PATIENTS
POTIONS &
PHYSICIANS

Celebrating *350* years

The Royal College Of Physicians Of Ireland

The College crest from the 1667 Charter:
The blue hand coming from the heavens represents God. The unusual method of pulse-taking
is copied directly from the crest of the Royal College of Physicians, London.

PATIENTS
POTIONS &
PHYSICIANS

A Social History of Medicine
in Ireland 1654–2004

Tony Farmar

A. & A. Farmar
In association with the
Royal College of Physicians of Ireland

British Library cataloguing in Publication Data
A CIP catalogue record for this book is available from the British Library.

Picture credits are detailed before the Index.

Picture research by Peter Costello
Index by Helen Litton
Text designed and set by Kevin Gurry at Cobalt
Cover design by Kevin Gurry at Cobalt
Printed and bound in Spain by GraphyCems

ISBN 1-899047-99-9

First published in 2004 by
A. & A. Farmar
Beech House
78 Ranelagh Village
Dublin 6
Ireland
Tel: 353 1 496 3625
Fax: 353 1 497 0107
Email: afarmar@iol.ie
Web: farmarbooks.com

In association with the
Royal College of Physicians of Ireland
Kildare Street
Dublin 2
Tel: 353 1 661 6677
Fax: 353 1 676 2920
Web: rcpi.ie

Contents

Acknowledgements

My first debt is to the Officers and staff of the Royal College of Physicians of Ireland; notably to Dr John Murphy, the Treasurer, who introduced me to the project, and Dr Michael Scott, the Sir Patrick Duns' Librarian, who was my 'minder' throughout the four years of writing. His comments and responses to the chapters were extremely valuable—not least of his contributions was the title. I would like to record gratitude also to the members of the Library Committee of the College, notably Dr John Fleetwood and Dr Paul Darragh, for their contributions. Dr T. Joseph McKenna, President of the College, and Dr John Murphy kindly read and commented on the last three chapters. It is important to state, however, that the opinions and judgements expressed in the book are mine, and should not be assumed to be the views of the College on any subject.

Dr Risteárd Mulcahy provided stimulating insights into doctoring as a career, as did Dr Peter Boylan.

Robert Mills of the College's Library was the essential collaborator without whom the treasures of the Library could not have been opened, and whose great knowledge of the College was always to hand. Mary O'Doherty the Archivist of the Royal College of Surgeons in Ireland was equally helpful.

I am grateful to Dr Larry Geary of UCC for reading and commenting on most of the chapters. Elizabeth McRory of Baltiboys House was extremely helpful in providing access to Elizabeth Smith's diaries of the 1850s. Dr Helen Dingwall of Strathclyde University provided valuable information about the Irish students at Reims. Declan McCourt kindly allowed me to quote from his father's detailed manuscript diaries of the experience of hospitalisation in the Blackrock Clinic and St Vincent's. Dr James McKenna and Professor Greta Jones allowed quotation from the ongoing oral history project called 'Candles in the Dark'.

I am once again grateful to my friends Frank Litton and the late Dr Geoffrey MacKechnie, a man with considerable experience of the patient's view of hospitals, for providing an arena in which the broader issues could be discussed.

Finally, a special thank-you to my partner Anna Farmar—from me for her encouragement, and on behalf of the reader for her highly professional, meticulous editing which clarified, elucidated and honed so much of the text.

Tony Farmar
September 2004

Foreword

The origins of the Royal College of Physicians in Ireland 350 years ago were based on a need to regulate the medical profession in Ireland and to confirm those who were appropriately trained to practice. At that time the College identified the minimum training requirements for those who were engaged in the practice of medicine. Only a small number of the practitioners achieved these standards. The evolution in medicine since its foundation is such that now the College's mission is 'to achieve and maintain high standards in specialist practice to ensure the health of the population' nationally and internationally.

These aims are achieved by the linked processes of education and assessment. The College, its Institute and Faculties, provide training and assessment in all the specialities of Medicine, Obstetrics and Gynaecology, Public Health Medicine, Occupational Medicine, Pathology and Paediatrics. At the time of the foundation of the College poverty was rife in a nation ravaged by disease and political strife. Today the country is prosperous, educated and confident. Achieving a high international standard of medical training is required to satisfy the assessments of the training programmes. It is appropriate at this point as the College faces significant changes in its physical base, with renovation and refurbishment of the building at 6 Kildare Street, and expanding international influence in both its spheres of education and examination, to reflect on the history of the College.

Tony Farmar's review of the maturation of the College within the context of societal change over these 350 years provides a fascinating record. From this history there are lessons to be learned and it will be helpful to apply this audit to future growth and development. Such development will be marked by a greater willingness of the College to become involved in discussion of issues as society looks for a more active role in decisions affecting management of its good health and of its diseases. In this way the College will respond not only to those needs recognised by Society, but it will educate society in general and medical practitioners by providing leadership to embrace the best of what is new while carefully examining the unproven and rejecting it if ill advised.

The College's role in protecting society by promoting high standards of education and practice remains unchanged through its history. The College which today enjoys its widest international membership and fellowship is more influential and active than ever before and carries an onerous responsibility to a rightly demanding profession and population. With confidence based in its historical roots, the College looks forward to playing an important role in the evolution of our society in the years ahead.

T. Joseph McKenna
President, Royal College of Physicians of Ireland
September 2004

A sophisticated sixteenth-century view of the four faces of the physician, as seen through the eyes of the patient: (top left) the godlike healer who saves his life; (top right) the caring angel who tends the sickbed; (bottom left) the ordinary man visiting a convalescent seen (on left) sitting by a fire in his bedroom; and finally (bottom right) the devil who insists on being paid. The images (after Hendrick Goltzius 1558–1617) are full of detail of contemporary medical life.

Chapter One
The Medical Encounter

'A richly diverse marketplace'

W E ALL GET SICK. We all spend time in discomfort or pain in the invalid's half-world—that break, or exile, from normal daily life. So commonplace is the experience, indeed, that it is not often discussed in historical writing. This book, which is published to celebrate the 350th anniversary of the founding of the Royal College of Physicians of Ireland (hereafter simply the College) in 1654, explores how the Irish have experienced disease and sickness, as patients and doctors, since the seventeenth century.

Medical history has usually focused on institutions, notably hospitals; the lives of well-known doctors; and occasionally specific diseases. Here the approach is more patient-centred, driven by three insights which are often underplayed in histories of learned or official medicine.

The first is that from the earliest days of the College there was always a richly diverse medical marketplace, in which the patient was the initiator and buyer.

The doctors at the bedside demonstrate the two key diagnostic signs in medieval medicine—the pulse and the urine.

Patients and their families invariably started the medical process by analysing and judging symptoms, and deciding the appropriate forum for care and cure. For most of the period what is now called 'primary health care' was in the hands of the leaders of the household, typically the mistress of the house herself. After that the sick person chose from a wide range of 'normal' or commercial services—at the top of the tree were the physicians, but it was always possible to consult a pharmacist, a wise woman or a homeopathist; an osteopath or a patent medicine vendor. And if these failed, there were more extra-terrestrial aids to be invoked: from Lourdes or Knock, from a holy well, from pishrogues or perhaps a healer, ideally the seventh son of a seventh son.

From its foundation the College was the Irish focus point for élite medicine, with all the prestige (and income) that implies. It was established to endorse and support formal medicine. Its members were at the apex of the medical pyramid, and had little contact with the varied fauna of unofficial medicine (in theory they were supposed to inspect apothecaries' shops, but this was strongly resisted by the apothecaries). As it happens, for most of the life of the College various forms of unofficial medicine have been quantitatively more important to most people than formal medicine. And it is not self-evident that official medicine was always kinder or more effective than other offerings.

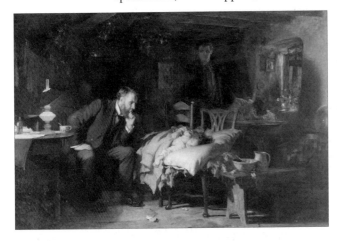

The second perception is that the flow of ideas by which medical decisions were made (especially by non-professionals) was never homogenous. Although the latest ideas swam clear and fast down the middle of the mental stream, at the edges, caught in eddies and in whirlpools, were notions and fears

The early-twentieth-century profession's favourite image of itself. Large framed prints of this painting, The Doctor (1891) by Luke Fildes, were common on Irish physicians' waiting room walls up to the 1960s.
(Tate Gallery London)

based on much older paradigms. The paramount need of the human mind is a locating narrative, and if the most approved modern sickness story were out of reach, older tales would be adapted. The propensity to hunt for and elaborate meaning is seen in the rich folklore of hospitals (don't leave flowers in the sick-room overnight, patients discharged on Saturday will quickly return, it is bad luck to conduct a patient into the operating theatre feet first, etc.). Doctors historically remained most comfortable with the ideas current in their student days, and patients often reached much further back. For instance, most people no longer believe that disease and pain are a chastisement from God, but the belief lingers, as GP Paul Henry reported in 1994. 'I think of the man crippled with arthritis. He took his ailment as retribution for lying down with a woman in damp grass in 1934. The justice, as he saw it, helped him come to terms with his aches and pains.'[1] Although older ideas do eventually wither away, it takes a surprising time, since one idea rarely completely ousts another. Patients happily turn up to surgery for anti-flu injections wearing red flannel chest protectors.

The third perception that colours the whole narrative is that medical encounters between doctors and patients did not take place in a purely technical environment, but were conducted in a fog of social and moral constraints. Gender, class, religious and even political differences were carried into the medical encounter by both patients and doctors and coloured actions and responses. As Oliver Wendell Holmes put it: 'Medicine, professedly founded on observation, is as sensitive to outside influences, political, religious, philosophical, imaginative as is the barometer to changes of atmosphere.'[2]

Two examples illustrate the deep forces at play. It was not until the late nineteenth century, for instance, that a physician would normally examine the undressed body of his patient, especially if young and female. Queen Victoria's physician first saw her in bed when she was actually dying, and was afterwards surprised to discover that she had both a hernia and a prolapse of the uterus.[3] In European literature the moment of the change is captured by Tolstoy in *Anna Karenina*. He describes vividly the shame felt by Princess Kitty Shcherbatsky when the 'celebrated specialist', a young man, insists on personally examining her body, the Princess' parents reluctantly agreeing. The specialist however proclaims that in the medical encounter, 'modesty in a girl [was] not merely a relic of the dark ages but an affront to himself.' In the early part of the century the French physician Laënnac devised his primitive stethoscope (now the iconic device of the physician) especially to avoid just this affront to a young woman's modesty.

Another example is the visceral reaction to the most important change in medical personnel since the Church forbade the clergy to practice in the early Middle Ages—the introduction of women doctors in the nineteenth century. (Women were of course always welcome as nurses and carers—it was their taking the leading role of physician or surgeon that provided the shock.) The reaction could take surprising forms. Male medical students objected to being taught anatomy in mixed classes, and when the first female Assistant Master of Holles Street was appointed in 1924, hospital legend records that one of the lady Governors objected strongly, saying: 'She

wouldn't have a woman obstetrician, and she didn't see why the poor should have to put up with something she wouldn't'.[4] Even today most men hate to consult a woman doctor if a man is available.

The knee stone, or cloch ghlúine, the ancient Irish remedy for rheumatism, was still in use in the late twentieth-century.

Serious disease has never been thought of simply as a bit of bad luck, an incidental infection—it has resonance. At the beginning of our period disease was customarily thought of as a punishment from God; the Enlightenment preferred to blame ill-managed living, and neglect of the so-called 'non-naturals' (good diet, sleep, exercise, mental calm etc.); the nineteenth century (before the discovery of germs) worried about climate and miasmata. Today we are concerned about the diseases of the winners and the losers of the affluent society, or perhaps our genetic inheritance.

Powerful feelings can be generated by disease. This might be the fear or contempt directed towards mental illness or sexually transmitted disease—and AIDS in our day. Or it might be the craven panic an epidemic can engender. It might be no more than the harmless snobbery associated with gout: in the late-nineteenth-century novel *Golden Lads and Lasses* Warren the butler is reconciled to his painful ailment because my lord had it also; as he says, complacently, 'it's a nobleman's disease.'[5] It might be the almost superstitious fear once attached to cancer (spoken of in hushed terms as 'the big C') or the stigma associated with tuberculosis—as Dr John O'Connell put it in his autobiography, describing a time when it was the major killer of young adults: 'Nobody ever admitted to having TB. Whatever else you had, you didn't have TB. Nobody in your family, seed, breed or generation had TB.'[6]

Another indicator of the deep forces at play, far beyond the simple therapeutics, lies in attitudes to the body, both living and dead. Outside the medical profession the dead body is almost as hedged with feeling as the living one. One of the hallmarks of Western medicine has been its impious willingness, in pursuit of anatomical knowledge, to violate the near universal taboo on opening and examining the dead. But the success of this strategy did not mean that the old instincts are not still strongly felt by non-doctors, as the rows about retained organs that broke out in 1999 made clear.

In order to portray the great changes in these matters from generation to generation I have used the freeze-frame technique adopted in a previous book, *Ordinary Lives.*[7] This enables intense scrutiny of chosen short periods, in which there is space to explore understandings from the mainstream to the exotic. The result is a series of pictures of successive eras, rather than a linear narrative of causations.

The first snapshot is of the state of Irish medicine in the 1650s, when the College was founded. Western medicine at this time had barely moved away from magic and the ancient classical theories of Galen and Hippocrates. Diseases, and especially epidemics, were generally interpreted as buffets from the hand of God. An outbreak of plague that terrifyingly had killed one-third of Dubliners was within living memory. The next shot focuses on a hundred years later. Enlightenment medicine now held sway, and men and women were conscious of a physical vulnerability which could be controlled only by close attention to disciplined habits of eating and drinking, sleep, exercise and evacuations, but above all calm of mind. They profoundly believed, as Laurence Sterne put it, that 'the mind and the body are like a jerkin and its lining—rumple one and you rumple the other.'[8]

A hundred and fifty years after the foundation of the College, Ireland was deeply involved in the Napoleonic Wars. Wars benefit medical development, especially surgery, and during these years surgery at last became respectable. At the same time the ancient division between physic and surgery began to break down. Surgery was given another lift in the 1850s by the introduction of anaesthesia.

The central problem of medicine however was still the ancient catch-all category 'Fever', into which single rubric doctors since Hippocrates had lumped febrile diseases from flu to typhus, from measles to diphtheria. As late as the 1870s the distinguished Professor of Medicine at Trinity, Sir William Stokes FRS

Eighteenth-century surgeons prided themselves on their speed and ruthlessness, here satirised by Rowlandson in a print of 1785.

insisted that typhus and typhoid were effectively the same, declaring 'you all know that typhus fever may relapse into typhoid fever, and typhoid into typhus.'[9]

By 1900 germ theory had exploded 2,000 years of speculation. As the great medical teacher William Osler triumphantly put it: 'We know the cause—the germ'.[10] He was talking about tuberculosis, the white plague of Ireland, which was to remain a major killer of young adults for another fifty years. For knowing the enemy did not mean that one could cure the disease. It did mean increased scepticism about the older cures, however. Doctors became increasingly conscious that, apart from opium, digitalis, quinine and a few others, most of the pharmacopoeia was of little more than placebo value. As a result a kind of therapeutic nihilism became fashionable, in which as Oliver St John Gogarty put it about his time in the hospital in Vienna, 'their idea of good medicine was a precise diagnosis confirmed by a painstaking autopsy'.[11] It has been argued that since doctors knew well their armamentarium was mostly shooting blanks, they gave more freely to the patient what they had—time and attention—and this was particularly appreciated.

Although the effectiveness enabled by antibiotics was still far in the future, the prestige of the medical profession rose to a height in the 1920s. Doctors were credited with a penetrating view of 'society without its mask' as the paediatrician Bob Collis put it.[12] Their presence at birth and death became expected. Although their prestige remained high, the conditions of the new state encouraged a kind of complacency in the profession. The quality of Irish medical training gradually sank below international standards, although this was more perceptible at specialist than GP level.

The nation's physical and sanitary conditions were not a priority for the post-1922 governments, and by the 1950s the Republic's health record had slipped behind Northern Ireland, especially after the introduction of the National Health Service there. While the availability of antibiotics meant that ordinary infectious diseases had lost their sting, large swathes of the population were without proper sanitation and were plagued by lice, fleas and other parasites. Although the Catholic Church had been to the forefront in providing medical charity, it and the profession combined to resist the state's tardy intervention in medical matters—but the international pressures of medicalisation were irresistible.

One of Lady Aberdeen's anti-TB caravans which travelled through Ireland in 1907 and 1908 spreading the word with lectures and demonstrations on the new germ theory.

Twenty-five years later, a new generation of doctors, armed with a growing array of antibiotics, cortisone, polio vaccinations, kidney transplants, coronary care units and the wonders of intensive neonatal care entered what should have been a brave new world of medical success and prestige. Somehow, however, it was not, and it is not clear why. Certainly, expenditure on medicine kept rising, and more and more people were employed, until by the mid 1970s one in twenty of the working population worked in the 'healthcare industry'. As doctors increasingly identified the so-called 'diseases of affluence or lifestyle', such as diabetes, obesity and heart disease' as major causes of death, patients became increasingly health-conscious, and attracted to fads and alternative medical regimes. The less positive characteristics of the modern medical environment—the disillusioned practitioners, the 'worried well', the growing popularity of intellectually shaky alternative medicines and finally the ever-rising costs of public medical expenditure—began to be visible.[13]

Following independence, the College, like other 'Royal' institutions in republican Ireland, had lost its position of leadership. It became little more than a medical gentlemen's club. In the 1970s, however, it enjoyed a resurgence, and concentrated on the vigorous provision of post-graduate medical qualifications and the setting of high standards in medical care that are its main preoccupations today.

The modern medical environment and the modern College are far removed from the world of the founder John Stearne, whose times we explore in the next chapter.

Chapter Two
The 1650s

'We must first begin with a prayer,
and then use physick.'

T HE WORLD IN WHICH the Royal College of Physicians of Ireland
was born is both familiar and very strange. It is
familiar in the sense that seventeenth-century ailments, discomforts and diseases were broadly the
same as ours. It is strange in the names people then gave to
their pains and the stories they told to explain them. It is
familiar in the sense that people trusted their doctors and carers to help them make sense of otherwise meaningless ills. It
is strange in the things these doctors and carers did, and, not
least, in that these things very often had the desired curative
effect. The hills, the trees and the creatures that inhabited
them are familiar. The way the people viewed the natural phenomena, and their own place in that world, is quite strange.

During the seventeenth century, between the Flight of the
Earls in 1607 and the Battle of the Boyne in 1690, the form of
Irish society was painfully broken and reset. By the end of the
century the old Gaelic order had been definitively superseded
by the new colonial power. As far as Irish medicine was concerned, this period certainly marked a fundamentally new
start; the basis of the old order of carers—the old Gaelic medical families and the monastic hospitals—had been swept
aside by history, leaving a mere rump of variously qualified
practitioners. The foundation of the Dublin Fraternity of
Physicians, the precursor of today's Royal College of Physicians of Ireland, in
1654, can reasonably be seen as the very turning point of the tide.

In previous centuries the Gaelic chiefs had had their hereditary doctors, and
there were occasional foreign-educated physicians, but most people looked
after their own family's ailments or addressed their needs to apothecaries and
barber surgeons, and in the country to wise women, herb or fairy doctors, and
the like. The numerous monastic hospitals of the Middle Ages had been sup-
pressed during the Reformation. In England just two hospitals survived of the
nearly 500 medieval foundations, and these two (St Bartholomew's and St

People of the book: the
learned physician, in his
careful professional
dress, and the literate
midwife discuss a case
with the patient. From
the first book in English
on midwifery, written
by James Wolveridge, a
Fellow of the College.

Thomas') served a London of nearly a million people. With 1.1 million people, as William Petty estimated, Ireland did not have a single hospital or hospice. The medical institutions of the future were represented by the tiny School of Medicine in Trinity College and the Guild of Barber Surgeons. In practice, virtually all medical needs were met inside the household; any kind of coherent, centralised medical profession was non-existent. So, when Cromwell arrived in Ireland in August 1649 to consolidate his rule, it was immediately necessary to import physicians from England to meet the needs of his 20,000-strong army. These men quickly became the leading practitioners in the country.

The theory of medicine[1]

In the foreground two physicians prepare a prescription for the patient in the bed, which will be filled by the apothecary at his shop in the background; from a work on prescribing (1650).

For those living in the seventeenth century the key to personal health, as it had been since ancient times, was to maintain a balance of the bodily fluids called humours, or spirits, specifically blood, phlegm, and yellow and black bile. The ideal, as set out by Galen in the second century, was to allow these spirits to move around the body so as to be neither too hot, nor too cold, nor bilious nor phlegmatic. The physical body was perceived simply as a container for a constant ebb and flow of fluids, much as a stew pot contains a stew (a homely metaphor frequently used). The right and healthy balance point was specific to the individual, so the physician had to interpret the physical signs (fevers, spots, diarrhoea etc.) in the light of a patient's normal health. As the physician attempted to restore the appropriate balance it was easy to mistake signs and address the wrong humour, or molest the body to no purpose. The analysis was complicated by the fact that the imbalance was constantly shifting, so diseases metamorphosed and also moved from one part of the body to another.

This view largely accounted for the treatment of technical anatomy which was thought of as interesting but not critical to the education of a physician, an attitude that survived to the eighteenth century. The lesions and symptoms found during an autopsy were, after all, merely effects, and said nothing as to the causes of disease. An anatomist, ran the common analogy, was like a brewer who paid more attention to his barrels than to the beer contained in them.

The whole Galenic system allowed physicians to create a readily understandable narrative of disease—epilepsy, for instance, was caused by phlegm blocking the pathways of the body, and the fits were the body's struggle to free itself. Different ages and different seasons were conducive to the excess of one humour

One of two portraits in the College traditionally supposed to depict John Stearne (1624–69); a copy of the original in the Provost's House, TCD.

over the others; spring was the time one was most at risk from an excess of blood, so a prophylactic bleeding was often suggested. (It was Nature's way—did not the monthly issue of blood in women ensure their health?) Humours could also take on a pathological (putrid, corrupt) character, perhaps through contagion, bad air or over-indulgence. The quality of the air the patient breathed could be adjusted, either by moving to a better place, or by fumigation. Evacuation techniques enabled the body to remove a plethora, or excess, of one humour over others and thus restore the essential balance.

To correct the imbalance the physician used drugs (mostly herbal, though there was a new trend to chemicals) to stimulate evacuation of whichever element was

The second supposed portrait of Stearne— evidently a different person, and by the wig style and other indications must have been painted many years after Stearne's death; attributed to Thomas Pooley (1646–1723).

corrupt, putrid or simply in excess, 'which', wrote Daniel Le Clerk in his *History of Physick* (published in English in 1699), 'is done either by Bleeding, by Stool, by Vomit, by Urine, by Tumors, by Abcesses, by Scabs, Pimples, Spots and other things; Nature easily reduces the rest to the condition they were in before the accession of the disease.'[2] Nature in fact often showed the way by inducing evacuations (vomiting, diarrhoea) which the physician, taking the hint, further encouraged with emetics or cathartics. On this scaffold an immense weight of learning was erected. Some said there were as many as 300 diseases. In the fourth of his *Travels*, Gulliver reported to his Houyhnhnm master that 'it would be endless to give him a Catalogue of all Diseases incident to human Bodies; for they could not be fewer than five or six Hundred spread over Limb or Joynt. In short every Part, external and intestine having Diseases appropriate to each.'[3] A recent tendency was to group diseases together into sets; thus the revolutionary German physician Paracelsus identified four generic diseases, which he called leprosy, gout, dropsy and falling-sickness, from which the others stemmed. (Gout, in this analysis included stone, colic, toothache, headache and others.) In 1694 Johann Bernhard Gladbach also reduced all diseases to four broad categories: fever, scurvy, cachexia and catarrh.[4]

The early years of Dr John Stearne

In 1641 a great rising commenced in the north of Ireland, deliberately incited, some believed, by the English Puritan administration in London. This led to the establishment of an uneasy alliance of Irish and Old English in the Confederation of Kilkenny, and a long attempt to establish Catholic home rule. Dublin, with its largely planter and Puritan population, was rightly identified by the Confederates as the seat of English power. A plot to capture the city in 1641 was betrayed, and for nine weary years Dublin was the core of resistance to the Confederates and a hotbed of lurid tales of their wrongdoings. Owen Roe O'Neill laid siege to Dublin in 1646 and Sir John Temple, whose father had been Provost of Trinity from 1609 to 1642, published the first edition of his *History of the Rebellion*, a book whose vividly exaggerated horror stories seared the Protestant imagination for generations. Using a medical analogy typical of the time, he described the Confederation's haste to evict the English and re-establish Catholicism. 'The rebels', he wrote, '. . . pretended the ill humours and distempers in the Kingdom to be grown to that height as required Cauteries, deep incisions, and indeed nothing was able to work so great a cure but universal Rebellion. This was certainly the disease, as appears by all the symptoms, and the joynt concurrence in opinion of all the great Physitians that held themselves wise enough to propose remedies and prescribe fit applications to so desperate a Malady.'

In the end, despite the distractions of their own civil war, the economic power of the City of London dictated the outcome; Cromwell landed in Ringsend in August 1649 and eventually established a parliamentary commission, initially under his own authority and later that of his son Henry.

It was against this background that Dr John Stearne initiated his Fraternity of Physicians in 1654. Stearne was born in 1624, with close connections to the Ussher family (whose most distinguished member had been Archbishop of Armagh since 1625). He had begun his education in Trinity at the age of fifteen, becoming a scholar two years later. During the disturbances of the early 1640s he fled to England. Under the protection of a friend of Archbishop Ussher's, he enjoyed nine studious years in England, at first in Cambridge, then moving to

William Petty (1623–87)—the young anatomist at Oxford, c.1653, by Isaac Fuller.

Oxford. As a student both of medicine and Hebrew, Stearne would have been exposed in Cambridge to the great debate of the day between those, following Descartes and Robert Boyle, who believed in a mechanical universe, and those, such as the much-loved neo-platonist Henry More, who believed that matter was too elaborate and designed to be inanimate, and must therefore be driven and shaped by spiritual entities animated by God.[5] In the 1660s More was offered the provostship of TCD, but turned it down. The neo-platonists envisaged a world full of spirits, of which the grossest manifestation would be ghosts. 'The isle is full of noises', as Caliban explained, 'that give delight, and hurt not.'

The implications for medical practice were important, and made such phenomena as the weapon salve explicable. In his notebooks the Dublin practitioner John Clavell described 'a way to cure a green wound and never come near the party wounded'. This involved washing a cloth with a drop of the wounded man's blood in a solution of ferrous sulphate for three days. (Other versions required the practitioner to apply acid to the actual weapon that caused the wound.) If the blood spot washed out the man would be cured, if not the wound was mortal. While this was going on, 'the party is to apply nothing to his wound but a change of clean linen'.[6] The alternative treatments were Clavell's prescription 'to stint the bleeding of a cut or wound', which involved burning a red cloth to powder and inserting the powder into the wound, or, more orthodoxly, to cauterise the wound by boiling oil or a red-hot metal tool. Practical medical men could hardly be blamed for adopting a remedy such as the weapon salve which no doubt worked better than alternatives, regardless of the actual mechanism. It was only in the next century that the lack of credible connection between action and result made the concept intolerable and it was dropped from the armamentarium.

Sometime in the 1640s Stearne moved to Oxford, an extremely Royalist town, which had been King Charles' headquarters until 1646—to Oxonian horror, the King himself was executed in 1649. Apart from the presence of William Petty as deputy to the Reader in Anatomy, the official Faculty of Medicine at Oxford was not distinguished. The Regius Professor of Medicine and Reader in Anatomy was the time-serving Sir Thomas Clayton, whom contemporaries described as of 'a timorous and effeminate humour, he could never endure the sight of a mangled or bloody body'. Petty, on the other hand, who came to Dublin in 1652 and became a leading light in the College, is reported to have 'exercised anatomy and chymistry much among the young scholars, to his and their great benefit'.[7] In his lectures he listed his conception of what a doctor should be; it is a curious combination of the scientist (e.g. 1–3), the practical doctor (8–11) the compassionate carer (6) and the practical man of affairs (7 and 12).

1. To be a naturalist at large.
2. To understand the fabric and generation of animals.
3. The diseases and deathes of them, but especially of man.
4. The senses of each disease, in its beginning, its state and determination.
5. The scales of salubrity from ayre, soile and way of life and extraordinary disorders.
6. The art of comforting and palliating payn and danger.
7. The art of begetting good opinions of himself.
8. The knowledge of all medicaments in use in the place of his practise, and especially of what grows thereabouts, and of the country pharmacopoeia.
9. What evills may be cured by the hand.
10. What by diet, ayres and water.
11. The proportion of casualties and diseases.
12. To make friends of patients and families and of women midwyves and nurses.[8]

Also in Oxford was Thomas Sydenham, later known as 'the English Hippocrates', studying post-graduate medicine. If Stearne and he met, it is unlikely they had much in common, for Sydenham was a radical who had already fought with the Parliamentary army, and he later became known for an equally radical, almost passive and nihilist, attitude to medical practice.

On his return to Dublin in 1652, Stearne was admitted as a Fellow of Trinity and soon became Professor of Medicine. Despite identification with the Anglican party (two of his books had prefaces by out-of-favour Anglican bishops), during the Cromwellian period Stearne accumulated offices in Trinity. He was evidently an active man, and favoured by Henry Cromwell to whom he dedicated another of his books. He became Registrar and Senior Proctor as well as conducting a medical practice of sufficient scope as to persuade the Fellows to allow him occasionally to sleep outside the college. In 1656, he became Hebrew Lecturer. Among Henry More's interests had been the Jewish Cabala, whose central idea was that the world had been created by using words, an idea reiterated in St John's Gospel: 'In the beginning was the Word'. Following this clue, Hebraists believed that one could gain insights into the deep structure of reality by studying God's language, Hebrew. In 1660 Stearne also became Professor of Law. During this time he wrote several books, mostly of a mixed theological, philosophical and medical nature with a strong taint of classical stoicism, so much so that his literary executor had to apologise for some of Stearne's extreme classicisms, and carefully place them in a proper Christian context.[9]

The new College

The tale of Stearne's foundation of the Fraternity of Physicians has been often told. The idea of a college of physicians had medieval origins and there had been a previous attempt to establish one in Ireland. The London College of Physicians had been founded in 1518, on a charter from Henry VII. Charles I had promised a group of Dubliners a similar charter, but they were to learn the fickleness of kings. In 1626 Charles I wrote to the Lord Deputy, Viscount Falkland, encouraging him to establish such a college with authority to control practice within a twelve-mile radius of the city. Later that year five Dublin doctors—Paul de Laune, (Falkland's physician and a Fellow of the College of Physicians in London), James Metcalfe, Dermot O'Meara, Christopher Talbot and John Verdon—wrote to the London college announcing that in answer to a petition the King had been pleased to found a college in Dublin to regulate medical practice and repress unqualified practitioners. They asked the London college to send copies of its statutes, charters etc. Unwilling to go to the expense of copying, the college replied that it would be better for someone to come over and explore their operation thoroughly and take advice. Perhaps they cynically wondered whether the King's approval did not mean quite as much as it seemed on the face of it. And so it turned out.[10] A year later de Laune had ceased to be Falkland's physician, and Falkland himself was recalled in 1629. The idea ran into the sand.

Stearne's attempt was more successful, perhaps because the very idea of frater-

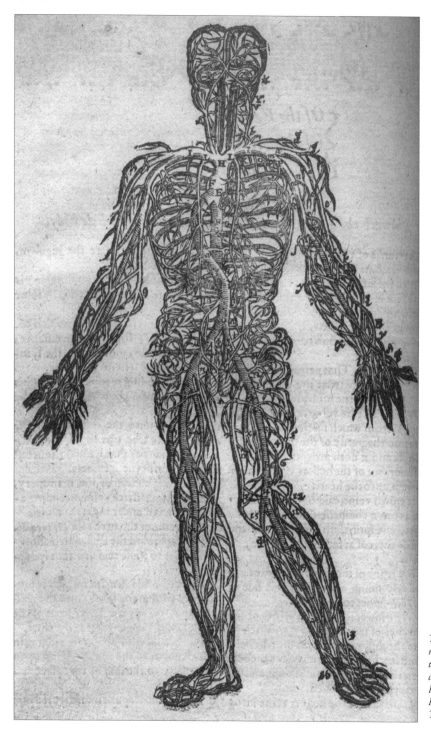

The irrepressible liveliness of this schema of the blood vessels is characteristic of Renaissance (pre-Harvey) anatomy, from Titian's workshop.

nities and colleges was in the air. The mystical 'invisible college' of the Rosicrucians was no doubt discussed in Cambridge, and in London Robert Boyle and others were floating ideas for what was eventually to become the Royal Society. In 1654 Stearne persuaded Trinity to let him acquire rooms in a run-down building called Trinity Hall, near what was to become the site of the

Bleeding and cupping were common remedies until the late nineteenth century, though they waxed and waned in popularity from generation to generation.

Central Hotel in Exchequer Street, 'for accommodating Physicians with a convenient place to meet in, in order to the erection of a College of Physicians as soon as possibly it could be erected'.[11] The building is identified as the Bridewell on John Speed's 1610 map of Dublin.

Stearne steered successfully through the very choppy waters of the change from the Cromwellian regime to the restored monarchy. Despite his relative prominence in the Puritan period he survived as a Fellow of Trinity, though he had to be re-established and sworn in afresh. He subsequently secured a deed from Trinity re-establishing the Fraternity of Physicians. Trinity Hall was to be 'from henceforth for ever converted to the sole and proper use and advantage of the study of medicine', and in 1662 Stearne himself was nominated President for life. Early members included William Petty, Lamb Gougleman, James Wolveridge and two known only by their surnames—Halle and Branchall.

Of the three strains of medical practitioner in Ireland—the Old Irish from learned families, the Old English and the New English—Stearne's fraternity was predominantly made up of the latter, though one at least of the Old English, Thomas Arthur, was widely consulted by the Puritan élite, including Henry Cromwell. Although Dr Widdess, in his history of the College, stated that 'religion did not affect membership' at this time, this seems unlikely, and in the 1680s the Catholic physicians of Ireland persuaded James II to allow them to establish their own college of physicians, based in Kilkenny.[12] Of course this came to nothing after the Protestant revolution of 1688. The official endorsement of the priority of learned medicine was reinforced in 1667 when Charles II granted a charter, in which fourteen Fellows were named, and the Fraternity formally became the College. The membership turnover was rapid—between then and the Charter of 1692 fifteen new Fellows were elected to fill vacancies. Among these was Ralph Howard, the only one elected in 1667 and still in place 25 years later.

Dublin in the seventeenth century

Dublin was a small place. Although various civil improvements had been initiated, such as a mint, an office for the registration of deeds, a court and a prison, 'in essence Dublin was still a medieval city with narrow streets and overcrowded houses'.[13] The city proper, inside the defensive walls, ran from the Castle to the Cornmarket, though there were extensive and scattered suburbs, notably to the south, and north across the river in Oxmantown. It is difficult for us to imagine the noise, the smell, the constant smoke, the insecurity, the rotting meat and other evidence of putrefaction (believed then to be one of the principal causes of disease) on every kerb. The squalor, the crowding and the constant presence of animals made Dublin a place where micro-parasites had easy access to victims.

Just as today in South-East Asia the influenza viruses mutate on the ricochet between pigs, poultry and humans living closely together, in the seventeenth century cities and towns were cauldrons of infection. The historian William McNeill has estimated that humans share 65 diseases with dogs, 50 with cattle, 46 with sheep and goats, 35 with horses and 26 with poultry.[14] All of these creatures ambled through the narrow lanes of Dublin, jostling against the human population. Constant small injuries, and vermin such as fleas, lice and rats, facilitated the crossfire of infection. The animals also joined with humans in fouling drinking water, and with enlarging the piles of suppurating filth around the city. Not surprisingly, the human population completely failed to reproduce itself—even in the relatively peaceful times between 1660 and 1680 deaths in the city were 64 per cent more than births.[15] Without a constant flow of migrants from the country Dublin would have been empty in less than a generation.

William Petty, writing in 1683, guessed that there were some 4,000 houses in Dublin, and about 1,600 deaths and 1,000 births in the city every year. Fewer than five deaths a day means that, in theory, a medical man could be personally acquainted with virtually every corpse. In practice, of course, very few of the poor would have seen a physician. Dublin houses, Petty believed, were crowded, with an average of eight people per house as opposed to fewer than five in London. For the first half of the seventeenth century the fabric of the city had been neglected—the results of an accidental explosion of stored gunpowder in 1597 (killing 126 people) had hardly been repaired—so the refugees from the country in the 1640s found many empty houses to squat in (including Trinity Hall). Although the city walls were in bad repair, as a result of private building initiatives, they represented a vital defence that could (with some considerable difficulty) be raised, as it was before the siege of 1646.

The disease world encountered by the first Fellows of the College can be identified from the list proposed by Sir William Petty (knighted in 1661) for the Bills of Mortality. These were regular monthly reports of the causes of deaths, originally established in London to give the literate early warning of outbreaks of plague. For the Dublin Bills Petty proposed the following classification of causes:

> Abortive and still-born; Aged above 70 years; Childbed-women; Consumption and French Pox; Convulsion, Small Pox; Dropsie and Tympany [swelled belly]; Epilepsie and Planet [intermittent fever]; Executed, Murdered, Drowned; Fever and Ague; Gout and Sciatica; Griping of the Guts; Head-ache and Megrim [migraine]; Measles; Palsey; Plague and Spotted Fever; Pleurisie; Quinsey [sore throat]; Rickets and Livergrown; Scowring, Vomiting, Bleeding; Stone; Teeth; Worms; Neither of all the other sorts.

These categories, he believed, were 'such as may be discerned by common sense and without Art'—which was just as well since the actual certification of cause was done by poor widows of the parish.[16]

The one Irish Bill that has survived was reproduced by Sir William Wilde in the Census of 1851, and records the deaths of 2,154 people in 1683/4. The city was overwhelmingly Protestant at this time, and the count was organised by Church of Ireland parish. Only members of the established Church and Quakers were included in the bills.[17] Sixty-two categories of cause of death were noted, including flux (78), 'hanged at the gallows' (10), surfeit (1) and 'hurt and ill-used by her master and mistress' (1). The largest category was 'Fever', regarded (as it was to be until the late nineteenth century) as a disease in its own right, rather than a symptom. The main categories, together accounting for nearly 90 per cent of the deaths, were:

Category	No. of deaths
Fever	527
Consumption	322
Convulsion	238
Teeth	187
Infants	178
Aged	159
Small pox	143
Meazels [sic]	122

Of course, death was only one, and not the most likely, outcome of any disease. More frequently there would have been an imperfect recovery and a subsequent weakening of the immune system. One ailment then piled on another. Even the great were not immune. In his early forties the Earl of Strafford, King Charles' Lord Deputy in Ireland 1633–9, suffered from rheumatism, as his biographer records: 'The damp climate seeping into his joints racked him with aches

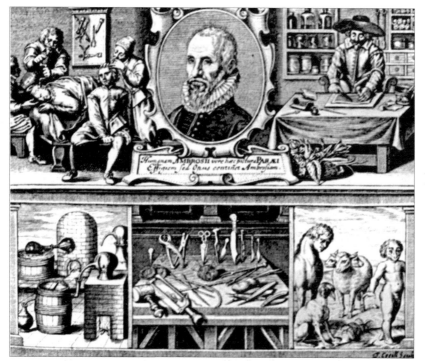

Unlike physicians, surgeons used a great many instruments. Shown here are the great French surgeon Ambroise Paré and some of his instruments.

and pains. His hands and feet were intermittently crippled by gouty swellings; he was tormented by insomnia and migraine; he had occasional fainting fits.' Later Strafford was attacked by the stone—this was painful 'above anything I have endured since a man', as he put it himself. In his late forties Strafford 'fought against his wasting illness but . . . exhausted by continuous dysentery and the blood-letting of his physicians he had not strength to stand; a week later an attack of pleurisy prostrated him.'[18] (The judicial axe put him out of his misery in 1641.)

The medical marketplace

Learned physicians, such as Stearne and his colleagues in the new Fraternity, were at the tip of the iceberg of medical aid and care. Below them the medical marketplace was diverse and ill regulated, and there was certainly very little in the way of professional structure. There were three formal sets of practitioners—physicians, surgeons and apothecaries. The logic of the division was simple: physicians were the men of learning who used the wisdom of the ancients to interpret what was happening inside a body; surgeons and apothecaries were in different ways practical men who worked with their hands. Thus was solved a recurrent dilemma of medical practice in that medicine is both a body of learned knowledge and a practical skill. Modern doctors are expected to be both knowledgeable and dextrous: unfortunately no amount of book learning will help the new practitioner find a vein in the arm of a distressed child.

At the top of the heap were physicians, graduates of famous universities. In theory, the bishops had the power to licence both physicians and surgeons, but it seems this was not done in Ireland, though it was in Britain. Physicians attached to the army were paid 5s a day (£91 a year); ministers of religion received 6s 8d, and surgeons 4s. We know that Sir William Petty earned £400 a year from his practice and the famous Dr Arthur in Limerick, had £300—and more than twice as much again from land speculation. In 1684 the Earl of Inchiquin paid a Dr Morice £40 for five weeks of constant attention to his wife, 'never leaving the house'. The following year, the Earl of Ossory paid 80 guineas 'to the Doctors when my lady had the smallpox'.[19]

The lack of professional structure made it easy for adventurers such as John Clavell to establish a practice in Dublin, armed with little more than a gentleman's knowledge of sickness and considerable self-assurance. Although it is unclear where he learned his medicine, Clavell, who came to Dublin in 1636 after a colourful career in London (including some time as highwayman), believed himself to have, as he put it, 'a gift in the art of physick'. A series of testimonials he collected from grateful patients suggest that they at least were satisfied. His casebook refers to curing Baron Louth and the son of the Archbishop of Dublin of vomiting and nausea, Lord Killilow of 'an old and sad malady, the Gout' and John Adams of Carrigrohan of a bloody flux. His most distinguished patient was Adam Loftus, the Lord Chancellor, whose kidney disease he relieved.

Although obviously a gifted salesman, Clavell was not a rogue. He took his work seriously, compounding his own medicines. This was partly because the prescriptions were special to himself, but also for safety and because he distrusted the local apothecaries. His recipes contained a mixture of folklore with a 'scientific' use of herbs, but no magic strictly so called. Epilepsy, however, does seem to have needed approaches akin to magic: one recipe prescribed the roasting to ashes of a live raven, another the drinking of a concoction of sea crab 'every full moon and new moon'. For a cough, 'take the oil of bitter almonds, wax, capon's grease, rose water. Boil them all together; then take black wool newly plucked from the sheep's neck and put therein, and put it warm, in a little bag, to the party's chest'. Dung, especially horse, goat and cow, was frequently used.

For surgical crises there were the barber surgeons or chirurgeons, whose first charter had been established in 1446 and renewed in 1572. The chirurgeons (the word is derived from two Greek words meaning hand and work) were concerned with practical operations on the fabric of the body. As the historian Andrew Wear put it, summarising a treatise of the 1630s:

> The first part of surgery treated wounds, ulcers, fractures, dislocations and also tumours, . . . the second part comprised separating parts of the body for either cosmetic or functional reasons . . . the third part dealt with what was superfluous to the body, such as a dead child in the womb, ruptures or hernias, limbs that had become mortified, wens, cataracts and stones as well as parts of the body such as a breast that had become cancerous . . . the fourth part made good defects of the body such as harelips.[20]

Educated by apprenticeship rather than university, chirurgeons operated in an emotional and practical environment quite different from the gentle, scholarly

care of the ideal physician. All of their operations involved pain, sometimes to an extreme degree, so they had to be both fast and merciless. Again, unlike physicians, who used no instruments until the nineteenth century, chirurgeons were craftsmen whose various tools for cutting, sawing, lancing, stitching and cauterising, were critical to their success. Military surgeons were given a special allowance for a horse to carry their surgical chest. The surgeon's skills were honed in particular by the knowledge gained during warfare. (It is said that the quality of English surgery fell back sharply during the peaceful years of the Tudors. The war-ravaged Italian peninsula enabled Italian surgery, on the other hand, to thrive.) Even military surgery had a very restricted range—the so-called 'capital' operations were undertaken in general by a group of men later described as 'itinerant empiricks, hardened in butchery, ready to commit such acts of cruelty as the sober regular practitioners would shudder to think of'.[21]

Has this gentlewoman been kicked in the face by a horse? Such injuries would have been commonplace, though of course any intervention would risk infection (1650).

Competing with these, in the 'normal' commercial medical market, were the one-remedy-meets-all men, empiricks, uroscopists and various cunning men and wise women, who could sometimes bring an enormous weight of inherited lore successfully to bear.[22] There were also, in a somewhat different category, seventh sons of seventh sons and other healers, including the famous Irish healer Valentine Greatrakes, who began a celebrated career of 'touching' for the King's Evil in 1662.

Medicine at home

Seventeenth-century medicine focused strongly on the individual's central role in the disease drama. Sick people were generally thought to have brought their ailment on themselves, probably by sin, or at the very least by excess worry, or by neglecting regular evacuations, diet, or proper air, or exercise, or sleep. Health was formed and sustained in the private, individual, sphere, where a person confronted pain, or indulged in immoral and self-destructive behaviour. It was then

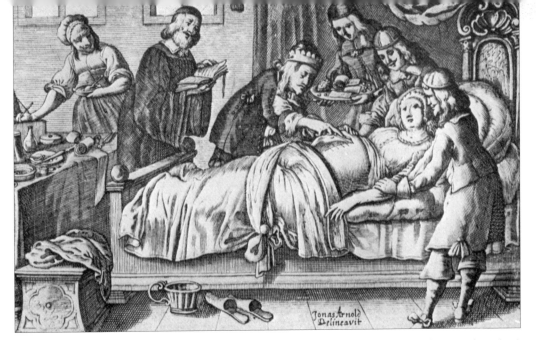

largely grappled with inside the family, though some kind of external medical advice was always available at all levels of society, even if it was only the wisdom and experience of a neighbour. It was not for two centuries or more that health became (except in epidemic times) a concern of the state.

In the seventeenth century most households had not only to initiate the medical encounter, but also to be medically self-sufficient to a very great degree. Medicine, like its close ally cookery, was primarily a domestic concern. The medical head of the household (usually, but not inevitably, the mistress) had to provide resources to cope with a wide range of ailments. These included 'industrial' accidents, on the farm, with animals, in the kitchen, as well as ordinary domestic medical events. Men and especially women stored medical recipes as they now might cookery tips, and swapped favourites. The library of a well-read scholar would contain up-to-date practitioners' medical treatises—Marsh's Library in Dublin, which combines collections from three non-medical scholars of the seventeenth century, contains several hundred medical books. One of the scholars was Stearne's son, a bishop, who continued collecting medical books long after his father's death.

The household recipe book, compiled by the mistress of the house, commonly contained instructions for medicine, cookery, perfumery and other domestic requirements. Thus the recipe book kept by Elizabeth O'Brien and Sarah Dudley in the late seventeenth and early eighteenth centuries has recipes for soups and fish and meat and puddings, and at the back: 'For the rickets, infallible', 'Plague water' and 'A medicine to cure the piles when they bleed'.[23] Lady Ranelagh, daughter of the Earl of Cork, and sister of the 'Sceptical Chymist', Robert Boyle, started a recipe book that was much more substantially oriented towards medicine. Out of the astonishing number of 713 recipes listed in the notebook compiled by herself and a successor, only a few are for cooking as such.[24]

Here for instance are some of the recipes indexed under B: 'Breasts to make little; Bloody flux; Bloody urine; Breasts sore; Bruises; Balsome, rare; Brain to comfort; Belly swelled with wind or water; Broath of chicken; Beef baked; Barrenness; Broath for a consumption; Blood to purify; Black jaundice; Bite of a

mad dog.' There are multiple recipes for treatments of certain diseases such as
sore and bloodshot eyes (caused by smoky fires?), for scurvy (a vaguer medical
term than it has since become), consumption, gout (not always distinguished
from rheumatism), stone, burns, fever, toothache, liver complaints and 'fitts'.
Often the recipe is identified not by what we would understand as a disease but
by the area affected, such as liver, kidney, lungs, spleen. In stubborn cases physicians would be drawn in, though not always with success. One recipe for scurvy
or dropsy, Lady Ranelagh declares, 'has cured in 9 or 10 days those that have been
given over by the doctors'. The marked difference between these books and their
modern equivalents is that there is no diagnostic guidance given—the user of the
book is expected to know her diseases.

Some of the recipes are for simple infusions of herbs for plasters or ointments;
others have a more fantastical element. A recipe for worms in children involves
taking earthworms that are 'knit together' leaving them in salt for three hours
then gutting and drying them in an oven. They are then beaten to a fine powder:
'Take also savin and dry and beat to powder, mix and lay out as much as will sit
on a twelve pence into a draught of muscadine with a littel sugar and drink it
morning and evening 3 days together at the full of the moon and in ye wane.'

There are echoes of sympathetic magic in many of the recipes. In the case of
fever, for instance, the suggestion was to take eleven stones out of the gizzards of
young swallows 'the sanguine coloured ones are best', 'quilting them in a riband
and applying them to the pulse of the left wrist'. This 'will turn any feaver in nine
howers'. It is so effective, Lady Ranelagh warns, that it 'has made some so cold
that they have bine brought to the fier to gett warmth'. In this world disease is
not an imbalance of humours as the orthodox medicine of the time had it, but a
malignant entity which fixes itself on various parts of the body. Ointments are
used 'to draw the pain'. This approach was widespread. The contemporary
German *dreckapotheke* or 'filth pharmacy' used excrements, noxious insects and
toads for similar reasons, and in Scotland David Rorie wrote of puppies and
pigeons being split open and laid for hours or days on the wound 'to draw the
tribble out'.[25] A century later, in his 1761 treatise *Avis au peuple* the physician
Samuel Tissot deplored the similar Swiss country practices, pointing out that the
resultant 'corruption and horrid stink' was not the result of the poison being
drawn out of the patient's body, as was believed, but simple decomposition.[26]

Lady Ranelagh's recipes assume an elaborate apparatus for cooking and distill-
ing and a large store cupboard: as well as simple ingredients such as wine vine-
gar, earthworms and hog's dung, and 'the watter of a man child and a pint of
womans milk' (part of 'a pretious watter for the eyes, it has don great cures')
plants such as scabious, eyebright and scurvy grass, and spices such as frankin-
cense are taken for granted. One of Elizabeth O'Brien's recipes, 'for the plague,
surfeit or feaver', called for no fewer than 30 different herbs to be steeped in white
wine. A similar panacea given by Lady Wray to Lady Ranelagh calls for 'flanders
oyle of bay 4 ounces, oyle of exeter 3 ounces, Venice turpentine half an ounce,

Axangia half an ounce' to be boiled with 'minium 4 ounces, Cerase one ounce, Perovium 2 ounces, Castle Soap one ounce'. This, Lady Wray claimed,

> . . . heals all wounds new and old, burns, scalds, felons, imposthumes, ulcers, fistulas, tetters, ringworms, St Anthony's Fire, sciatica, sprains, bruises, aches, King's Evil, strengthens sinews, draws out thorns, heals the gout, easeth the chollick, being layd to the belly, and if layd to the back it easeth the stone in the kidney.

Neither John Clavell, Elizabeth Butler nor Lady Ranelagh give us much idea of the reasoning behind the use of these recipes. Learned medicine worried greatly about this issue. In theory, as part of God's providence, there were growing on Irish soil herbs that were appropriate for the kind of diseases Irish people suffered from—scurvy grass for scurvy, feverfew for fever, eyebright for eye trouble and so on. In a letter to the Royal Society in 1763 the English clergyman Edward Stone invoked this 'doctrine of signatures' to support his discovery of the effectiveness of powdered willow bark (a primitive aspirin) in treating agues. Some believed that God encouraged the willows to flourish in just the damp areas most susceptible to fever. Often God had been considerate enough to indicate by a 'signature' what the plant might be useful for—yellow plants evidently came in handy for jaundice, for instance. In practice the matter was complicated by the patient's usually having more than one disease (or symp-

This quite sick young woman has apparently, for reasons of modesty, got out of bed to present herself to the physician.

toms appearing in various parts of the body), or the pure herb ('simple') might be too strong and cause internal damage. So dilutants and other herbs were compounded together, to produce increasingly fantastic amalgams.

Some of Clavell's recipes are marked 'probatum' or described as 'excellent' and a few carry the simple comment 'it helpeth'. Lady Wray said that her mixture performed wonders, but what did she, or indeed the Boyle family member who so carefully copied down the recipe and the recommendation, actually expect from it? Was it no more than simple empiricism, so that whatever seemed to work was valued? How did one choose between twenty or more remedies for gout or ague? Obviously there may have been simple practical reasons—one recipe was simply the easiest to prepare, or such and such a vital ingredient was not available (not every household, after all, can produce a spare pint of woman's milk) or the intended patient preferred this rather than that. But no doubt there were also therapeutic reasons: one was to be preferred if certain subsidiary symptoms were present, or another recipe seemed to work better for women than men, or certain recipes worked better at different seasons. Spring for instance was the time devoted to blood, air, childhood—Galenic medical approaches would take this into account. The justification of learned medicine was that it provided a formal mechanism, a narrative, by which medicines could be judged.

Medical encounters

Having tried the various household remedies, and decided that specialised care was required, the patient might call in a physician. Robert Burton, author of the best-known medical book of the day, *The Anatomy of Melancholy*, gives a vivid account of the four attributes conducive to success in the medical encounter. The first was that the patient should not be 'too niggardly miserable of his purse' and in saving a few coins neglect God's precious gift of health; on the other hand, equally deplorable were those who are 'too apt to take physic on every occasion, to aggravate every slender passion, imperfection, impediment; that if their finger do but ache, run, ride, send for a physician, as many gentlewomen do, that are sick without a cause'. The next desideratum was that the patient be honest and face the truth 'that out of bashfulness he do not conceal his grief'. As Burton points out, ''tis part of his cure to wish his own health, and not to defer it too long'. The third of Burton's requirements was that 'the patient be of good cheer, and have sure hope that his physician can help him . . . to this we may add perseverance, obedience and constancy; not to change his physician or to dislike him on every toy'. 'Last of all', says Burton, 'it is required that the patient be not too bold to practise upon himself, without an approved physician's consent, or to try conclusions if he read a receipt in a book; for so, many grossly mistake, and do themselves more harm than good.'[27] It is difficult to imagine any doctor, from that day to this, disagreeing with these sentiments.

Galenic theory was not only concerned with the patient's body. The land, the crops it grew, the air and water flowing round it deeply affected the inhabitants' humoural balance—and hence propensity to certain types of illness and length of life. Visiting Oxford in the 1680s, young Thomas Molyneux, a future President of the College, heard the learned Professor of Medicine, Dr Luff, discuss Chapter 5 of Genesis, which makes it clear that people lived very much longer just before and after the Flood. The pre-Flood patriarchs lived over 900 years before they died; even after the Flood their descendants to the time of Abraham averaged over 300 years of life. The puzzle was to understand what it was that enabled

these men to live so much longer than moderns. Some believed that the earth, being now over 5,600 years old, was emanating putrid airs that shortened lives.[28] Others thought it was something to do with the fact that after the Flood humans became weaker, and unable to digest vegetables and fruits, so God commanded Noah to eat meat (Genesis 9.2–3).[29]

Molyneux moved on to Leiden, where he became friendly with the philosopher and physician (then in exile) John Locke. Through Locke, Molyneux met Thomas Sydenham and found him, as he later told Locke, 'so thoroughly skill'd in all useful Knowledge of his profession and withal so communicative that his Acquaintance was a very great advantage to me'.[30]

Irish people growing up in, and eating food produced under, the cold wet conditions of the country were peculiarly susceptible to two generally non-fatal diseases: Irish ague (a kind of malaria) and looseness (dysentery). Irish ague, the physician Gerald Boate said, was

> . . . commonly accompanied with a great pain in the head and in all the bones, great weakness, drought, losse of all manner of appetite, and want of sleep, and for the most part idleness or raving, and restlessness and tossings, but no very great nor constant heat; is hard to be cured, for those that understand this disease, and seek to overcome it, do it not by purging, which cannot be used at any time without great and present danger; for the fermentation of the humours which caused the disease is hereby mightily increased and the patient weakens; and hardly with bleeding, which seldom is used with success otherwise than in the very beginning; but with strengthening medicines and good cordials: in which case, and if all necessary prescription be well observed, very few persons doe lose their lives: except when some extraordinary and pestilent malignity commeth to it as it befalleth in some yeares, with so great violence that notwithstanding all good helps, some are carried to their graves.[31]

The other characteristic ailment was simply called 'looseness', though several kinds could be distinguished. Gerald Boate elaborated:

> The Looseness doth also greatly reign in Ireland, as well among those of the countrie as among strangers . . . those that betimes make use of good medicines are without difficulty cured of it. But they that let the Looseness take its course do commonly after some days get the bleeding with it whereby the disease doth not only grow much more troublesome and painfull, but a great deal harder to be cured.

In his travels in Ireland in the 1630s, William Brereton, a future Parliamentary commander, suffered, and typically mentioned several of his own and others' prescriptions, but not those of a physician:

(Opposite) Valentine Greatrakes from Waterford had a flourishing local practice in Ireland both before and after his spectacular London vogue, beginning with the cure of local boy William Maher (Easter 1662). Seen through the window, a cured patient jauntily returns home, while another patient arrives.

THOMÆ MOLYNEUX EQ:AUR: M.D.
Obiit. 13. Oct: A.D. MDCCXXXIII. Æt: 72.

(Left) Sir Patrick Dun (1642–1713), who bequeathed money to establish professorships to develop the first formal medical education in Ireland.

(Right) Sir Thomas Molyneux (1661–1733): like many subsequent Presidents of the College, he studied at Leiden where he met John Locke; he later worked in London with Thomas Sydenham. He was President of the College in 1702, 1709, 1713, and 1720.

At my coming to Carrickfergus, and being troubled with an extreme flux, not as yet come to so great height as a bloody flux, my hostess, Mrs Wharton, directed me the use of cinnamon in burnt claret wine, or rather red wine, also the syrup and conserve of sloes well boiled, after they have been strained and mingled according to discretion with sugar; they are to be boiled with sugar until they be cleared, having been first boiled in water until they be softened, and then strained . . . The best things I found were these: usequebaugh with the yolk of an egg first and last, fast two hours before it; cinnamon water is also good and diacinamo-mum; but I found cinnamon water so distemper them in parting with my water as to put me to much pain and torment. . . . Sir Marmaduke Lloyde prescribed barley boiled in a bag as hot as may be to be placed in your close stool or under you when you go to stool, the fume hereof hath an excellent virtue; this was old Dr. Butler's direction to him, and to ride as far and as fast as he possibly could endure for a whole day. Sir Urian Leigh affirmed the fume of sage burnt upon a chafing-dish of coals often renewed placed in the close stool to have cured many.[12]

Two diseases that had formerly caused great distress seemed to be dying out. The first was leprosy, which had been common, but now seemed to have gone. For Boate, the reason was simple. This 'horrible and loathsome disease' had been caused by excessive consumption of salmon out of season. When the English parliament forbade this, the disease disappeared. Alas, the natives were not grateful, for as Boate complained, 'which great benefit, with so many others, that hateful people hath rewarded with seeking utterly to exterminate their benefactors'.

The second horror was plague. Since its first appearance in Ireland in the fourteenth century, the peculiar sudden virulence of the plague left society with a profound sense of helplessness. During an outbreak, men and women died, in great pain, only days, sometimes hours, after catching the disease. The physical symptoms were apocalyptic in intensity, as if the victim's body were exploding from inside. In 1348 the Irish chronicler wrote: 'many died of boils and abcesses and pustules, which erupted on their shins or under their armpits; others died frantic with pain in their head and others spitting blood'. No wonder people regarded plague as a blow from the hand of God.

The first reaction of the rich (and their medical advisors) to an outbreak was to escape into the country, leaving the poor to breathe the polluted air that was felt to be the immediate cause. In 1665, on medical advice, the Mayor of London caused bonfires to be lit throughout the city and kept going day and night to sweeten the air, and schoolboys at Eton were flogged for not smoking their prophylatic tobacco pipes. With a case-mortality rate of up to 80 per cent, a third or in extreme cases half, of a town's population could die, with all the resultant social disruption.

Ireland was not attacked so frequently as England, where plague re-appeared every twenty years. According to Sir William Wilde there had been five or six great outbursts since the fourteenth century, the most recent in Dublin being in the summer of 1575 when as much as one-third of the city's population died.[33] An outbreak in 1650 was reported to have 'exceedingly depopulated' the city.[34] Plague's effects were cataclysmic, and its causes obscure (diagnosis being confused by the fact that there are at least three separate forms of the disease—the pneumonic version, conveyed by droplets, being considerably more virulent than the rat-flea-carried version, and the rare septicaemic form more fatal still). Mysteriously, after 1660 it seems to have virtually disappeared from Ireland and Britain, though this, of course, was only clear long afterwards. An outbreak of plague in Marseilles in 1720 caused widespread fears of its reappearance in Ireland, and a flurry of pamphlets.

It was, wrote Robert Burton, 'those crying sins of ours which pull these several plagues and miseries upon our head'.[35] Public immorality—that 'high provokeinge of God'—was thus a health issue. This did not mean, as some feared, that physicians' attempts to effect cures were akin to a blasphemous attempt to thwart God's pleasure. As Burton explained, 'God works by means, as Christ cured the blind man with clay and spittle'.[36] It was the responsibility of the physician to identify and apply correctly the cures that God had created in the minerals, herbs, plants etc. Of course this work was done under God. As Burton put it: 'We must first begin with a prayer, and then use physick'.[37]

By the 1650s Galen's views were beginning to be considered critically. Most notably this occurred in anatomy, as his errors were brought to light; but also in medicine. However, the old orthodoxy was not immediately abandoned. William Harvey's now classic *De Motu Cordis et Sanguinis* (1628), which described the circulation of the blood, aroused the opposition of learned and public alike, not least because to accept criticism of Galen in this particular threw the whole of his theory into doubt. And that cast a shadow over 1,500 years of medical theory and practice. It was as if an academic biologist today had proved that mycobacterium tuberculosis was not in fact responsible for tuberculosis, and thus undermined germ theory as a whole. As it happens, it is always easier to extinguish a theory than to extirpate practices based on it. We shall see that Galenic injunctions continued to be part of popular medical lore as late as the twentieth century.

During the second half of the seventeenth century mechanical and analytic ideas associated with Descartes, Boyle and Locke also began to affect the way physicians thought about the body and sickness. The shift from the Galenic idea that diseases were manifestations of essentially unquantifiable imbalances between fluids, to an idea that they were classifiable, objective and related to each other by species and genus, just like plants, began. By the eighteenth century, particularly under the influence of Thomas Molyneux's friend, Thomas Sydenham, diseases were seen as specific collections of symptoms whose causes might be inscrutable, but which had a definite objective existence.

Chapter Three
The 1750s

Seeking 'the chearful circulation of the blood and juices'

MEDICINE WAS PRACTISED IN a strikingly different intellectual and social world only a hundred years after the foundation of the College. The occult mysteries of neo-platonism, alchemy and magic had faded into the shadows whence they came.[1] Even astrology, which, following Hippocrates, had long been regarded as an essential weapon in the physician's armoury, was mocked, at least by the sophisticated. In the *Pharmacopoeia* published by the College in 1746, most of the remedies from the science of older times—such as the so-called *dreckapotheke*, in which the loathsomeness of disease was matched with remedies such as human fat, moss from a dead man's skull, dried mice, millipedes and spiders' webs—had been eliminated, leaving only a residual feeling that to be effective a medicine had to taste nasty.[2] A few ancient nostrums remained, such as the famous medieval standby Venice Treacle or *Theriaca andromachi*. Venice Treacle, of which viper's flesh was considered the active ingredient, was first concocted as an antidote to snakebite and was later refined by Andromachus of Crete, on the order of Nero, to be effective against other poisons. By the Middle Ages it had become a general cure-all. The 61 separate ingredients (or 72 in the official recipe of the Faculté de Médicine of Paris) included viper's flesh, narcotics, foetid substances, bitters, saccharine, balsams, earth and opium.

Eighteenth-century thinkers dreamed of a world without essential mystery, in which all reasonable questions could be answered, and the answers would be mutually compatible. Descartes, Boyle, Newton and others had shown the thinking public that knowable, quantified laws governed the planets and the sublunary world, and the search was on for similar laws in medicine and other human sciences. The dangerous, passionate religious enthusiasm of the seventeenth century had dissolved in the rational acid of the Enlightenment, leaving a calm indifference. Some of this calm was shaken, however, by the earthquake which destroyed Lisbon in 1755, the shock effects of which were felt in Cork. The

John Locke (1632–1704), the eighteenth-century philosopher, was a friend of Robert Boyle and William and Thomas Molyneux. He studied medicine at Oxford, and collaborated with Thomas Sydenham in various writings. He continued to practice medicine in a small way to the end of his life.

An essential key to health in the mid-eighteenth century was mental control, here epitomised by a calm Georgian interior of family life; ascribed to Strickland Lowry. (National Gallery of Ireland)

meaningless destruction of a European capital jolted many people's confidence in the essential rationality of things.

Most men and women were still believers, but their belief was guided by books with titles such as *The Reasonableness of Christianity* by John Locke and *Christianity not Mysterious* by the Irishman John Toland. Following Locke, human reason was revered as the only faculty by which anything, even God's revelation itself, could be assessed. Luckily, reason generally led to the conclusion that the standards and values of the Protestant gentry were the ideal. At the same time, even in Dublin, full-blown deists and freethinkers were to be found—'a set of men not infrequent in this city', as Edmund Burke wrote later in the century. But since freethinking implied tolerance, and tolerance implied equality for Catholics, this was not a position the Ascendancy generally adopted. Much devout practice of religion was not, on the other hand, expected. When in 1759 Lady Kildare took it into her head to go to her local church on a Saturday, 'the man told me I cou'd not go to my seat, which was not ready, for that no quality was ever expected at Church of a week-day'.[3]

In the 1750s Dublin was in the middle of an impressive surge of growth that saw its population rise from 93,000 in 1716 to 140,000 in the 1750s to nearly 200,000 by the end of the century. However, since the number of births in the city still did not exceed deaths (and was not to do so until the late nineteenth century) this growth came from migration, especially from the Catholic population of surrounding Leinster. As a result, the strongly Protestant character of the city that Stearne and Petty knew became steadily diluted. In 1716 some two-thirds of Dubliners were Protestant; by the end of the century this proportion had sunk to less than one-third. The profession (and the College) by contrast was to remain Protestant for a long time—it was not until the 1911 Census that Catholic physicians numbered even half of those working in Dublin.

The city was also enjoying the social and political benefits of the increased prosperity of the country as a whole. As the historians of Trinity College put it,

> . . . by 1753 the ice of early Georgian Dublin was breaking up fast. The siege mentality which had dominated Irish Protestantism since 1641 had at last disappeared, for even the most nervous Whig can hardly have taken seriously after about 1750 the threat of a Jacobite restoration, and the Ascendancy was by now so firmly established that some relaxation of the penal laws could be contemplated. There grew up accordingly a new spirit, confident, expansive and relatively tolerant, with its exuberance tempered in art and literature, if not always in life, by the canons of classical good taste.[4]

The medical marketplace

Since the early days described in the previous chapter, the College had finally received formal Royal endorsement, first by Charles II in 1667 and subsequently by William and Mary in 1692. The 1692 Charter established the cumbersomely named 'The King and Queen's College of Physicians of Ireland', which was the formal title of the College until the late nineteenth century. As well as powers to regulate physicians, in theory this new Charter gave the College extensive powers of control over apothecaries and practitioners in the Dublin area. In practice, these powers were never ratified by legislation, largely because of successful lobbying by the apothecaries, who did not, of course, feel the need for such supervision.

The major development in the College in the 1740s had been the enactment, at last, of Sir Patrick Dun's will. In his *Memoir* of Sir Patrick, T. W. Belcher (Hon. Librarian of the College) records that his family were originally from Aberdeen, where Dun's great-grandmother had been burned as a witch.[5] Appointed physician to the Lord Lieutenant in the 1670s, Dun became a successful society physician and also a member of the sophisticated circle of the Dublin Philosophical Society. He was elected President of the College for the first time in 1681, and subsequently was re-elected seven times. When he died in 1713 his celebrated will, establishing a professorship of physick in the College, fell into legal complexities. A professor was appointed finally in 1717, but legal scrapping with Sir Patrick's widow was not finally resolved until 1741. By this time Sir Patrick's leases, following the sharply rising trend of the economy, had greatly increased in value. Now there was finance enough for three professorships (physick, surgery and midwifery, and pharmacy and *materia medica*). Lady Dun died in 1748, at which

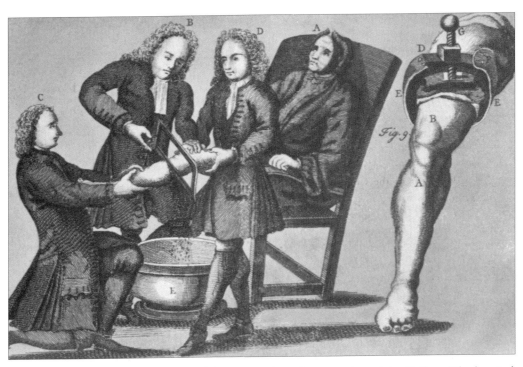

From a surgical text-book of the period, a highly stylised view of an amputation—the patient is not even grasping the arm of the chair! (1743)

point Sir Patrick's library came into the possession of the College. The hospital was finally established much later, in 1791.

Dublin was tolerably well-supplied with medical practitioners of various sorts. A compilation of names and trades for 1738 identifies 30 physicians, 19 surgeons and 11 apothecaries, not to mention druggists, patent medicine sellers and oculists.[6] To the irritation of the College, the apothecaries could not be prevented either from visiting patients or prescribing. Surgeons also could not be limited to the knife and cautery. In his textbook *Chirurgical Pharmacy* (published in Dublin in 1761) Robert Doussie distinguishes the field of general pharmacy from that appropriate to surgery, which dealt with 'the cure of disorders of particular parts only'. This included skin diseases (certain cancers and syphilis were so defined) as well as more obvious local injuries. But Doussie recognised that the distinction is artificial, and surgeons were typically treated as a kind of general practitioner by the public. There was, in fact, an informal hierarchy: some ailments and injuries were susceptible to home remedies, others required the apothecary to confirm that they were indeed serious. The apothecary might prescribe himself (though he was not supposed to charge for anything other than medicines) or he might hand the case over to a surgeon or a physician. Of course it was also possible to call in a surgeon or a physician directly.

Only half of the physicians would have been attached to the College. Some years later, in 1754, there were 12 Fellows, 4 'candidates' (awaiting a vacancy in the list of Fellows) and 9 Licentiates, of whom 3 were Licentiates in the relatively new speciality of midwifery. Of those not attached to the College, many would have been Catholics and therefore ineligible. By 1780 there were, according to Wilson's *Dublin Directory*, 49 physicians practising in the city, of whom 11 were Catholic. There were 66 surgeons of whom perhaps 10 were Catholic; although the Royal College of Surgeons in Ireland had, from its foundation in 1784, a visible Catholic presence, Catholics were an even smaller minority among surgeons than among physicians.[7] The rest of the country was much less plentifully supplied with medical attendants.

A typical medical training for a top physician such as John Anderson (1708–61), President of the College in 1751, started with an arts degree from TCD, followed by study in Leiden under the great Boerhaave; Anderson then returned to take his MB in 1738 and his MD in 1741. He was physician at Mercer's Hospital. A year or two in Leiden regularly formed part of the high-flying Irish physicians' training. Between 1730 and 1767 men trained by Boerhaave filled the College's presidential chair no fewer than 23 times. In all, some 122 Irish medical students passed through his hands.[8] Rather less prominent were the 542 Irish students who studied in Reims between 1620 and 1753.[9] These courses were said to be cheaper than Leiden, and the examinations easier—but above all the local religion was Catholic.

Boerhaave, who also lectured in chemistry and botany, encouraged a wide scientific interest. In his lectures and clinical discussions students learned a new mechanistic view of the functions of the body, stressing the insights of the new sciences rather than the subtle balances of the classical writers. In particular, Boerhaave treated Galen's theory of humours and qualities seriously but shortly: in the end, the great man was 'mistaken' and 'in error'. The anatomists had struck the first blows, and now the most respected physician in Europe added his word.[10] There was, on the other hand, no substitute for long study of the modern and especially the ancient authors, who still had many insights to give into disease. The physician's training was determinedly holistic, being aimed at knowing 'the animal frame in its perfect state; the various laws of its oeconomy, the functions of its organs . . . from that he is led to know its imperfections or diseased state'.[11]

The experience of sickness

For all the apparent calm—the measured grandeur of its buildings, the dignified tread of its prose—the eighteenth century, particularly the first half, was a period in which sickness, pain and death were ever-present. The narratives of sickness recorded how an apparently trivial imprudence could have dire consequences even for the most learned. In his 'Life of Boerhaave', published in 1739, Samuel Johnson related how the great man was laid up in agony for months simply as a result of going straight from his bed to walk on the dewy grass one morning. Contemporary diaries and letters are full of accounts of people being confined for weeks with what are described as colds, of apparently trivial accidents rapidly taking a near fatal turn, of reports of earache, sore eyes, bad teeth. Little Mary-Anne FitzGerald died of fever so suddenly that her aunt fretted that she had neglected her—but the doctor assured Lady Louisa Conolly that nothing could have been done. 'The state of her blood was so foul that the most trifling illness was sufficient to produce the very malignant and rapid fever of which she died.' This, wrote Lady Louisa, 'is to be accounted for by her imprudence in the frequent improper wetting of feet, keeping on damp clothes and subjecting herself to the sudden transition of colds and heats . . . her constitution had a tendency to obstructions of every kind, bowels and pores'.[12]

Life expectancy at birth in England actually fell between 1720 and 1750, and even before the famine of the 1740s the Irish rural population suffered periodic surges and declines. Not only did many children die, but those who survived seem to have been weakened. The cumulative insult of poor nutrition and not-quite-cured ailments meant that small bruises and injuries took long to repair. In addition, health-conscious parents deliberately kept their children on 'lowering' diets to prevent fevers; in practice these must have reduced their resistance to infection. In his pamphlet *The Case of Five Children who were inoculated in Dublin on the 26th of August 1725* a future President of the College, Bryan Robinson, wrote with approval: 'A gentleman had six children, five sons and a daughter, who from their infancy had been kept to a regular cooling diet and had scarcely tasted flesh.' Once they were inoculated, they were allowed even less: 'They were kept from flesh meat and were only allowed bread and milk, bread and butter, light puddings, tea with milk and things of that nature.' Sick people were also systematically under-nourished, on the theory, as the popular Swiss writer Tissot, put it, that 'as long as a sick person has a bad humour or ferment in his stomach his weakness increases in proportion to the food he receives. For this being corrupted by the infected matter it meets there proves incapable of nourishing and becomes a conjunct or additional cause of the distemper.'[13]

Babies and very young children were, of course, the most vulnerable, even in the grandest households. Emily Lennox, who became Duchess of Leinster, had twenty-two children between 1748 and 1778. Of these seven died at or before the age of five. The household of the premier duke in the country had therefore a child mortality rate as bad as countries in sub-Saharan Africa today.[14] The duchess did employ the services of the fashionable men-midwives, with their emblematic instrument the forceps, but no doubt the fact that only one of her children died immediately after birth was more a tribute to her own constitution than to any contribution of the new profession. The children managed an average lifespan of thirty-three years (the average life expectancy of the British aristocracy at the time was just over thirty-six years). The seven children born to her after the age of thirty-five averaged a mere twenty-two years of life each.

Although historians have suggested otherwise, in fact this vulnerability did not ease the heartache. In 1755 Emily was brought to bed with a daughter, but the child quickly died.

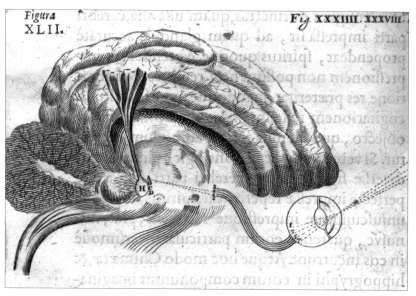

Figura
XLII.

Fig. XXXIIII. XXXVIII.

Were nerves tubular or solid? The former implied the existence of some form of nervous analogy to blood in which messages from the brain were carried to the body. If the latter it was a puzzle to know how this conveyance operated (1680).

This poor dear little thing who was as beautiful as it is possible for any thing of that age to be. I saw the sweet little creature but once and was delighted with it. That night the first symptoms of its illness appeared but it seems it was born with some inward disorder which nothing cou'd have cured.[15]

Even in rich households worms and bedbugs were not unlikely. Staying in London, Lady Kildare wrote to her husband on 10 May 1761: 'I am all over bug-bites . . . tormented all night with these bugs cou'd not sleep'. And some years later her sister Sarah puzzles over a daughter's failure to thrive: 'The point is doubtful whether she has worms or obstructions to remove, or if her complaint is an habitual weakness'.[16] And simple accidents would happen: in 1761 five-year-old Charles FitzGerald tumbled out of a cart while playing, and hurt his leg: 'Dear little Charles', wrote his mother, Emily, to her sister, 'is lame; he has a sore leg. I have quite an hospital here, but I hope it won't signify. He is mighty comical about it, calls it the gout.' (A little lord would, of course, play at having the aristocratic gout rather than some more plebeian ailment.) A week later, 'Charles breaks out in scabs and blotches more and more every day; both his feet sore.'

Following Boerhaave, by far the most influential medical teacher of the age, doctors considered the human body 'as composed of tubulous fibres that constitute hydraulic machines and solid matter not properly part of such machines'.[17] The tubes contained fluids which were moved round the body by the action of the solids, and the solids were in turn 'nourished, preserved and restored' by the fluids.[18] The whole system was kept in motion by 'a vital economy peculiar to animals'. Much attention was paid to hydraulics, for instance by Bryan Robinson

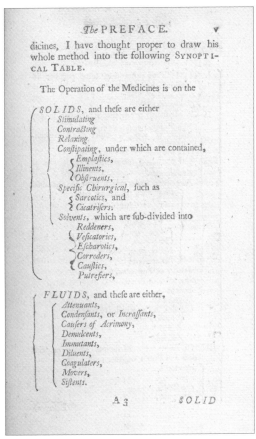

The PREFACE.   v

dicines, I have thought proper to draw his whole method into the following SYNOPTI-CAL TABLE.

The Operation of the Medicines is on the

SOLIDS, and thefe are either
  Stimulating
  Contracting
  Relaxing
  Conftipating, under which are contained,
    Emplaftics,
    Illinents,
    Obftruents,
  Specific Chirurgical, such as
    Sarcotics, and
    Cicatrifers.
  Solvents, which are fub-divided into
    Reddeners,
    Veficatories,
    Efcharotics,
    Corroders,
    Cauftics,
    Putrefiers,

FLUIDS, and thefe are either,
  Attenuants,
  Condenfants, or Incraffants,
  Caufers of Acrimony,
  Demulcents,
  Immutants,
  Diluents,
  Coagulaters,
  Movers,
  Siftents.

A 3   SOLID

Hermann Boerhaave (1668–1738) the great Dutch physician and teacher of the early eighteenth century, whose courses at Leiden attracted students from all over Europe.

in his treatise on *Animal Oeconomy* (1732) which is full of diagrams visualising flows though idealised tubes. Although the fluids went under the traditional name of humours, they were by no means the same as envisaged by Hippocrates and Galen. 'The fluids . . . may be reduced to five kinds: the alimentary juice or chyle, blood, lymph, oil and the secreted humours.'[19] Fluids were subject to two general classes of 'depravity': viscosity, or stickiness, and sharpness, or acrimony, which arose when foreign elements impeded its natural flow, and therefore its ability to nourish the solid parts of the body. Little Lord Charles' physician diagnosed 'a great sharpness in his blood, or [he] wou'd have been well long ago'.

Faced with the bewildering range of human disease, the profession had evolved a formidable armoury. In his *Treatise on the Powers of Medicines* Boerhaave identified over 80 different types of medicine, distinguishing between those acting on the solids or the fluids or both. Each type then had specifics for various intended actions such as stimulating, relaxing, contracting, condensing etc. For each of these actions any one of several remedies made from a single herb (simples) might be suggested. In 1761 the Dublin surgeon Robert Doussie, dealing with pharmacy for the cure of topical diseases only (i.e. those affecting particular parts), divided external medicines into sixteen classes, and listed a further thirteen classes of medicines to be used internally.[20]

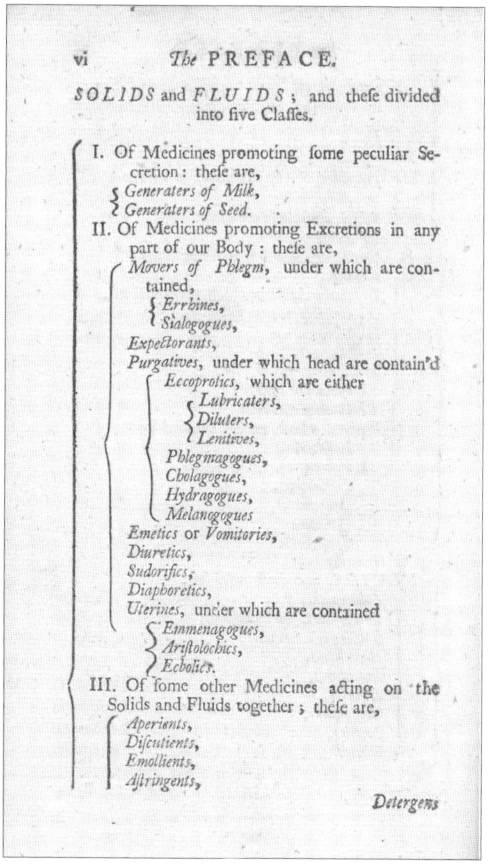

vi *The* PREFACE.

SOLIDS and *FLUIDS*; and theſe divided into five Claſſes.

- I. Of Medicines promoting ſome peculiar Secretion: theſe are,
  - *Generaters of Milk,*
  - *Generaters of Seed.*
- II. Of Medicines promoting Excretions in any part of our Body: theſe are,
  - *Movers of Phlegm*, under which are contained,
    - *Errhines,*
    - *Sialogogues,*
  - *Expectorants,*
  - *Purgatives*, under which head are contain'd
    - *Eccoprotics*, which are either
      - *Lubricaters,*
      - *Diluters,*
      - *Lenitives,*
    - *Phlegmagogues,*
    - *Cholagogues,*
    - *Hydragogues,*
    - *Melanogogues*
  - *Emetics* or *Vomitories,*
  - *Diuretics,*
  - *Sudorifics,*
  - *Diaphoretics,*
  - *Uterines*, under which are contained
    - *Emmenagogues,*
    - *Ariſtolochics,*
    - *Ecbolics.*
- III. Of ſome other Medicines acting on the Solids and Fluids together; theſe are,
  - *Aperients,*
  - *Diſcutients,*
  - *Emollients,*
  - *Aſtringents,*

Detergens

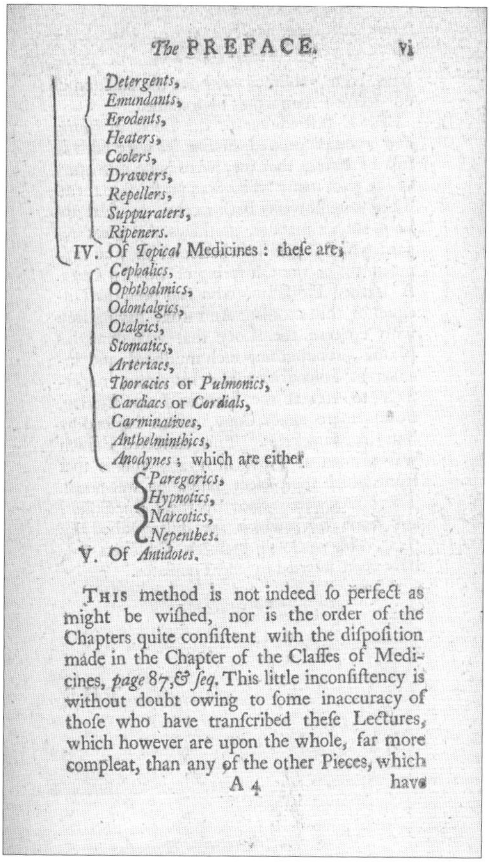

The PREFACE. vii

  - *Detergents,*
  - *Emundants,*
  - *Erodents,*
  - *Heaters,*
  - *Coolers,*
  - *Drawers,*
  - *Repellers,*
  - *Suppuraters,*
  - *Ripeners.*
- IV. Of *Topical* Medicines: theſe are,
  - *Cephalics,*
  - *Ophthalmics,*
  - *Odontalgics,*
  - *Otalgics,*
  - *Stomatics,*
  - *Arteriacs,*
  - *Thoracics* or *Pulmonics,*
  - *Cardiacs* or *Cordials,*
  - *Carminatives,*
  - *Anthelminthics,*
  - *Anodynes*; which are either
    - *Paregorics,*
    - *Hypnotics,*
    - *Narcotics,*
    - *Nepenthes.*
- V. Of *Antidotes.*

THIS method is not indeed ſo perfect as might be wiſhed, nor is the order of the Chapters quite conſiſtent with the diſpoſition made in the Chapter of the Claſſes of Medicines, *page* 87, *& ſeq.* This little inconſiſtency is without doubt owing to ſome inaccuracy of thoſe who have tranſcribed theſe Lectures, which however are upon the whole, far more compleat, than any of the other Pieces, which

A 4 have

In his System of Medicine *Boerhaave identified some 80 types of medical action that could be produced by medicines. He often recommends a complex prescription of several drugs, herbs or concoctions to produce a single effect.*

At the end of sickness there was, of course, death. The Bills of Mortality (still covering Protestant deaths only) reported that 1,897 people had been buried in Dublin in 1754, with the major assigned causes as follows:

Fever	413
Aged	308
Smallpox	292
Fits	140
Teeth	136
Decay	112
Infants	108
Consumption	93
Childbed	44
Measles	2
Flux	20
Spotted fever	18

Since the causes were still being assigned by elderly women employed by the parish, they lack technical polish. The combined categories 'aged' and 'infants' are no more than life stages, and they are followed by the catch-all 'fever'. The easily recognised and deadly smallpox accounted for fully 15 per cent of all deaths. 'Fits' and 'teeth' are hardly precise terms, though presumably 'consumption' and 'measles' would be recognisable.

Not that learned physicians could do much better—just at this time, Jean-Jacques Buhier's book *Dissertation sur les signes de la mort* (published in a pirated translation in Dublin in 1748) alerted the public to an uncertainty about the fact of death itself—and the potential horrors of premature burial, which haunted the European imagination for generations. Every country had its legends about the survivors of premature burial—a Mrs Marjorie McCall from Lurgan was popularly supposed to have a tablet on her eventual gravestone reading 'Lived once—buried twice'.

Sickroom ritual

The rituals of sickroom attendance were well established. In 1759 Swift's friend Mrs Delany described how her god-daughter became extremely ill:

> I sent on Friday night for Dr Quin, who is a very sensible, good physician and an ingenious and agreeable man. [Quin, who had a large fashionable practice, was President of the College no fewer than seven times.] Had an emetic in case it should be wanted; but he desired it might not be given till the next morning, and when he came he would not venture to give it, but said she must be blooded; no marks appeared until Saturday night, and the doctor pronounced it the small pox with every favourable symptom. Mrs Hamilton of Finglass has offered (and I gladly accept) her assistance to nurse. She has a great deal of experience with her children and friends and has sense and spirit, which will be useful to all, and a great relief to my mind . . . This is the eighth day. Mrs Hamilton lies in a little bed in the dressing-room next to Sally and will not suffer me to sit up beyond my usual hour. As she is very watchful, and never goes to bed when at home and alone before two o'clock, it makes me comply easily. The nursekeeper is also a very sober, good sort of woman, and used to tend the small pox, but it is too critical a distemper to trust entirely to any nursekeeper til after the turn.[21]

The rhythm of fever was well known: anxious watching and care, especially at night when the crisis was most likely to occur, were essential until the disease took 'a right turn' and then all was well—as Bishop Synge, writing with paternal anxiety to his daughter Alicia in the 1750s, put it. Her fever having subsided 'is I am sure an indication of returning health'. The fact that she was still lean and weak was a good sign, 'fullness or colour would be a continuation of disease'.[22]

As we have seen, smallpox was a potent scourge which, like TB in a later generation, particularly attacked the young. Most recovered, but some were horribly pock-marked, and some blinded. For a young, unmarried woman without much of a fortune this could be ruinous, as Mrs Delany described: 'Visit a young lady who has just recovered of the smallpox. I think I never saw a prettier creature than she was before that malicious distemper seized her . . . all the men were dying while she was in danger but . . . now they will not acknowledge her for a divinity since she is divested of those charms that occasioned their devotion'.[23] In 1764, young Charles FitzGerald, then aged nine, was struck. He made a good recovery, to the delight of his aunt Lady Holland, but doubts remained: 'I do most sincerely and from my heart give you joy, my sweet siss, of Lord Charles' recovery. I'm impatient to hear again, and now begin to think of his pretty phiz; will he be mark'd? Tho' I believe your alarm had been too great to think of his beauty.'[24] Charles survived unmarked, and lived to a reasonable age.

'A very sensible, good physician'—Sir Henry Quin, the most fashionable Dublin physician of the mid eighteenth century. Six times President of the College and King's Professor of the Practice of Medicine.

Such was the fear of smallpox that inoculation, introduced to Britain in the early eighteenth century, aroused much interest. The great proponent in society was Lady Mary Wortley Montagu, wife of the British Ambassador to Turkey, who described how people there 'send to one another to know if any of their family has a mind to have the smallpox; they make parties for this purpose . . . every year thousands undergo this operation and there is no example of anyone who has died'.[25] At least in the early days, European experience was more equivocal. In the description of an inoculation, Bryan Robinson described how the fourth son of a family had caught smallpox in the normal way—'his pocks being distinct and good' it was decided to inoculate the rest of the family. 'They were each of them prepared for the Distemper by two doses of a purging infusion'; but unfortunately the experience was not a happy one. Two of the sons died within ten days of the inoculation process, including the eldest, aged thirteen. It was later estimated that 1 in 100 died of inoculation—which was considerably better than 10 or 20 in 100 who died of natural smallpox, but enough to make the practice controversial.

Until travelling inoculators started to spread across the country (they were still active in the 1850s) inoculation was an expensive business requiring elaborate preparation by purges etc. and often several weeks of medical attention once the disease had been caught. The possibility of a bad outcome was used by opponents of the technique; others argued from scripture—did not Saint Paul teach that one should not do evil to produce good? There was another more sinister point. To inoculate was deliberately to foster a very infectious disease. This might be good for the patient who was likely to get only an attenuated form, but the peo-

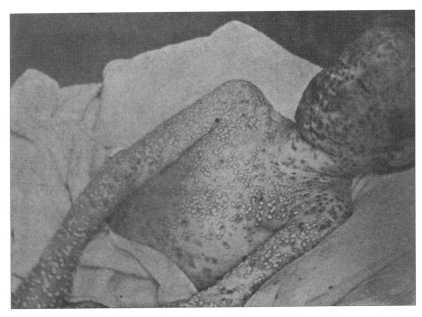

*The horror
of smallpox.*

ple around were exposed to smallpox in its full strength. Inoculation was, in fact, made illegal in Paris in 1763, after an epidemic had been blamed on inoculators. To its proponents, however, inoculation was perhaps the first really effective medical technique for preventing disease.[26]

Like many in their position, the Lennox sisters were keen 'physicians', and kept up with medical theory. In the letter previously quoted, Lady Holland remarked: 'I don't think it impossible but the humours may take a turn after so great a discharge as a full smallpox must occasion and that he may get the better of his other disorders the sooner for it.' The belief was that in the course of Nature's struggle with one set of morbid particles it often happened that particles that might have caused other symptoms were flushed out at the same time. This led to a philosophical acceptance of certain manageable conditions such as gout, which among other advantages located the 'badness' in the feet (toe and heel) well away from the dangerously vulnerable inner body. In his influential *Practice of Physic*, John Gregory noted that 'after a regular fit of the gout the patient enjoys perfect health, and gets free from many complaints he had before been subject to—it has sometimes removed epilepsy, and other nervous disorders, asthma, dropsy, gutta serena, intermittent fevers, nephritic and stomachic complaints and sometimes alternates with these disorders'.[27]

From the point of view of treatment, control and stimulation of appropriate evacuations was still the critical discipline. Depending on the disease one might encourage sweating by sudorifics, or reduce bodily heat by cooling; a 'comfortable vomit', as it was often called, could be induced if Nature seemed that way inclined. Vomits and evacuations of all sorts were a regular concern of physicians, particularly the quantity and quality of urine and stools. Clysters and enemas were equally popular. In *Gulliver's Travels* Swift mordantly described current medical practice: 'in all Diseases Nature is forced out of her Seat; therefore to replace her in it, the Body must be treated in a Manner directly contrary, by interchanging the Use of each Orifice: forcing Solids and Liquids in at the anus and making Evacuations at the Mouth'.[28] More gently, Dr Johnson recommended his friend John Perkins, about to embark on a voyage, to 'get a smart seasickness if you can'.[29]

Bryan Robinson was a strong proponent of vomits, believing that they effectively stimulated heat and motion in the blood. *In Virtues and Operations of Medicine* Robinson described fifteen cases of the dramatic effects of vomits, including 'Case 6: When I attended Dr Steevens' hospital in the year 1737 I took five or six men who from pleurisies had a hectick fever, attended with a spitting of purulent matter, and night sweats, and sent them out all free from those complaints by vomiting them every day, and allowing them the flesh diet of the house.'[30] Others were less keen, including Lord Kildare's Dr Duncan who feared that too frequent use of vomits such as mustard or horseradish could lead to dependence.[31]

In 1752 Bishop Synge, believing his daughter was keeping the details of her ill-health from him, wrote to her:

Dean Swift (1667–1745) founded St Patrick's Hospital for the mentally ill, but took a sardonic view of the activities of contemporary physicians, perhaps as result of his own ill-health.

> Upon the whole I saw something was wrong, and that the seat of the disorder was Stomach and bowels. But by your account the Vomit shew'd you had a clean stomach, and the Doctor says only that you threw up some tough phlegm, not much. It's having purged you, Mrs J says, had been of great use. For what, thought I? How are my Dear Girl's bowels affected? There is a latent disorder which does not yet fully shew itself; and the longer it is in shewing itself, the worse it may prove.[32]

Bleeding provided an opportunity for the poisons carried in the blood to be flushed out. It was normally done from the arm by a surgeon, but sometimes a

Dr Steevens' Hospital, the second Dublin voluntary hospital, opened in 1733. From the beginning doctors such as Bryan Robinson (who reported the medicinal effects of vomits) were conscious of the opportunity presented by wards full of fever patients.

physician might decide to stimulate the flow from a particular spot, perhaps by the use of leeches. Artificially created blisters mimicked the evacuative effects of sores naturally produced.

Except among the very devout and evangelistic, ill-health was no longer seen as a punishment for specific immorality. On the other hand, one did have responsibility to preserve one's own health as far as possible. By the age of forty, as the saying had it, one was either a fool or a physician. For individuals the starting point was the six so-called 'non-naturals' (called thus in contrast to the natural processes inside the body). These went back to Galen, and were: the air breathed, food and drink, sleep, exercise, evacuations (of all sorts) and mental calm. The medical, as opposed to aesthetic, virtues of cleanliness were not widely appreciated until the acceptance of germ theory.

In a world thick with smoke and foul smells (of which people were becoming increasingly conscious) it was natural to concern oneself with the air quality. Especially in towns, the 'filth and nastiness, their deleterious smokes, noxious vapours and foul air etc.', as one author put it,[33] were potent sources of corruption. Many physicians believed that the apparently random outbreaks of epidemics were traceable to sour exhalations from the earth (as, for instance, after earthquakes) that infected the air; the well-known seasonality of diseases (diarrhoea in the summer, ague in the winter) was self-evidently caused by seasonal changes in the air; and finally to particular weather shifts, 'for instance pleurisies, quinces and the like which generally happen when an intense and long-continued cold spell is immediately succeeded by a sudden heat'.[34] This theory gave doctors a professional interest in weather changes which lasted until the end of the nineteenth century. College Licentiate John Rutty's magisterial *Chronological History of the Weather and Seasons* (1770) covered 40 seasons of observations. The *Dublin Journal of Medical Science* regularly carried weather summaries, and in

1894 Sir John Moore (President of the College 1898–9) published his *Meteorology Practical and Applied*, though by this time Koch and Pasteur had pointed the profession in a different direction.

Careful regulation of eating and drinking was important. People constantly considered whether such and such a foodstuff was 'cooling' or 'heating'; thus Bishop Synge asked his daughter to check whether buttermilk was wholesome for breakfast, 'even Ned [apothecary Edward Curtis] need not fear it's being too cool, if Wine enough at dinner will ballance it'. By simple physical association, red meat and red wine were heating, chicken and milk were cooling. Spa waters, particularly those with iron content, were valued as supplying extremely valuable minerals, and in 1757 John Rutty produced a reference book, *The Mineral Waters of Ireland*, detailing their specific chemical virtues.

Regular sex was commonly regarded as essential to long-term health for men and for women, though when the Duke of Leinster hinted as such to his sister-in-law, she would have none of it: 'I should quarrel with the Duke of Leinster as I do with all men that fancy that they are so mighty necessary to a woman's health and happiness; it's abominably indelicate and I don't believe a word of it. I'm sure one sees many an old virgin mighty well and mighty comfortable.'[35]

Theriac, or Venice Treacle; a panacea with at least 70 ingredients, some very costly including viper's flesh and opium. This handsome jar, specially made for the Jesuits, indicates how precious Theriac was. (Science and Society Picture Library London)

Although there had always been taboos, it does seem that Lady Holland's reference to indelicacy marks a shift in sensibility. Starting with the upper class, women, and later men, seem to have become increasingly reticent and self-conscious about bodily matters. This trend was not reversed until the twentieth century, and in some respects has not yet been for men, as their reluctance to attend to their health suggests. An indication of this shift lies in the letters Bishop Synge wrote while he was concerned that his daughter Alicia, by then aged eighteen, should from modesty conceal the fact of her period from the doctor. (We can hardly imagine his successors writing to their daughters on such a subject.) To the bishop it was important because, lacking this information, her doctor might dangerously misprescribe. He was convinced that his wife's death had been due to this cause, and that of a Mrs Southwell: 'A severe cold, got at a critical time and conceal'd by the false modesty which ruins multitudes, laid the foundation of irremediable disorders.'[36] In his contemporary best-seller *Domestic Medicine* (aimed primarily, as the title implies, at women) William Buchan bluntly warns against such pudeur. 'Delicacy is doubtless a virtue; but that can never be reckoned true delicacy which induces any one to risk his health or hazard his life.'[37]

There was, of course, no question of full physical examination. The nearest the physician got to physically touching the patient was checking the pulse and then only for qualitative indicators—was it weak or strong, regular or intermittent? The physician would scrutinise the outward appearance and examine urine or stools, and the qualities of any blood drawn, but by far the most important technique was a critical hearing of the patient's own account of symptoms and what was felt about them. The physician's enquiry as to how the patient felt was more than mere courtesy. Instruments of quantitative measurement were a nineteenth-century innovation whose use was relevant to the more atomised approach to disease which replaced the whole-body approach of the eighteenth century. Writing in 1769 Edward Foster thought a thermometer 'a necessary piece of furniture' for his ideal hospital, but it was for measuring the air temperature.[38]

The last and most important of the 'non-naturals' were calmness of mind and control of the passions. These were prized not only for their own sakes, but as the essential bedrock of health. It was no coincidence that Swift's calmly rational Houyhnhnms knew nothing of disease. The mind, it was thought, controlled the flow of 'animal spirits' to the body, which in turn stimulated all physical activity

BOTANALOGIA
UNIVERSALIS
Hibernica,
Or, A General IRISH
HERBAL
Calculated for this KINGDOM,
GIVING AN
ACCOUNT
Of the *Herbs Shrubs*, and *Trees*, Naturally Produced therein, in *English*, *Irish*, and *Latin*; with a true Description of them, and their *Medicinal* Virtues and Qualities.
To which are added, Two Short
TREATISES
One Concerning the *Chalybeat*, *Waters*, Shewing their Origin, Situation, *Medicinal* Virtues, &c.
Another of the *Prophylactic*, Or, *Hygiastic* Part of *Medicine*, Shewing how *Health* may be preserved, and *Distempers* which human Bodies are subject to, prevented.
Author Job, K'Eogh, A. B. Chaplain to the Rt. Hon. the Lord KINGSTON.
He causeth the Grass to grow for the Cattle, and the Herb for the Service of Man. Psal. 104. 14. V.
CORKE, Printed and sold by GEORGE HARRISON at the Corner of Meeting house Lane, 1735.

and motion. Laurence Sterne wrote: 'A man's body and his mind . . . are exactly like a jerkin, and a jerkin's lining; rumple the one,—you rumple the other.'[39] While his undergraduate son was dying Bishop Synge wrote to his then thirteen-year-old daughter assuring her that 'I do and will take all possible care of my self as to diet, sleep and exercise . . . compose yourself my dear and learn thus early that resignation to the Will of God which is the best indeed the only support and stay of the mind and body under afflictions.'[40]

The importance of mental control added a special sting to the gravity of nervous afflictions. The exact mechanism of nervous disorder was unclear. Writers differed on the question as to whether nerves were tubular or solid. There was unanimity, however, in the new weight given to afflictions of the nervous system. In his deeply personal book *The English Malady* George Cheyne wrote:

> Of all the Miseries that afflict Human Life and relate principally to the Body, in this Valley of Tears, I think, Nervous Disorders, in their extream and last Degrees, are the most deplorable, and, beyond all comparison, the worst. It was the Observation of a learned and judicious Physician that he had seen persons labouring under the most exquisite Pains of Gout, Stone, Colic, Cancer and all the other Distempers that can tear the human Machine, yet he had observ'd them all willing to prolong their wretched Beings and scarce any ready to lay down chearfully the Load of Clay, (we will except those who were supernaturally supported) but such as labour'd under a constant, internal Anxiety, meaning those most sinking, suffocating, and strangling Nervous Disorders; it is truly the only Misery almost, to be dreaded and avoided in Life, if by any means, it can possibly. Tho' other Evils be Burdens, yet an erected Spirit may bear them, but when the Supports are fallen, and cover the Man with their Ruins, the Desolation is perfect.[41]

Cheyne's title comes from the eighteenth-century idea that the English were peculiarly prone to suffer from 'nervous Distempers, Spleen, Vapours, and Lowness of Spirits', as he put it. On the other hand, like gout, these were ailments of the distinguished—it was only those 'of the liveliest and quickest natural parts' who were likely so to suffer. ('Some consolation for many hours passed in Pain' runs a marginal note to the copy of Cheyne's book in the College, bought in Dublin in June 1733 by Lord Orrery.) It was in these years that a new speciality of 'mad doctor' grew up to help those afflicted. St Patrick's, Ireland's first hospital specifically for the insane, was established in 1746.

Patent medicine

For those for whom the simple observance of the non-naturals was not enough, there was by the middle of the eighteenth century a cornucopia of patent medicines available for self-dosing. This market was dominated by brand-names, usually invoking the name of some well-known doctor—typical was Dover's

(Opposite) Plants and flowers were a universal source of medicaments, which botanists were beginning to explore in a more detailed manner, drawing on centuries of older knowledge. This herbal was published in Cork in 1735.

Powders (largely liquorice and opium, used for many generations for colds). Richard Dickson, of the Elixir Warehouse, or Elaboratory, situated in Silver Court, Castle Street, regularly advertised his wares, medical and cosmetic, in *Pue's Occurrences* in the 1750s. Thus on 18 August 1752 he announced:

> A general collection of such choice remedies as . . . Montpelier's Bolus, 'Colbura' Lotions, famous French Water for the Venereal Disease—curing it in all its symptoms from the slightest infection to the most inveterate degree of that most terrible distemper without salivations, any confinement and very little trouble—Also, the great Reparative Elixir for broken constitutions, Elixir for Gleets, Palsy Drops, Prolific Elixir, Golden Pills, Lotion for the Itch, Spanish Balls, Steel Pills, Lip Salve, German Pills, Boerhaave's Drops, Great Remedy for Agues, Worm Powders, Purging Sugar Pills, Gout Oils, Pills for Rheumatism, Nun's White Pot or beautifying Italian Cream for the face, Chemical Liquor for colouring red or grey hair, liquid soap, Sal-Volatile, Spirits of Hartshorn, Carmelite Water, Honey Water, Hungary Water, Spirits of Scurvy-Grass, London Electuary Asthmatic Drops and Lavendar Water.

Most of these were non-specific in their application. The celebrated Viper Drops (taking up the supposedly active ingredient in Venice Treacle) 'promoted the chearful circulation of the blood and juices, raising all the fluids from their languid depressed state to one more florid and sparkling'. As well as 'restoring juvenile bloom', this had the effect of curing barrenness in women and 'also gleets, impotency, coldness and imbecility in men'. This was expensive, at £1 3s for a large bottle and 11s 6d for a small, at a time when the Duchess of Leinster paid her housekeeper £25 a year. Turlington's Original Balsam of Life was specifically for gout and stone, but was also 'excellent for women in their lying-in when they have any faintness or sickness. Also infants may safely take it for any nervous case, convulsions or windy disorder.'[42]

As well as these branded remedies, the medical market was well supplied with self-help books such as John Wesley's *Primitive Physick* (1747, published in Dublin 1751) and George Cheyne's *Essay on Health and Long Life* (1724, Dublin edition 1725). The most famous such book, which was taken by many an emigrating family to the US and remained in print until the early twentieth century, was William Buchan's *Domestic Medicine*, published in Edinburgh in 1769 and in Dublin in 1781. With or without such aids, the mistress of the house remained the source of a great deal of immediate medical care, often with her own recipes such as we have seen in the seventeenth century. In 1758 Mrs Delany recounted how

> I have been acting as surgeon as poor John [an employee] cut a terrible gash in the fleshy part of the inside of his hand. I washed it well with arquebuzade and put on the black plaster and in a few hours it was easy, and I hope it will soon be well . . . the receipt for tooth-ache is trefoil leaves made into a little pellet and put to the tooth or tied up in muslin and held between the teeth.[43]

(Opposite) Bishop Berkeley's famous treatise Siris *(1744), on the benefits of tar water as a panacea. The basic ingredient, turpentine, has a long tradition in medicine. He came across it during his time in America.*

The hospital movement

No fewer than eight hospitals that survived into the twentieth century were founded in Dublin in the first half of the eighteenth century: Jervis Street (1718), Dr Steevens' (1733), Mercer's (1734), Incurables (1743), the Rotunda (1745), Swift's (St Patrick's, 1757), Westmoreland Lock (1755), the Meath (1756); there were also others that did not survive so long, such as the New Charitable Infirmary in Francis Street (1752). These institutions eventually became the critical focus for the profession, taking over some of the College's role in that respect. Various factors came together to stimulate their foundation. As the country became relatively prosperous there was a chance to set up institutions to care for those less well-off, and, critically, there was a social imperative encouraged by the Enlightenment feeling that illness and disability were not simply God's punishments, but misfortunes about which something could be done. The prospectus of the Hospital for Incurables (now the Royal Hospital, Donnybrook) in 1743 reveals a curious mix of motives. As Watson's *Almanack* for 1750 noted:

> Since the Opening III miserable Creatures have been admitted. 28 are now in the House. They are maintained, furnished with cloaths, linen and other Necessaries and when they die are decently buried . . . The wretched are here maintained, their infirmities palliated, and the Publick in a great measure freed from those disagreeable sights so frequently heretofore met with in our streets.

There is no doubt that some of those unfortunates must have indeed been distressing sights, but it is indicative of a distinct shift both in political philosophy and sensibility that it was felt they could and should be removed from the streets, and not simply left to themselves.

There were certainly practical advantages for the doctors involved in these hospitals, in terms of both professional skills and of advancement. Not only did the steady flow of patients expand their experience, but the fund-raising functions, endowed beds and the issuing of tickets brought them in contact with the great and the good, who sooner or later needed medical attention themselves. Eventually these unpaid consultancy positions became sources of great prestige.

The middle- and upper-class pre-occupation with disease, and the eighteenth-century love of music and masquerade, no doubt made the fund-raising of hospital promoters easier. Of course, there had been hospitals before, usually with a monastic basis, or as houses of seclusion against outbreaks of plague and fever. The hospitals of the eighteenth century were by contrast 'not just places of custody and death, but places of healing and teaching'.[44] They were also places, as we have seen, where an increasing squeamishness about physical matters could be contained. In the long run they became the central arena for the medical encounter. By the twentieth century their sociological importance as channels of medical power could hardly be exaggerated.

The operation of these hospitals was simple. As the notice for Mercer's in Watson's *Almanack* (1750) describes:

> Great numbers of such poor sick, maimed or wounded Persons as appear to be curable and proper objects are there relieved. Physical and Surgical Advice and Medicines are given to all. Sick Poor have at any one time been supplied with Diet, Washing, Lodging and Medicines in the House, and a great Number of Out-Patients are daily attended and furnished with Advice and medicines at the House. Dr John Anderson, Physician, visits on Mondays and Fridays. Messrs John Stone, Geo. Daunt, Rice Gibbin, Joseph Shewbridge, Geo Whittingham, and Rathborn Mills, Surgeons, visit daily in their turns and all serve without fee or reward. The number of patients received into the house from 30 Sept 1748 to 30 Sept 1749 were 327. The number of out patients attended within the said time were 4,174.

'Proper objects' only, one notes—other hospitals, including the Rotunda, required a ticket of approval from ministers or church wardens, or gentlemen connected to the hospital. The preponderance of surgeons over physicians is typical (though the North Infirmary, which opened in Cork in 1744 with eleven physicians to five surgeons, was an exception[45]). Hospitals were an important way for surgeons to advance their profession as separate from barbers (the Royal College of Surgeons in Ireland was not founded until 1784).

We have no record of the daily life inside these institutions, though some inkling can be gained from Edward Foster's 1768 *Essay on Hospitals*, which followed the 1765 Act enabling grand juries to impose a tax to support them. His ideal hospital had three floors; the ground, being inclined to be damp, was

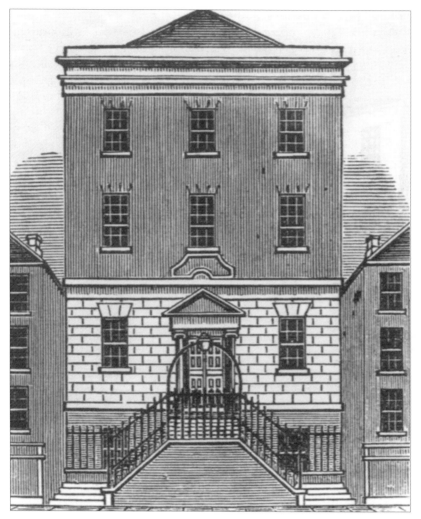

The Meath Hospital opened in 1753. Before finally moving to Long Lane it had several adresses. This is the hospital, in a town house in the Coombe, in 1771.

reserved for offices and other service rooms. The first floor held the wards, one big ward with twenty beds and several small wards for two to four patients. He recommended a quota of one nurse to ten patients. On the third floor were removed the noisier or more noxious activities such as 'the Operation Room [lest] the cries of the patient undergoing any operations should disturb the other sick, and lest the noise and heat of the kitchen, the noise of the apothecary's shop, the moisture and noise of the wash-room, the smell of the necessary house or the contagious miasmata from the dead room' disturb the other patients. This last room, he noted 'ought to be next the operation room that the dead may be easily conveyed into it to be opened or otherwise examined [and] as far distant as possible from the wards lest the patients may be disturbed by the necessary noise

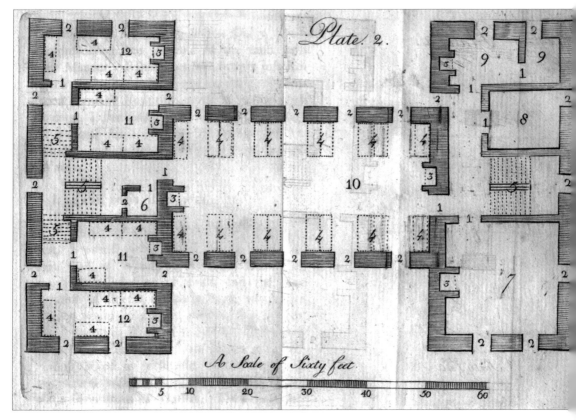

Plate 2.

A Scale of Sixty feet.

5   10   20   30   40   50   60

The ground plan of the ward floor of Edward Foster's ideal county hospital (1768). The beds (two singles or a double?) in the main ward (10) are five feet wide, and are evidently intended to accommodate two patients.

of the friends of the defunct in doing their last offices; or that thoughts of a dead person lying in the same house may not produce bad effects in weak minds.'[46] In his proposed annual budget, incidentally, he noted that the maintenance cost for patients would be 5d per day, and allowed £100 a year for a physician and a similar amount for a surgeon (too much, he wrote, £60 would be quite enough!)

Perhaps Boerhaave's most long-lasting contribution was the system of clinical instruction he developed. At the hospital of St Cecilia in Leiden two of the wards had been specially adapted for teaching, with galleries along the walls for students and local practitioners. Twice a week, it is said, he would demonstrate particular cases, and detail his prescriptions. A few days later the students would be able to see what effect his treatments had had. The hospitals founded in the eighteenth century in Ireland made little original allowance for the teaching function. Systematic teaching at the Rotunda (founded in 1745) only began under the third Master, William Collum, 20 years after the hospital's foundation.[47] Similarly, the first reference to pupils in the minutes of the Richmond occurs in 1796, 23 years after the hospital opened; a formal medical school was only established in 1813.[48]

Medical contribution to culture

Stearne and Petty had been prominent intellectuals in their societies, and Sir Thomas Molyneux, four-times President of the College, was a worthy successor, publishing papers in the *Proceedings* of the Royal Society on zoology, botany and geology as well as medicine. In the eighteenth century College Presidents and other prominent physicians retained a central role in intellectual, specifically scientific, life in Ireland. It is no surprise to see them prominent among the founders of the Dublin (later Royal Dublin) Society in 1731, where Drs Molyneux, Le Hunte (President of the College 1729, 1741), McNaughton (President of the College 1732) and Stephens (President of the College 1733, 1742 and 1759) were among the first fourteen members of the society.

Although it was not until the 1780s that specialist medical bookshops appeared in Dublin, there were certainly more medical books published in Ireland in the eighteenth century than in the twentieth. Bryan Robinson, who has already been quoted, had a breadth of interest which included exploration of the implications of Sir Isaac Newton's ether theory for medical analysis. Among other active writers were the eye specialist Sylvester O'Halloran, author of numerous medical treatises and a popular *History of Ireland*, and Fielding Ould, the second Master of the Rotunda, whose *Midwifery* (1742) was fiercely attacked by Thomas Southwell, a Fellow of the College, for elementary errors, an attack to which Sir Charles Cameron believed Ould 'had laid himself open with respect to his anatomical knowledge'. Perhaps this partly explains the intransigence of the College, which for years refused to recognise midwifery as appropriate to the exalted status of a physician.

Throughout the century the College regularly gave assistance to natural scientists, such as the £30 donated to Dr John Rutty towards the publication of his *Natural History of the County of Dublin* (1772). The historian of the chemistry profession underlines the importance of the profession as the natural source of scientists in Ireland: 'From the sixteenth to the early nineteenth century medicine was practically the only entry into science. Professional chemistry developed out of the practice of medicine . . . practically all the teachers of chemistry were medical men, or at least they had medical qualifications or honorary MDs. In TCD from 1711 to 1903 all the chemistry men had the MD.' Perhaps the most distinguished of these medical scientists was David MacBride, who came to practice medicine in Dublin in 1751. His researches into 'fixed air' (carbon dioxide) gave him a European reputation wider than any Irish scientist since Boyle. His scientific interest in carbon dioxide grew directly out of his medical practice, since he had noticed its role in putrefaction and digestion, and he believed that lack of it caused scurvy.[49]

There is a special fascination in the carefully calm stoicism with which the people of the eighteenth century met the considerable pains of everyday life. It is

David MacBride, one of the founders of the Meath Hospital, Fellow of the College and a scientist with a European reputation greater than any Irishman since Robert Boyle. His researches into the process of putrefaction led to discoveries about the nature of air.

difficult to believe that this self-conscious response to the understandings about the relations between mind and body did not profoundly affect their attitude to other aspects of life such as art and architecture. The physicians of the day have been frequently derided (by their contemporaries and ours) as no better than brutal frauds with gold-topped canes. In fact, most were surely like Mrs Delany's 'very sensible, good physician' Dr Henry Quin, providing a calming reassurance and a comfortable prognosis in stressful times. Although, to our eyes, the medicine they practised seems futile, even dangerous, the best men of the medical profession were certainly not idle. The enthusiasm for founding hospitals, and other interventions in public life, are certainly to their credit. It could surely be argued that the profession was more important to the general intellectual life of the country in the eighteenth century than it has ever been since.

Chapter Four
The 1800s

'The dreadful steel'

WAR HAS GENERALLY been good for the development of medicine, and the Napoleonic wars between 1795 and 1815 were no exception. Irish-trained surgeons were in great demand in both the army and the navy, and to meet the need new structures were established to train them. The profession had finally broken the degrading association with barbers in the ancient Guild of Barber Surgeons, and had set up the Royal College of Surgeons in Ireland in 1784. From 1789 the College was based in Mercer Street, moving to new premises on St Stephen's Green in 1810. It quickly established schools of anatomy and surgery, and began to license surgeons to practice.

There had been a school of anatomy in Trinity since 1711 where, in the late 1770s as a student, Jonah Barrington used to attend the occasional demonstration. 'Whenever I heard of a fresh subject or a remarkable corpse being obtained for dissection I frequently attended the lectures and many were the beauteous women and fine young fellows then carved into scraps and joints *pro bono publico*.' Despite this, and an uncle who had been a naval surgeon and had explained the use of his various instruments, Barrington demonstrated his late-eighteenth-century sensitivity by deciding against joining the profession himself—'my horror and disgust of animal putridity in all its branches was so great that surgical practice by me was necessarily out of the question'.[1]

A number of private medical schools sprang up in Dublin at this time, starting with Mr Kirby's in Peter Street where, among other things, he was famous for using corpses to demonstrate the effects of gunshot wounds. To cater for the needs of the evolving profession William Gilbert set up a medical library in the 1780s, and by 1794 he was issuing annual catalogues of medical books for sale.[2] But to train surgeons anatomical 'subjects' were needed, and there was no formal way of acquiring enough. An Act of 1799 consigning the executed bodies of murderers 'to the hall of the surgeons' company', was quite insufficient to supply the growing demand for surgical knowledge and education. The solution adopted put the fledgling profession in a lurid light.

Technically it was not a crime to steal a body from a graveyard—as a legal handbook of 1812 put it, 'stealing the corpse itself (though a matter of great indecency and indictable) is no felony unless some of the grave-cloths be stolen with it. But, Rex *v* Lynn, it is a high misdemeanour and *contra bonos mores* for which the party may be indicted even though the body be taken for the purpose of dissection only.'³ Ethically it was another matter, although the surgeons asserted that the study of anatomy was so important that a higher good should prevail and it was argued that 'exhumation, in fact, if performed with the necessary secrecy is perhaps the best of all ways to avoid offending the feelings of the public'.⁴ (This approach has a long history—when Dr John O'Connell was a student in the Richmond in the 1950s, post-mortems were done without permission, at the dead of night, to avoid awkward questions.⁵) The instinct to preserve the human body intact is not, of course, exclusive to Christianity—Islam and great civilisations such as those of China and Greece all forbade dissection.⁶

The actual work of raising the corpses was usually done by professionals (who indeed got so adept that they organised an export trade to Britain), but medical students and even their teachers took part—one of the prescribed duties of a demonstrator at the RCSI was to 'undertake the direction of the resurrection parties'.⁷ At this time Dublin's dead were buried in the parochial graveyards around the city, in small suburban graveyards and, above all, in Bully's Acre or Hospital Fields, between the Royal Hospital, Kilmainham, and the River Liffey—the destination of most of the Catholic poor. As many as 3,000 corpses a year were buried here, and the graveyard was only closed in 1832, at the height of the cholera epidemic of that year. Replacement cemeteries were opened at Goldenbridge (1829), Glasnevin (1832) and Mount Jerome (1836).

Strikingly different attitudes to the bodies of the recently deceased remain a source of alienation between doctors and the public. The controversy that flared up in 1999 about organ retention vividly demonstrates this chasm. Certainly, the necessary clinical detachment of the profession has in the past degenerated into a disrespect, particularly for the poor. Religious and class differences no doubt increased detachment in the past. Alive, in hospital, the poor were the subjects on which fledgling surgeons and physicians learned their craft. Dead, they were exposed to post-mortem dismemberment that people believed imperilled their hopes of resurrection. This was, after all, a society in which indignities inflicted to the corpse of a felon (including dissection) were regarded as a profoundly significant punishment. These beliefs did not die with the passing of the Anatomy Act 1832, which regulated the supply of corpses and rendered the 'sack-em-ups' redundant, nor were they limited to the ignorant. When the wife of Sir Andrew Horne, the first Master of Holles Street and President of the College 1908–9, had a leg amputated due to diabetes, it was carefully preserved and later buried with her.⁸

It is curious to imagine future pillars of society—including, for instance, a future Catholic President of the College, Sir Dominic Corrigan—gathering in Kilmainham or some country graveyard at the dead of a winter night (for obvious reasons dissection was not a summer activity), furiously digging, and then cracking open the top of the coffin prior to hauling the partly decomposed body

out by a noose around the neck. To be of use, the corpse had to be only recently buried, just when the grief of friends and relatives was rawest. Grave-robbery
was for all these reasons deeply unpopular and, if caught, the students could
expect a rough time. Relatives would watch in graveyards for weeks after an interment; mighty fences, slabs and other protections were erected by those who
could afford them. But the poor did not have such protection, and it was usually their corpses, dragged from two- or three-week-old graves, stripped, tied neck
and heels, bundled into a sack, jolted through Dublin in the dark and then
dumped onto the dissection table, that formed the staple of the surgeon's training. Apart from the very dubious ethical status of these cadavers, they were, as
John Cheyne, first Professor of Medicine at the RCSI, noted dryly, not particularly suitable for teaching: 'The condition of the capillary system cannot be well
learnt from an examination of the bodies which are usually brought into a public dissecting room.'[9]

Surgery was a special art, as separate from what physicians did as perhaps den-
tistry is today, with its own disciplines and techniques. The surgeon's job was still
largely concerned with the external fabric of the body. He looked after ulcers and
fractures, removed stones, repaired accidental dislocations and breakages; his
clerk applied dressings and bandages, and removed stitches from wounds. He was
also called in to remove dead foetuses, cancerous organs and to deal with burns
and other skin ailments (including syphilis). In the army and navy, of course, the
destination of most of the students, surgeons were also required to prescribe
internal treatments, so there was constant pressure to upgrade their general

*Mort guard in
Drumcondra grave-
yard, evidence of
grave robbing and
the social investment
to prevent it.*

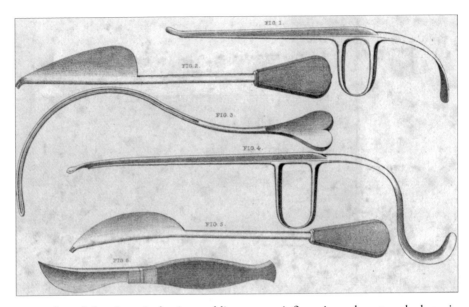

William Dease's surgical instruments—a considerable step up in technical sophistication from Paré's. Dease was one of the most energetic of the founders of the College of Surgeons, and designed many of his own instruments.

knowledge. In 1765 the Act enabling county infirmaries to be set up had specified that surgeons appointed to such infirmaries should be certified by a competent board. The board, consisting of the Surgeon-General and surgeons from Steevens' and Mercer's hospitals, examined candidates on 'osteology [bones], myology [muscles], angiology [arteries, veins, lymph glands], neurology [nerves] and splanchnology [viscera]; surgery, including wounds, fractures and dislocations, tumours and ulcers, operations of the head, operations of the trunk, operations of the extremities, chirurgical pharmacy'.[10] This formidable (if narrow) curriculum is very evidently focused on surgery rather than medicine as a whole. In his history of the medical schools of the RCSI, J. D. H. Widdess described how contemporary teaching encouraged students to explore one system (muscular, nervous etc.) at a time throughout the body. This led to great detailed knowledge, but little sense of how the systems interact; as Widdess said, 'one might as well attempt to explain the mechanism of a watch by taking it to pieces, describing each part minutely, but never showing how one wheel moves the other'.[11]

Unlike physicians, surgeons used a variety of instruments to achieve their ends. In the *Instructions from the Army Medical Board of Ireland to Regimental Surgeons* (1806), 'a complete set of instruments, with the modern improvements for regimental hospitals' is laid down. They are:

> An amputating saw, with spare blade, 1 metacarpal saw, with ditto, 24 curved needles, 2 amputating knives, 1 catlin [a double-edged knife], 2 tenaculums [a fine hook on a handle for holding blood vessels prior to tying], 1 bullet forceps, 1 pair of bone nippers, 2 screw tourniquets, 4 field tourniquets with handle, 2 callico compresses, 2 trephines with sliding keys [a sophistication of the trepan], 1

trephine forceps, 1 elevator [for raising portions of bone that have been depressed by the trephine], 1 lenticulator, a brush, key instruments for teeth to fit trephine handle, 8 scalpels, 2 silver catheters, 1 trocar with spring and introductory canulas [a triangular device to be introduced into a wound to expedite the flow of fluids away from the body], 1 ditto, ditto and canula for hydrocele, 1 probang [a whale-bone rod designed to push bodies lodged in the throat into the stomach], 1 long silver probe, 1 long bougie.[12]

Because the surgeon's activities were carried out on the unanaesthetised human body, surgery and pain were closely linked. All this lancing, cutting and suturing had to be done with speed and in awkward circumstances. The surgeon had to be quick, dextrous, physically strong and, to a large degree, merciless. As the physician Edward Foster put it, he had to have 'undaunted resolution, capable of making him steady to persevere in his patient's good though to his unspeakable pain and torture; to be staggered neither by tears, sighs or groans, the sight of blood or even death's pale image'.[13]

No description in English exemplifies this better than the novelist Fanny Burney's remarkable account of her mastectomy at the age of fifty-nine:

30 September 1811
When the dreadful steel was plunged into the breast—cutting through veins, arteries, flesh, nerves, I needed no injunction not to restrain my cries. I began a scream that lasted intermittingly during the whole time of the incisions—& I almost marvel that it rings not in my ears still! so excruciating was the agony. When the wound was made & the instrument withdrawn, the pain seemed undiminished for the air that suddenly rushed into those delicate parts felt like a mass of minute but sharp poniards that were tearing the edges of the wound—but when again I felt the instrument—describing a curve, cutting against the grain, if I may say so, while the flesh resisted in a manner so forcible as to oppose and tire the hand of the operator, who was forced to change from the right to the left— then indeed I thought I must have expired. I attempted no more to open my eyes—they felt as if hermetically shut, & so firm closed that the eyelids seemed indented into the cheeks. The instrument this second time withdrawn, I concluded the operation over—oh no! presently the terrible cutting was renewed— & worse than ever, to separate the bottom, the foundation of this dreadful gland from the parts to which it adhered—again all description would be baffled . . .[14]

The operation lasted fully twenty minutes. After it she opened her eyes and saw her surgeon 'my good Dr Larry, pale nearly as myself, his face streaked with blood, & his expression depicting grief, apprehension & almost horrour'. It was, however, a success; Fanny Burney lived for another twenty-nine years, and at the end of the description she wrote 'I am at this moment quite well! . . . all has ended happily'.

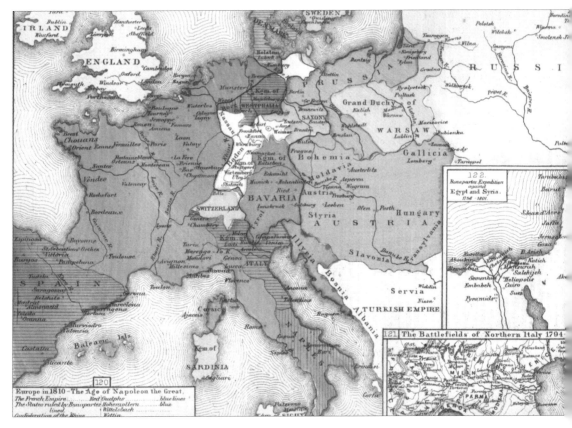

In 1805 England, Wales and Scotland had 10 million people and Ireland 5.2 million. France and its dependent states under Napoleon's rule mustered 54 million. The map also makes it clear how critical was the navy's role in preventing an invasion.

The social status of surgery took time to improve. As late as the 1780s, as the surgeon Sir Philip Crampton recalled, 'surgery was immeasurably below medicine in everything which could ground a claim to public confidence and respect'.[15] Surgeons had generally been uneducated men, whose claim to knowledge was exclusively based on an apprenticeship. As Edward Foster (a physician) dismissively put it, the surgeon 'was only at first made use of to take the trouble of any operative duty off the physician's hands such as dressing sores etc.'[16] However, Foster also complained, with overt class consciousness, how surgeons were creeping into the physicians' territory, as he put it, like pettifogging attorneys pretending to practice at the Bar. Even so, in 1806 the College attempted to preserve its position by forbidding Fellows or Licentiates from consulting with a surgeon (or anyone else) on a purely medical case. Over time, the practice of surgery became more respectable until, on the opening of the medical school of the Royal College of Surgeons in Ireland in 1791 Clement Archer, surgeon to the police and first lecturer in surgical pharmacology, was able to riposte to the kind of prejudice displayed by Foster and his fellow-physicians, declaring roundly 'we are not the servants or slaves of physicians, trained up to use the knife, the saw, the cautery and the many instruments of the science under the immediate inspection and direction of self-important dogmatical philosophers, too proud or too enervated by luxury to bloody their own fingers'.[17]

Part of this change in status came from the kind of persons presenting themselves at the new professional schools, and the fact that the curriculum was by no means limited to practical anatomy, detailed knowledge of which some old-fashioned surgeons thought could only inhibit the vigorous action required of a practising surgeon. Students were required to pass an examination in Latin and Greek before going on to study anatomy, surgery and surgical pharmacy. In his syllabus for the latter course, Clement Archer recommended that the students read Lavoisier's *Elements of Chemistry*, Priestley on *Airs*, 'Mr Kirwan's work on Phlogiston with the observations and comments of the French chemists and the reply of the author to their strictures', the *Apparatus Medicaminum* of Dr Murray of Gottingen 'and many parts of the *Materia Medica* of the late Dr Cullen of Edinburgh'.[18] Twenty-nine years after its foundation the RCSI established a chair in the theory and practice of medicine. It seems that pressure from the Army Board (a major destination for its qualified men) looking for medical qualifications as well as surgical initiated this change.[19] A few years later the apothecaries were established into the Corporation of Apothecaries' Hall, and the old Guild of Barber Surgeons, which was not dissolved until the late nineteenth century, consisted of barbers only. It remained normal, however, for a trainee surgeon to be apprenticed for five, or even seven, years to a qualified surgeon.

The long war

From the College's point of view, the Act of Union, passed in 1800, was momentous in its long-term consequences, but immediately changed little, apart from the departure of some rich clients. In due course the doctors themselves and their professional colleagues would inhabit the fine houses that the aristocracy had vacated, but in 1804 (150 years after the foundation of the College) the great fact was the continuing war with France. In the early months of that year the long-feared French invasion of Britain and Ireland seemed agonisingly close. Everyone knew that at least 70,000 troops were camped in Boulogne waiting for favourable conditions to cross the Channel. It was expected that the large French fleet in Brest would attack Ireland at the same time. Invasion attempts had already been made in Ireland in 1796 and 1798, not to mention a small expeditionary force that landed in Wales in 1797.

Tension was particularly marked in the early weeks of 1804. On 5 January the *Freeman's Journal* reported: 'that the Corsican Despot and his band of brigands will make an attempt without delay on this country is now hourly expected'; 17 January: 'the [London] newspapers are still at variance with respect to the time the invasion will be effected'; 9 February: 'that our shores are intended to be assailed we are thoroughly persuaded' for the simple reason that 'it is [in Ireland] only that Britain is vulnerable'; 14 February: 'it is the opinion of some of the best informed that the French expedition may almost be hourly expected'.

If (when) he came, the numbers would be very much on Napoleon's side: England, Wales and Scotland together had only 10 million people, and Ireland had 5.2 million. These faced 24 million people in metropolitan France, and a further 30 million or so Europeans who now came under French rule, as a result of Napoleon's extraordinary military successes. The conquered Dutch, Spanish and Germans all supplied ships and men to the invasion forces. To add to the sense of vulnerability, there was no knowing how the ordinary Irish in the country might react to a French invasion. There had certainly been little public support when Robert Emmet (the son of a Licentiate of the College[20]) tried his sad little coup in July 1803. On the other hand, the Rising of 1798 had shown how serious a threat an enraged peasantry, unassisted by the French, could become. Even in England there was very considerable doubt as to whether farm labourers and the urban working class would support the existing regime, or would simply acquiesce in a French take-over.

Eventually a stroke of naval genius changed the situation completely. In October 1805 Nelson and his ships comprehensively smashed the French fleet at the Battle of Trafalgar. As long as the British fleet maintained its dominance of the sea there could be no invasion. Napoleon at once recognised the new reality, and returned to land warfare of which he was the supreme master. The ruling classes of these islands heaved a great sigh of relief. The erection of Nelson's pillars, in the middle of Dublin and London, paid for by upper- and middle-class subscription, was no more than just.

On the whole, the continuing war with Napoleon's forces was good for the Irish economy, with an augmented demand for its products—prices doubled during the war period, and wages and rents followed suit. By 1815 exports of grain had increased six-fold from their level in 1800; beef, mutton and pork exports doubled in the same period. Manufacturing did well also, with, for instance, a surging demand for woollens which kept several thousand people in Kilkenny and Cork city occupied.[21] The use of Cork harbour as the victualling point for Wellington's Iberian peninsular army gave a further boost to the local economy.

Well supplied with potatoes and turf, the Irish peasantry was often described by contemporaries as the healthiest in the world. The potato was seen as a wonder food: the political economist Adam Smith famously noted that an acre sown with potatoes provided three times the nourishment of a similar area of wheat, and at less expense. Furthermore, since 'the strongest men and the most beautiful women in the British dominions' came from the lowest rank of Irish, who fed largely on potatoes, there could be no doubt as to the tuber's healthful and nourishing qualities. Throughout the eighteenth century the Irish peasantry became increasingly dependent on the potato. Its crucial disadvantage was that, unlike corn, it could not be stored for any length of time, so no reserve stocks could be held. It was too bulky to be economically transportable. But, with the harvest

R Power
Operated on July 20th
Died this aug 11th 1817

failures of the 1740s a distant memory, there were few people to suspect the forth-coming famines. In the words of the surveyor of Cork in 1810, 'this excellent root is daily getting into greater esteem in all parts of the Empire', but especially in Ireland where potatoes were 'pleasant, mealy and nourishing'.[22]

The medical marketplace

It was perhaps just as well that the Irish were healthy, for there were few doctors outside the cities, and not many inside. To serve a population of some 200,000 people, in 1805 there were 87 physicians in Dublin (45 of whom were Fellows or Licentiates of the College) and 93 surgeons (81 connected to the RCSI). By comparison, there were 50 licensed pawnbrokers, and over 1,000 attorneys.[23] The enormous demand for medical practitioners generated by the Napoleonic wars meant that for those who stayed in Ireland there were lucrative opportunities. In Dublin Dr Robert Perceval, President of the College in 1799, was reputed to earn as much as £7,000 a year, as much as Daniel O'Connell at the height of his

A messy and painful business—a drawing-room operation in fashionable Merrion Square for a tumour (1817)—unfortunately, as the caption relates, the patient died within a few weeks.

career.[24] A top country practitioner could earn £1,500 a year.

The experience of sickness very much depended on class. Three broad groups, the urban poor, the rural poor and 'the better sort', each had quite different expectations and experiences of sickness. By far the worst off were the urban poor, particularly the inhabitants of the Dublin slums. In his *Treatise on the Principal Diseases of Dublin* (1810) Martin Tuomy, a Fellow of the College, explained how 'the miserable accommodation of their dwellings, the scantiness of their cloathing, the low and innutritious nature of their diet and intemperate use of spirituous liquors together with the vicissitudes of our climate' led to 'a train of disease . . . fevers, diseases of the chest, acute and chronic, of the stomach and bowels, rheumatic and dropsical complaints; these ever abound'.[25] Susceptibility to fever, he wrote, rose from the miserable living conditions of the urban poor, the 'foul, stagnant, corrupted air as of dirty cellars and garrets' and the diet which consisted largely of tea and whiskey, or 'raw, spoiled, indigestible food'.[26]

In general, towns, and especially cities, were thought of as unclean places compared to the healthy countryside; they were dangerous to both morals and health. As William Buchan, author of the great best-seller *Domestic Medicine*,[27] put it, 'the whole atmosphere of a large town is one contaminated mass, abounding with various kinds of infection'. Although there was both social and political prejudice in this view, there was no doubt that mortality was greater in towns. The country was, as the urbane Sydney Smith insisted, 'a kind of healthy grave' even though there was not much medical care available. In his *Personal Sketches* Jonah Barrington, who was born in Abbeyleix in 1760, recalled that

> . . . there was seldom more than one regular doctor in a circuit of twenty miles. A farrier never came to physic a gentlemen's horse that some boxes of pills were not deducted from his bags for the general use of the ladies and gentlemen of the family and usually succeeded vastly better than those of the apothecary. As to the farriers I reflected that as man was only a mechanical animal and a horse one of the same description, there was no reason why a drug that was good for a pampered gelding might not also be good for the hard-goer mounted on him . . .[28]

Another approach to treating minor ailments was to call in the traditional wise women, called colloughs.

> They were held in the highest estimation as understanding the cure (that is if God pleased) of all disorders. Their *materia medica* did not consist of gums, resins, and hot iron—as the farriers' did—but leaves of bushes, bark of trees, weeds from churchyards and mushrooms from fairy grounds; rue, garlic, rosemary, birds-nests, foxglove etc; in desperate cases they sometimes found it advisable to put a charm into the bolus or stoop and then it was sure to be 'firm and good' . . . No collough ever could be a doctor whilst she had a tooth remaining in her head, as

the remedy was always reduced to pulp by her own mumbling of its materials, and the contact of an old grinder would destroy the purity of the charms and simples and leave the cure they would say, no better than a farrier's.[29]

Barrington vividly evokes the scene as

> . . . our old collough Jug Coyle . . . sat by the corner of the hob, by the great long turf fire in the kitchen exactly in the position of the Indian squaws, munching and mumbling for use an apron-full of her morning's gatherings in the fields, mouthing the beliefs that the learned had long discarded: 'what would the poor Irishers have done in owld times but for their colloughs . . . God never sent any disorder into a country that he did not likewise send something to cure it with . . . God or the Virgin, and I'm sure I can't say which of them, planted the cures. Sure they must have made people who knew how to pick them up in the fields or what good is there growing there? Well, then it was to the colloughs sure enough God gave the knowledge of picking the cures up—because he knew well that they were owld and helpless and it would be a charity to employ them.'

According to Sir William Wilde however, the 'callaghs' (as he designated them) were also capable of much more sinister activities particularly in creating love-charms and abortifacients. One recipe for an effective love-charm required the callagh and her client to go to a graveyard and exhume a nine-days-buried male corpse, from which, with a black-handled knife, they would cut a long strip of skin. This would be sprinkled with water from the hollow of an old stone, incanted over, and then used to bind the affections of the chosen lover. A similar charm could be used to procure an abortion, though more typically drastic herbal purgatives were used.[30]

Jug Coyle could hardly have done worse than the two physicians who had attended Barrington's father's last hours. The regular family physician Dr Dennis Mulhall (who was 'a matter-of-fact doctor, and despised anatomy') and his colleague Dr Fletcher were called in.

> The two learned gentlemen attended my poor father with the greatest assiduity and daily prescribed for him a certain portion of every drug that the Stradbally apothecary could supply; but these were not very numerous; and as everything loses its vigour with age, so the Stradbally drugs, having been for some years waiting for customers, of course fell off in their efficacy till at length they each became what the two doctors ultimately turned my father into: a *caput mortuum*.[31]

The 'better sort', those who could afford the physician's fees, were expected to be tender and lack the robust good health of the labourer. Some wondered if the rich were actually worse off as a result of medical attention. Robert Graves, in his classic textbook *The Practice of Medicine* (1848), wrote that 'in the epidemics of

1816, 1817, 1818 and 1819 it was found by accurate computation that the rate of mortality was much higher among the rich . . . the true explanation was that the poor did not get so much medicine and that in them the *vis medicatrix* had more fair play'.[32] Notwithstanding, patients continued to fill the waiting rooms, and physicians were able to make comfortable livings.

Mary O'Connell, a portrait from life (1820).

One ailment that the poor did not yet suffer from was 'nerves'. Following George Cheyne and the Edinburgh physician William Cullen, physicians began to ascribe upper-class debility to 'nerves', a state that was not exactly illness, but certainly indicated vulnerability. The development can be detected in letters to the Duchess of Leinster from her sisters. Writing in 1760, Lady Caroline Fox confided: 'I take vitriol drops and drink selzer-water and I think they have done me good for two different complaints I had; but I'm sorry to find how nervous (or what's called so) I am when the least thing ails me, or hurries or fatigues me.'[33] Thirty years later, the term needed no glossing and had become less alarming. After a beloved niece died suddenly, another sister wrote: 'Poor Mr Conolly has been terribly affected, and it fell very much on his nerves, as it has done upon my dear Harriet's. But thank God, they are both better and [Dr] Lindsay assures me that I need not be uneasy about either of them for that the complaint in their heads proceeded only from the shock and that their pulses were in no way affected.'[34] By the 1800s to classify a disorder as nervous was reassuringly to reduce its seriousness. In 1801 Daniel O'Connell's wife Mary described her fever, which had laid her up for weeks, as merely 'nervous'.[35]

Lawrence Sterne had likened the association of the mind and body to a jerkin and its lining; by the early nineteenth century this association had become looser, though by no means detached. We can see this in O'Connell's letter to his newly pregnant wife: 'They say, my heart, that the state of the mother's mind when pregnant much affects the temper and even the understanding of her progeny. I do not deceive you in this particular though I do not either attach much credit to notions of the kind. Yet they are not to be entirely despised. There may be something in it.'[36] Calmness and lack of mental agitation were still important. O'Connell regularly urges his wife to keep up her spirits in face of his absences and financial difficulties 'lest your mind should injure your state of health', which was always frail.[37]

Between the very poor, for whom free medicine was increasingly available, and the rich, who could afford to pay, there were those who were neither. 'Such persons are unable to fee the physician', wrote William Harty, a Fellow of the College, in 1808,

> . . . though equal to the purchase of medicine, when attacked by disease they are either ashamed to apply to a public dispensary for relief or if they do are from their circumstance refused it; they are compelled to apply where they can obtain advice and medicine not best but cheapest, to the ignorant though licensed quack, to the surgical intruder or take a chance with the apothecary better qualified than either . . . a few illnesses in a family of this description have too often transformed the decent inhabitants of a neat habitation into the wretched inmates of a miserable hovel.[38]

This problem will always arise when some medicine is free and some charged for; it is still a source of controversy between the medical profession and the public.

As well as the traditional practitioners there were other choices for the patient apart from the physician or surgeon. For most families the apothecary, as later the pharmacist, was the first point of call—to check if an ailment was serious or not. To the disgust of the College, apothecaries could not be prevented from prescribing, and would leave their shops and attend patients. Not only was this exposing patients to men whose sole education was in pharmacy, complained the Fellows, but it also took the apothecaries from their proper business of preparing concoctions to the physicians' orders. To add to the irritation, it was reported that no fewer than eight apothecaries were rich enough to be seen riding in their carriages around town.[39]

There were also quacks 'whose gross ignorance is notorious' as the College complained in 1806, adding interestingly, 'though their number is not so great in this country as in England, yet they do much mischief'. The RCSI confirmed that 'the number of empirics professing to practice surgery in Dublin is not considerable; and that in these places and in the country at large their number and practice have gradually decreased for some years past'.[40]

Finally, patent medicines were still plentiful, such as, for instance, Godbold's Vegetable Balsam. An advertisement in the *Freeman's Journal* of 19 January 1804 illustrated how the advertiser at least saw its role.

> Mr Wade, 26 Charlemont Street . . . in consequence of a cold caught last Easter Sunday was reduced to such a state as to be at last ordered by his physician to Dundrum for goats' whey, air and exercise. This proved unavailing. A second physician was called in—their united prescriptions were unable to stop the progress of a most rapid decline; having heard of Vegetable Balsam he immedi-

ately took it and, in consequence of the instant benefit he received, persevered until it effected a total and radical cure.

Also advertised regularly in the *Freeman's Journal* was Dr Samuel Solomon's *Guide to Health*, an eccentric volume written primarily as a promotional vehicle for Solomon's Cordial Balm of Gilead.[41] This was described as an 'anti-impetig- ine abstergent lotion'—impetigo was a term variously used to mean simply itch, or could be extended to syphilis, scrofula and other skin diseases; an abstergent was a cleansing ointment. The ointment was dear, at half a guinea a box. The book is in three parts: the first deals with nervous diseases, for which the Balm of Gilead was ideal; the second is a ferocious discourse on the evils of onanism (a favourite theme with Enlightenment doctors); the third consists of a series of essays on the virtues of hot and cold bathing.

The main inheritance of the sixteenth-century drekapotheke *school was the idea that to be effective medicine had to be nasty, as James Gillray suggests in* Taking Physic (1800).

Being sick

Anyone who reached adulthood in the early nineteenth century had shown some hardihood. Philosophers urged their readers not to repine the shortness and hazards of life, but to take consolation that they at least had survived.[42] Over half of the babies born died before the age of ten; and, from a variety of ailments, less than one in ten would reach anything like old age. An article in the *Freeman's Journal*, in 1804, told its readers that

... of 1,000 persons, 23 die in the birth, 277 from getting of teeth, convulsions, worms; 80 from smallpox (by which is meant not the cowpox) seven in the measles; eight in childbed; 191 of consumptions, asthmas and other diseases of the breast; 12 of lethargy and apoplexy; and 41 of dropsy, omitting other diseases not so well ascertained. So that 78 of 1,000 attain what may be called old age.[43]

The view that illness was at bottom ascribable to imprudence of some sort was still widely accepted. William Buchan bluntly declared that 'diseases seldom come by accident, but are the effect of improper conduct'. Directly so in the case of syphilis and gout, of course. But even in the case of smallpox, which was known to be caused by infection, 'children who have over-heated themselves with running, wrestling etc., or adults after a debauch are very apt to be seized'. The poor could not avoid bad air, but since much of their sickness was caused by excess alcohol, the point still stood. Daniel O'Connell agreed: 'Almost all the dis- eases of persons in the upper classes do at middle life arise from repletion or over- much food in the stomach.'[44] Apoplexy and gout were certainly of this class.

Following the evangelical revival at the end of the eighteenth century, some reverted to the older idea of the direct intervention of God. 'The Lord', wrote the Cork merchant Nicholas Cummins in 1811, 'has for some days been visiting me with a little gentle chastisement. My left arm pit is sore. May he accompany his visitation with a Blessing, for Christ's sake, Amen.'[45]

However caused, the threat of illness was a constant worry. In the letters between Daniel and Mary O'Connell (starting with their clandestine engagement in 1800) much space was devoted to health and sickness, descriptions of ailments and reassurances of health. In 1814 little Ellen O'Connell (aged nine) fell ill, possibly as a result of a violent toothache. 'When it became clear that Ellen had fever, her hair was cut to allow ice caps to be placed on her head'; this did not reduce the fever, so a Dr O'Riordan was called in, with Dr Tuomy. Their opinions differed, one diagnosing water on the brain, the other brain fever (another term for typhus). A third opinion, from a Dr Mackey, was sought, and he agreed with the brain fever theory. Ellen's head was immediately blistered, and she was bled in both arms by leeches, to little effect, so finally Mackey lanced the temporal artery. Ellen recovered, but only after two months during which time matters were serious enough to warrant bringing in a priest for the last rites.[46]

The diaries of Lady Selina, wife of the celebrated surgeon Sir Philip Crampton (1777–1858), from a few years later abound with reference to illness.[47] They open in January 1813 with Sir Philip, who was then aged thirty-six, suffering a bout of sickness which continued for virtually two months:

2 January	'Philip still very middling at home all day . . . had a very bad night with the Gout';
22 January	'Philip very ill with gout and pains in his sides. All day in bed, up in the evening very bad pains all night in both feet and sides';
28 January	'P so much better went downstairs to the drawing room for 2 hours caught a severe cold & very ill all night';
29 January	'cupped and leeched in the morning very great pain in the shoulders and chest';
30 January	'in great pain in the breast and back bled in the arm in the evening'.

Finally, by 21 February Philip was able to go out, and called at the Castle 'tho' not free from pain after his drive'. At last she was able to record: 25 February 'Philip much better'.

Although she had been a doctor's wife for some twenty years, Lady Crampton rarely uses technical descriptive vocabulary, but simply refers to being ill, thus 'very ill all day in labour' (1 March 1817), or 'Philip still very ill a blister put on his breast which made him very restless all day and night' (31 January 1817). She was, however, conscious that a 'wandering' disease was serious. On 30 October 1816 she took fright because her daughter reported that a pain which began in the breast and throat had 'gone down to her stomach and belly'. Although a couple

of doses of senna saw to that trouble she had been so alarmed that she summoned Sir Philip from the Park where for the best part of a month he had been staying in attendance on the Lord Lieutenant. She does not record him prescribing otherwise for his family, certainly not in childbirth, for which she seems to have had a traditional midwife rather than the fashionable male accoucheur. 13 June 1815: 'labour pains about 2 o'clock got up at 4 o'clock called up the servants sent to the country in the gig for Nurse by Dobson & for Mrs Hull.' By his wife's account Sir Philip certainly did not let himself be distracted from his social or professional duties, as a diary entry records: 'in great pain all this day with after-pains took opium draught. Philip dined at the Park'.

Most medical encounters, even operations, occurred in the home. Since there were no instruments or diagnostic tests that the physician could deploy, an experienced mother or wife could just as well (or better) interpret a fevered cheek or the cold and shivering of an ague. Anyone interested could, and did, produce her family's own range of pills, plasters and powders, not to mention boluses, cataplasms and electuaries. In Sheridan Le Fanu's story 'The Familiar', set in the late eighteenth century, he describes the familiar character of Lady L—— 'who, like most old ladies of the day, was deep in family receipts, and a great pretender to medical science'.[48] Lacking a personal recipe book, the mother of the house could rely on an increasing range of texts to help her interpret and treat the family's health problems. Goldsmith's Tony Lumpkin complained to his fond mother: 'you have been dosing me ever since I was born. I have gone through every receipt in the *Complete Housewife* ten times over'.[49]

Professional attention was required when these simple remedies failed, and the heavy armaments of the *materia medica* were brought in, together with reassuringly elaborate instruction as to regimen: the exact doses, the frequency and timings, the degree of warmth or cool required, the types of food and drink allowed— 'to be taken in a wine glass of warm water half an hour after the last meal of the day' etc.

Understanding disease

Physicians struggled to make sense of the apparently protean nature of disease. The underlying theory postulated some failure in the process whereby the inputs to the body (diet, climate, air), the process (exercise, mental stress etc.) and the outputs (urine, stools, perspiration) maintained an equilibrium. Often physicians would blame a combination of failures as the cause of mischief, such as the 'confined foul air, an inactive sedentary life and frequently great distress of mind' that Martin Tuomy identified as the cause of the virulence of gaol fever. Phthisis, or tuberculosis, was stimulated by 'foul, poisonous and impure air' combined with 'depressing passions and affections of the mind, which by repressing perspiration' let otherwise evacuated poisons settle on the lungs.[50] It was the physician's job to correct the process and re-establish equilibrium.

The touchstone of any theory was 'fever', variously subdivided, a category that was to puzzle physicians until the late nineteenth century. Fooled by the common symptoms (high temperature, shivering, headache, thirst, hot skin, perhaps mental wandering) many physicians considered that typhus, enteric, scarlet fevers and other similar diseases such as influenza, diphtheria and measles, were manifestations of one generic disease. Confusingly, 'fever' *tout court* was often used to refer to typhus. Exactly how fever was caused was a matter of great discussion.

Contemporary physicians thought of the sick body as a complex ecology in which disease could migrate from one area to another and from one form to another. Thomas Mills believed that fever 'was of one kind, of which there are many varieties . . . depend[ing] on the organ or part particularly affected'.[51] The very worst form of gout, another iconic disease, was wandering or flying gout, which was regarded as a most dangerous condition, particularly if it moved from the feet to the head or chest. In a letter to her sister, Lady Louisa Conolly confides her worries about their brother the Duke of Richmond: 'I thought that the most trifling illness might end fatally . . . [however] I will trust in God that the fixing of the gout may be accomplished and that his precious health may be restored.'[52]

In his *Lectures on the Nature and Treatment of Fever* (1853) Dominic Corrigan (President of the College 1859–63) was obliged first to discuss 'the differing opinions as to the nature of the disease', some thinking it a primary disease, others believing it to be merely the 'consequence of some local or structural lesion'.[53] Whatever determination one came to, infectious fever was undoubtedly important, especially as for climatic or other reasons Ireland was felt to be particularly conducive to it. Martin Tuomy wrote: 'Fever is entitled to particular attention as being a disease perhaps the most universal and constant with which this country is afflicted.'[54] William Harty recorded in the 1808 *Report of the Sick Poor Institution* that of the 3,300 people treated that year for acute conditions just half were for fever of various sorts and a further 500 were for inflammation of various organs (eye, kidney, lungs, liver etc.).[55] William Buchan wrote that since 'more than half of mankind is said to perish by fevers' it was important to understand how to prevent or treat them. Medical writers devoted large proportions of their time to the subject. Thus, for instance, half of the important late-eighteenth-century text *Practice of Physic* (1774) by Dr John Gregory was devoted to fevers of one sort or another (intermittent, spotted, low, continuing, putrid, nervous, miliary, etc). Nearly 60 years later, in his *Practice of Medicine* (1848, based on lectures delivered to students in the Meath in the 1830s), Robert Graves devoted 23 out of 70 chapters to fevers.[56]

Thomas Mills, Fellow of the College. Extensive bleeding had gone out of fashion in Ireland by the late eighteenth century. Following ideas he had learned in Edinburgh Mills was an enthusiastic reviver of the practice.

Medical men struggled to make sense of their very limited information. Jonah Barrington sarcastically described how 'each son of Galen now strikes out his own system; composes his own syllabus; and finishes his patients according to his own proper fancy'. Notable among these 'systems' was that of the British physician John Brown (1735–88) who held that all life was the result of stimulation of tissues, and disease was simply the result of excessive or insufficient stimulation. Broadly speaking, he proposed opium in the first case and alcohol in the second.

The French physician Broussais (1772–1838) similarly reduced all disease to irritation or inflammation. Reasoning that the crucial response to fever was to lower the amount of inflammation or heat in the body he prescribed various 'antiphlogistic' remedies, notably heroic amounts of bloodletting, which had been going out of use. Robert Graves, lecturing in the 1830s, noted that

> . . . we live among systems. It is true that the practice founded on the mechanical, mathematical, chemical and humoral physiologies has been long since abandoned; but the destructive system of Brown has but lately quitted the stage, where its place is occupied on the Continent by those of Broussais and Rasori, and in Great Britain by the system which derives all diseases either from derangement of the digestive function or from inflammation.[57]

Hospital medicine

Following an unusually severe outbreak of 'fever' at the beginning of the century Dr T. A. Murray and his colleagues established the Fever Hospital and House of Recovery (from fever) in Cork Street. When it opened, in May 1804, it had 80 beds, but this was quickly increased to 180. Six physicians were attached to the hospital, three working in the wards and three visiting the sick in their dwellings. The object was, as far as possible, to check the infectiousness of fever by removing sick people from their homes. This was easier said than done, since the poor feared and distrusted hospitals. William Harty, one of the visiting physicians, admitted that at times 'opposition to removal has been so obstinate' that he was obliged to pretend that he was not allowed to provide medical care at home.

Another of the Cork Street physicians, William Stoker (cousin of Bram), described how the hospital contained two separate buildings, one for those still contagious and a convalescent wing (carefully placed up-wind of the contagious fever wards).[58] A patient could expect to spend about twelve days in the fever wards and a further six days in the convalescent ward. On arrival (in the special sprung carriage designed for the purpose, to prevent sick people having to use public hackneys and sedan chairs), the new patient 'is stripped of his wearing apparel and his hands and feet being washed in warm water, he is provided with clean linen and conveyed to bed, the wards being ventilated and kept at a moderate temperature'.[59] Hospital practice was no more uniform then than now. The Royal Infirmary in Edinburgh was, for instance, more thorough in its washing, there 'patients on admission are carried directly to the ward where they are to lie. The nurses immediately undress them, wash their face, breast, arms, feet and legs, or if need be their whole body with tepid water and soap'[60] though mere washing would hardly have been sufficient to disinfest the newcomers.

There was at this time a furious debate about the use of bloodletting, especially in cases of fever. Although all doctors took blood from time to time, over the course of the eighteenth century sentiment had turned against it. By the end of the century, however, under the influence of the great American physician Benjamin Rush and of Broussais in France, bloodletting came strongly back in

The Rotunda Gardens were created for fund-raising events as well as ordinary entertainments—Sunday evening was the fashionable time to visit in Georgian times.

favour in advanced circles. Edinburgh physicians were enthusiastic, recommending 'the lancet steadily and freely employed' and 'the excellence of that remedy in fever'.[61] Even though, as William Harty claimed, Dubliners were much more robust than their counterparts in England,[62] most Dublin physicians were generally more conservative. In his *Treatise*, Martin Tuomy barely mentions bleeding for fever, except in the case of headaches, when leeches might be applied to the temple. He preferred emetics and purgatives as the main line of attack. Harty, speaking for the Sick Poor Institution, agreed, finding 'decided good effects from purgatives, which in some instances have been administered daily for 14, nay 21 days'.[63] In Cork Street, too, most of the physicians went in for a less 'heroic' regime, preferring purgatives, wines, emetics and fomentation (warm bathing) of the feet. Bleeding was adopted only in special circumstances. Writing about scarlet fever, Martin Tuomy notes that 'general bloodletting in this town is seldom admissible; and in some cases where it was tried it proved hurtful'.[64]

However, there was one physician in Cork Street who adopted extensive bleeding on the Edinburgh lines. This was Thomas Mills, a Licentiate of the College, who described his practice in his *Essay on Blood-letting in Fever* (1813). Mills was a great proponent of the utility of bleeding in typhus, typically taking between four and six ounces a session. Patients might have sessions on three or four consecutive days, typically reporting 'relief' or 'great relief' afterwards.[65]

The argument depended on which model of fever was adopted. The more conservative school urged that fever was essentially a debility and 'a putrescency of the fluids' for which strengthening wine in large or small quantity was appropriate. Bloodletting simply worsened the debility. Mills argued that the debility of fever was not caused by a fundamental lesion, but simply by a temporary oppression, like 'a strong vigorous man placed under a great weight'. Vigorous bleeding removed the weight. 'Look at the hardy peasant', he continued in a characteristic piece of contemporary medical argument,

> . . . this hour he whistles over his plough; the hour following he is attacked with brain-fever or enteritis; to walk he is unable, he lies down and calls for relief; the pulse is weak and frequent; there is great oppression of strength, there is vomiting and pain of the head and bowels; administer food, wine, alkalis and other stimulants and he dies; employ evacuants and he lives, and the relief thus obtained is immediate.[66]

Shifts in medical practice were occurring in prescribing styles also. Part of this was caused by a lack of standardisation. Some physicians used the terms laid down in the 1746 *Pharmacopoeia*, others used the 1788 revision, while still others prescribed according to one or other of the Edinburgh editions.[67] When the *Pharmacopoeia Collegii Medicorum Regis et Reginae in Hibernia* was finally published in 1805, the preface pointed out the dangers of such variety: a tincture often called *Elix Pareg.* contained one grain of opium in one version and four in another.

There was a marked change in prescribing styles over the period, as we can see in William Moore's study of prescriptions fulfilled by his family apothecary's shop between 1780 and 1836.[68] Moore analysed 1,200 prescriptions fulfilled from each of three periods (1780–98, 1800–17, 1818–36) and identified quite marked differences in medical preferences. In general it seems as if there was a trend away from the more violent remedies of the mid century. During that 60-year period, for instance, emetics (to produce the 'comfortable vomit' recommended by Dr Johnson) fell from 74 to 7 prescriptions supplied, while leeches (the gentle bloodsuckers strongly championed by Broussais) rose from 1 to 45. The strong purgative Jalap (from South America—'odour nauseous, taste sweetish and slightly pungent, the resinous part griping violently') was gradually dropped from 136 prescriptions in the first period to only 14 in the third, in favour of less violent purgatives, such as senna and rhubarb.[69]

William Moore's statistics show that purgatives and mercury preparations were the leading medicines at the turn of the century, representing 45 per cent of the prescriptions fulfilled. Saline preparations were also popular, especially Epsom salts (sulphate of magnesia). Another major change in the use of medicine was the increasing prescription of the mercury-based blue pills and calomel which over the 60 years rose from 5 per cent to 15 per cent of all prescriptions. Diaphoretics (used to stimulate sweating) fell off markedly as a class, their place being taken by expectorants, notably the astringent Hippo (*Euphorbia corolla*).

A new configuration

At the beginning of this chapter we saw the major changes that occurred in the status of surgeons. As anatomy became respectable, gradually an important shift in the focus of medical theory occurred as well. Attention to anatomy forced attention away from the subtle ecology of fluids to specifically located and identifiable lesions. As the great Dublin physician William Stokes put it, many years later, 'before pathological anatomy became a science it was held that a large number of diseases depended on the alterations of the fluids. But when anatomy was directed to the investigation of disease medical opinion underwent a change . . . disease was then an alteration of the solids, the living tissues of the body.'[70]

At the same time men slowly perceived that the absolute divide between medicine and surgery could not be sustained; by the 1840s the two strands of practice were inexorably coming together, it being acknowledged that 'there cannot be a good physician who has not the knowledge of a surgeon, or a good surgeon who has not the knowledge of a physician.'[71] This laid the ground for a new configuration of medical practice, whereby all doctors would be trained in both disciplines (and midwifery too), and some would become specialists and some generalists. Not that the old barriers came down quickly. The College in particular maintained a somewhat stand-offish posture, requiring a surgeon wishing to join their ranks to divest himself of any connection with the College of Surgeons.

The change was happening (more quickly) in France, too. In 1788 the Sociéte Royale de Médicine prepared a *Nouveau Plan* for the structure of French medicine and the training of physicians, the crucial ingredient of which was the uniting of medicine and surgery. A further important element was that this training would be combined with a residence in hospitals. Men were no longer simply to 'walk the wards', to follow this great man or that in a long procession punctuated by clustering three or four deep round a bed so that half-understood descriptions in dog Latin could be heard over others' shoulders.

In Paris also the so-called 'clinical gaze' was evolving—a cold, numerate exploration of the body, regardless of the patient's own assessments. It is no coincidence that the iconic instrument of the physician—the stethoscope—was developed in France. Allied to this was a new approach to clinical teaching which appeared in Germany, where the intern was encouraged to study a small number of cases and to suggest methods of treatment. It was particularly this idea that Robert Graves and his ally William Stokes introduced into the Meath Hospital in the 1820s, at the beginning of the heroic age of the Irish school of medicine. The reputation of the Irish school was still high when the College celebrated its 200th anniversary in 1854. By that time a quite new idea of the roles of doctor and patient had developed, as we shall see.

Chapter Five
The 1850s

'Our great object is to be practical men'

VERY FEW MEDICAL advances have made so immediate and acceptable an impact on ordinary people as the introduction of anaesthesia
in the late 1840s. Writing at the end of his long life in medicine,
Lombe Atthill, (President of the College 1888–9) vividly remembered
how 'a few, but only a few, bore heroically the pain which must be inflicted by
even the most skilful surgeon; and the groans, cries and struggles of the many
were distressing to hear and see.'[1] All this was
now to be a thing of the past. As later with polio
vaccines, the wholehearted speed of the public's
acceptance of the new technique revealed the
depth of the dread. Although, as all doctors
knew, early anaesthesia was certainly not perfect, and was by no means free of fatal accidents
and side-effects, the public knew what it wanted.

The first successful operation using ether was
performed in Massachusetts in October 1846;
word of this astonishing technique flashed
across the Atlantic, and within two months it
had been tried in England, for an amputation
through the thigh. The first Irish operation
(using an apparatus for inhaling the ether
vapour made the day before by the surgeon
himself) was performed on 1 January 1847 by John McDonnell in the Richmond
Hospital. The first attempt to make the patient, a young girl, unconscious failed,
but the second succeeded and she endured an amputation of her arm with only
slight signs of discomfort. In his account of the event McDonnell ranked the new
technique with vaccination as among the greatest benefits of medical science.[2]

So widespread was the professional acceptance of anaesthesia that when a few
months later the American discoverers attempted to patent the idea, it had
become too common to control. News travelled fast to the public also, with successful cases being eagerly reported in the press. On 31 January 1847 Elizabeth
Smith of Baltiboys, County Wicklow wrote in her diary:

*Homeopathy, developed
by Samuel Hahnemann
(1755–1833) after
rejecting the costly poly-
pharmacy of the time. It
became a fashionable
alternative therapy,
with its appealing stress
on minimal use of drugs
and the body's ability to
heal itself.*

> We are all taken up with this surgical discovery, or rather with the wonderful use
> to which the vapour of ether can be applied in surgical cases. By inhaling it, the
> nerves become so senseless that the most painful operations are performed during
> a state of perfect unconsciousness on the part of the patient who falling back in a
> sort of swoon dreams of soaring through Elysium in an extasy of happiness while
> limbs are amputated, teeth extracted, cancers and tumours removed.[3]

A baby had already been born under anaesthesia when she wrote this, but the practice was controversial. There were both theological and practical objections. Genesis clearly stated 'in sorrow thou shalt bring forth children', an injunction taken extremely seriously by many, particularly those influenced by evangelical thinking. A more practical objection was that the use of chloroform (which quickly replaced ether as the preferred agent) could be dangerous. The first death in childbirth under anaesthetic occurred in January 1848. Pragmatic doctors argued also that pain was essential; its object might be mysterious, but it was risky to tamper with such things. Pragmatic patients were less than enthusiastic about this argument. However, childbirth under anaesthesia was still controversial in 1853 when Queen Victoria decided to have it for the birth of her eighth child.[4] While the *Lancet* snorted with disbelief that the Queen should have been exposed to so dangerous a technique, the *Dublin Medical Press* noted: 'This will it is hoped remove much of the lingering professional and popular prejudice against the use of anaesthesia in midwifery'.

The novelist Charles Lever, a qualified doctor, had by then had a tooth removed under ether, and had no doubt of the boon that this discovery provided. 'Pain', as he put it in an article in the *Dublin Review* (September 1850), 'even short and passing, is of mightiest moment in the tale of life. How many from dread of it have done base acts?' In a long review article Lever described the genesis of the idea of anaesthesia (a word he deplored), noting how chloroform quickly replaced ether as being quicker and having fewer side effects. In the past, attempts had been made to deaden the nerves with alcohol, opium and other drugs, or even loud distracting noises. Practical surgeons thought that some of these techniques still had their uses. In 1854, seven years after the first use of ether in Dublin, the *Dublin Medical Press* published an article arguing the advantages of intense cold over chloroform—its perfect safety, ease of administration, lack of chloroform's considerable and dangerous side-effects, not to mention 'the assistance which the patient may give to the operator in assuming convenient postures instead of it's being necessary, as in using chloroform, to have an assistant to repress his involuntary movements and struggles.'[5] But the writer was obliged to admit that the public had completely accepted chloroform, and nothing less than perfectly pain-free operations would do, and ice could not provide that.

Nine years after the first operation under anaesthesia, Surgeon Richard Butcher of the RCSI, in his *Operative and Conservative* Surgery, made no bones about his adherence to the old ways for operations to the jaw, where there was a

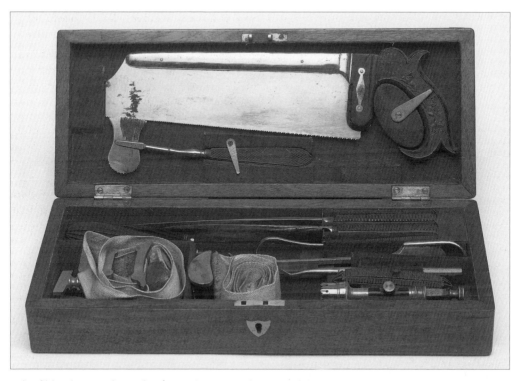

risk of blood going down the throat. 'Severe as the pain of these operations may be', he comments, 'it is better endured than the risk of suffocation.' It would not have been much consolation to the prospective patient to learn that 'cases will seldom occur where the chisel and mallet will be required'; saws likewise could be dispensed with in favour of 'well-formed cutting pliers and powerful scissors, if the operator possess the required strength to use them'.[6]

A surgeon's amputation saw and other instruments designed for use at home rather than in a hospital (mid nineteenth century).

Noting how now 'surgical operations of the most racking character can be performed without the slightest knowledge of the fact by the person under the knife', Charles Lever prophesied that the new technique would have a great practical and social impact on the surgical profession. Previously the premium had been on speed and an almost callous ability to ignore another's pain; surgeons boasted of being able to remove limbs in seconds. Lever, however, from his medical training, knew that such professional speed had its drawbacks. Now, he wrote, lives that 'under the old system would have been endangered by the benevolent hurry of the operator . . . have the full benefit of cautious judgement'. Lever also perceived another benefit to the profession. Although a few surgeons, such as Sir Philip Crampton, had risen to social heights, the discipline had not been much regarded. In the new conditions, 'many high-toned minds who formerly would have shrunk from the profession . . . will now contribute to refine and raise it in the social scale.'

Medicine after the Famine

The Great Famine of the late 1840s, with its accompanying devastating epidemics, brought about revolution at the bottom and the top of the social scale. The 'middling sort of people', who included the great majority of the medical profession, were much less affected. The very poorest, the cottier class, were largely wiped out—the 1851 Census found nearly 400,000 fewer mud cabins than ten years before. At the other end of the scale, the Encumbered Estates Court had enabled the transfer of a quarter of the land of Ireland at knock-down prices from bankrupt Ascendancy landlords to more solvent incomers (virtually all Irish). The resultant social vacuum was to be filled by the professional and business class.

Robert Graves (1796–1853) one of the most distinguished physicians and teachers of the heroic age of Irish medicine.

The first half of the nineteenth century had been heroic years for Irish medicine. The 'Irish school' of clinicians gave to men such as Robert Graves, William Stokes, Abraham Colles, John Cheyne and Dominic Corrigan (all Protestant, except the last) international celebrity. In the professional honours list represented by eponyms, these men scored richly, with Graves' disease, Corrigan's pulse, Cheyne-Stokes breathing, Montgomery's tubercles, Stokes-Adams heart block and others. In fact, of the 2,500 medical men and women listed in one compendium of eponyms, there are nine Irish names (all men, as it happens); of these, seven were born between 1790 and 1810. The school was famous overseas, introducing new methods of bedside clinical training to the English-speaking world. The Dublin doctors were also fertile and innovative in specialist studies, notably of the eye and ear, and in the development of medical instrumentation. While still an undergraduate, William Stokes wrote the first English-language text on ausculation, the pioneering French technique for exploring the chest. The surgeon Francis Rynd developed the use of the hypodermic syringe, Francis Cruise the endoscope, and William Wilde numerous specific tools and techniques in his speciality of aural medicine.

The introduction of such instruments coincided with a shift in the way clinicians operated. Led by the stethoscope, instrumentation (reinforced by morbid anatomy) gradually became the way in which physicians explored what was happening inside the patient's body. Students were trained in precise observation of the patient's external signs. The so-called 'clinical gaze' became part of the public persona of the professional man. But for years instruments such as the ther-

An early form of hypodermic syringe, for direct delivery of medicine into the system, was invented by Dr Francis Rynd in 1845. These kits, from the RCPI's collection, are also designed for use in the patient's home.

mometer were for specialists only. In the Rotunda, for instance, accurate and regular recording of pulse and temperature did not occur until as late as 1884. Atthill, who was elected Master of the Rotunda in 1878, introduced the use of the clinical thermometer 'but had not encouraged it, believing it worried patients unnecessarily'.[7] His view was shared by Dr George Kidd, then Master of the Coombe Hospital.

Encouraged in particular by Robert Graves, the ancient art of pulse-taking moved from the purely qualitative to include a quantative note. Previous to this an astonishingly rich vocabulary had evolved to describe various states of the pulse (which was still the only part of the patient a physician could freely touch, and touching was not the only taboo—in 1853 the editor of the *Dublin Medical Press* Arthur Jacob complained bitterly of 'the wickedness of visual inspection of young women'[8]). A medical dictionary published in 1848 includes the following terms to describe pulses: 'ardent, caprizant, complex, convulsive, deep, depressed, formicant, intricate, jarring, languid, long, supple'. Some pulses were diagnostic and were believed to reveal organic problems such as 'hepatic pulse [liver], intestinal, nasal, pectoral, stomachal, urinal'.[9] (The modern acupuncturist who maintains that there are six pulses on each arm, and 28 diagnostic states of each, is in the same tradition.) In his *Practice of Medicine* Graves included both numbers and descriptions, in an attempt to identify the stage a fever had reached: 'pulse 100 distinctly dicrotous and sharp', he noted, or 'pulse 112 dicrotous and wiry; pulse 84 soft and regular; pulse 140 and remarkably shabby'.[10]

The century had started with the medieval separation of the three branches of practitioners, as represented by the Royal Colleges. They were still functionally separated and hierarchically ordered—physicians, surgeons and apothecaries. This venerable division of labour relied on an urban assumption that each type of practitioner would be equally available to patients. It began to break down when men began to be sent to military outposts and country districts where they would very likely be the only practitioner for miles. To meet the situation, a new type of medical man, with qualifications in surgery and medicine (and also midwifery) emerged. In 1813 the College of Surgeons, under pressure from the Army Board, had appointed a professor of physick, and in 1837 Apothecaries' Hall established a medical school in the building in Cecilia Street that was later to house the Catholic University Medical School. It became common to have some qualification and hospital experience in three medical areas—medicine, surgery and midwifery, as well as a licence from Apothecaries' Hall. Although it was still a matter of controversy among the more conservative, it was generally accepted that it was not demeaning for a physician or surgeon to mix his own medicines—the only thing they certainly could not do was run a shop. Just as the barber surgeons had split generations before, now the erstwhile apothecaries either became general practitioners or stayed with the retail trade and called themselves chemists or druggists. Those men with multiple qualifications, most typically qualifications in surgery and apothecary, usually called themselves 'general practitioners'.

The 1851 Census identified some 6,800 people in the category called 'ministering to health'; this included about 1,200 physicians and the same number of surgeons, plus 650 apothecaries (see Table 5.1), though in practice many of these would have had multiple qualifications. There were therefore just over 3,000 formally qualified practitioners for a population of 6.5 million in the whole island. These were not of course evenly spread across the country—43 per cent of 'ministers' were based in Leinster, looking after 25 per cent of the population. In the Republic in 2001 there were 6,300 qualified medical practitioners for a much smaller population, but the really significant change in the structure is in the number of professionally qualified nurses. In 1851 the Census identified a mere 2,752 nurse-tenders and 572 midwives in the whole country (though no doubt there were many more with informal practices); in 2001 there were 32,429 registered nurses and 9,228 para-medics.

Table 5.1: 'Ministering to health' in 1851

Physicians	1,223
Surgeons	1,216
Dentists	80
Apothecaries	648
Druggists (unqualified)	260
Leech dealers	5
Midwives	572
Nurse-tenders	2,752
'Quacks' [sic]	55
Total 'Ministering to health'	**6,811**

Source: Census 1851 (not including medical students)

Despite the social and economic gains of the Catholic middle class since the late eighteenth century, the medical world was still dominated by Protestants. At the top levels, and in Dublin, the degree of dominance was much greater. In the process of establishing the Catholic University Medical School in Cecilia Street, the university Rector, John Henry (later Cardinal) Newman reported to the Hierarchy in 1854 that

> . . . out of the 62 medical officers altogether in the various hospitals, the Catholics do not exceed the number of ten. Again out of the five medical schools in Dublin (exclusive of our university) three have no Catholic lecturers at all, and the other two have only one each; so that on the whole, out of 49 lecturers only 2 are Catholic. Putting the two lists together we find that out of 111 medical practitioners in situations of trust and authority, 12 are Catholic and 99 Protestant.[11]

The establishment of overtly Catholic hospitals, notably St Vincent's in 1834 and the Mater in 1861, provided an outlet for the graduates of Cecilia Street, but change came slowly. According to the 1861 Census, Protestants represented 66 per cent of physicians and 70 per cent of surgeons in the country.

Other opportunities for the sons of the burgeoning middle class (Catholic and Protestant) were limited, so the Dublin medical schools continued to produce far more qualified men than the country could absorb. Only the favoured few, very often aided by family connections, could expect to work in the élite Dublin hospitals. As a result, competition for dispensary and county infirmary positions was severe, and kept a downward pressure on salaries. The Empire remained an important employer as it had been since the Napoleonic wars: a survey of the 90 early graduates of Cecilia Street who continued in medicine revealed that 54 practised in Ireland (mostly in the dispensary service) and 36 in the army, navy or imperial service.[12] One-quarter of the army surgeons during the Crimean campaign (1854–5) were of Irish origin.[13] Over half of the surgeons sent by the British army to the unhealthy West African or West Indian stations were Irish-born.[14]

Dispensary doctors were elected by boards of guardians made up of local worthies, who tended to be parochial in outlook and protective of the rates. As a result, many dispensary doctors were paid quite badly, often as little as £50 a year, though they did have the opportunity to make more by private practice—if they could find it. But the subsidised presence of over 700 medical practitioners across the country was appreciated since, as the *Dublin Medical Press* put it, 'there [was] not a county, at least south of the Boyne, with the exception of Cork and Tipperary, in which three physicians or surgeons could live on their income. To the dispensary then, the peer as well as the peasant is indebted for having an efficient medical attendant.'[15]

Outside the dispensary system practitioners could set up their plates where they liked, so medical coverage was greater in the north and east than in the south and west. Towns and spas tended to attract a disproportionate weight of medical assistance. The *Medical Directory* of 1852 records no fewer than eleven practitioners based in Cobh (then called Queenstown). Mallow, another favoured spa, had five resident doctors; Clifden in Connemara had two. Alexander Knox's *Irish Watering Places* (1845) is full of physicians' toutings for business, such as Dr A. Thomson's praise of his own place of residence: 'There is no place within Great Britain or Ireland so well adapted for the winter residence of a consumptive as Cove'.[16]

How typical it was it is impossible to say, but we do have a detailed picture of morbidity in one dispensary district in south-east Ireland at this time. In 1854 Joseph Edmundson, Licentiate of the College, analysed the previous two years of his dispensary in Carrick-on-Suir.[17] Edmundson had taken his Licentiate of the Society of Apothecaries in 1842 and then received the slightly dubious MD from the Aberdeen university, St Andrew's, two years later, becoming MRCS (England) in 1845.[18]

A travelling drug kit. These kits typically included opium and other strong drugs— note the scales for careful measuring of proportions. From the RCPI's collection.

Edmundson's district contained 4,500 households at this time, spread over three counties. He listed 5,565 medical cases, of which 3,724 were described as cured, 661 were sent on to hospital (mostly fever and dysentery cases) and 51 died. The 1,129 remaining he recorded as either 'relieved' or 'lost sight of'. It was a laborious life, into which it is difficult to see how he could have fitted any time for private practice. The patients (equally divided between male and female) made 18,700 visits to the dispensary over the two-year period.[19] He also made 4,200 visits to patients in their own homes. No mention is made in the article of any assistance in the practice, though the *Medical Directory* records that Anthony O'Ryan (LRCS 1842) was medical officer in the Carrick-on-Suir workhouse and fever hospitals.

By far the most common ailment was scabies, accounting for 20 per cent of cases most of which Edmundson was able to eradicate. The next largest category is 'fever' with 580 cases of whom 5 died. Most of the fever cases were sent out of his care to hospital. There were also dysentery and diarrhoea, quite a lot of bronchitis and pneumonia, and 200 or so sexually transmitted diseases, no doubt a consequence of a nearby barracks. (The 1854 *Report on Dublin Hospitals* recorded that provincial garrison towns Cork, Fermoy, Clonmel, Athlone and Templemore all reported particular problems with venereal diseases.) Eye diseases were common (including 99 conjunctivitis and 34 ophthalmia). Injuries and fractures, reflecting the hazards of an agricultural society, were also numerous.

Edmundson was somewhat sensitive about the death rate, which amounted to just under 1 per cent of his patients. As others had done, he complained that he was often called in at the last minute, and that 'the want of ventilation, cleanliness and clothing, the impossibility of procuring the requisite dietary and the unwillingness of the pauper patients and their friends to adhere to the physician's directions' were everyday difficulties. The biggest single cause of death was phthi-

sis, followed by fevers, bronchitis, and scrofula.

Marking a great difference with later general practice, during the period analysed by Edmundson he dealt with only 33 pregnancies, most of which were difficult cases. As he wrote, 'the midwifery practice is very laborious, the cases are always of a formidable character, the medical officer being never summoned to attend any except those of a serious nature', these being the ones where the case had run beyond the skills of the local midwife or traditional birth attendant. As a result he reported that 2 mothers and 9 infants died. Most of the mothers (26 out of 33) were over thirty, and one, on her 15th pregnancy, was forty-eight—she was one of the maternal deaths. Three-quarters of the labours lasted twelve hours or more, and seven lasted for three days or more.

The dispensary doctor's position was socially isolating for these sons of the middle class. Nearly one-third of Irish practitioners worked on their own in country districts, often far from colleagues.[20] Apart from the priest and the parson, the only educated company was likely to be the local landlord, who rarely thought of a doctor as an equal. The novelist and editor Charles Lever, who had himself been a country practitioner, wrote sourly about 'Doctor Dill [who] had been a poor dispensary doctor for some thirty years, with a small practice, and two or three grand patrons at some miles off who employed him for the servants, or for the children in "mild cases" and even extended to him a sort of contemptuous courtesy that serves to make a proud man a bear and an humble one a sycophant.'[21]

Lever's Dr Dill had plenty to be sour about, not least the danger. A survey conducted by James Cusack, President of the College of Surgeons, and William Stokes (President of the College 1849–50), estimated that in the terrible year 1847, 178 practitioners died, or 1 in 15. In the five years between 1843 and 1848, 443 practitioners died, by far the largest number of them succumbing to fever. Tragically, nearly half of these were comparatively young men, under forty years of age. Like the Catholic priests in Penal times, in these years the Irish medical profession really earned its subsequent esteem. In the 1851 Census report, covering the previous ten years, William Wilde confirmed that the average age at death of the medical men in the city of Dublin was between thirty and thirty-five years. (Three of the five medical suicides in the decade were under thirty.) They died from infections caught in fever hospitals, and also, as Cusack and Stokes put it, from 'labouring among the poor in wild and thinly populated districts, where the medical man has often to ride or drive for many hours, exposed to cold and wet, and frequently at night, suffering great fatigue and then becoming exposed to concentrated contagion in some of the wretched isolated hovels of the peasantry.'[22] Not that this prevented coroners' juries from being bluntly critical when the occasion arose—22 verdicts between 1841 and 1851 identified the cause of death as 'unskilful medical treatment'.[23] On a lighter note William Stokes quotes a colleague on the hazards of the carefully compiled heaps of manure that lay outside most farm doors. On a night visit it was a distinct puzzle how to avoid 'sticking, ankle deep in mire or filth, or perhaps coming to worse grief in the shape of a souse in a slough of despond'.[24]

Apart from simply recognising that so many of their former pupils had died in this way, Cusack and Stokes wanted to highlight the parlous state in which these doctors so often left their families. Dispensary practice was not a rich living, but 'of all the professions', they noted, 'the medical is the only one in which a necessity exists for its members entering the marriage state'. 'In Ireland', they continued, 'the feeling which leads to this state of things is peculiarly strong; and as a consequence a large number of junior practitioners, at the time they fall victims to fever or other diseases, leave behind them an unprotected and unprovided family.'[25] At meetings of the revived Irish Medical Association in the early 1850s (the original Medical Association of Ireland, set up in 1839, had foundered in the 1840s) the dispensary doctors noisily aired their grievances about pay and conditions. Not only were the boards of guardians notoriously parsimonious with salaries, holiday allowances and medical necessities, they were not above giving themselves favours. A regular complaint was the practice of guardians of awarding themselves and their political cronies attendance tickets, thus entitling them to free medical attention. Being obliged to supply free medicine to those who could very well afford to pay shut off the practitioner's only chance of building up a private practice and thus escaping the treadmill of dispensary work.[26]

Doctor as sage

While these professional changes were occurring an idea of the medical practitioner as sage began to evolve, at least for the middle class (oral history suggests that the poor were more ambivalent). By dint of practice among the poor in hospitals and the rich in his consulting rooms, the doctor became the holder of 'a deep insight into the world' as the *Dublin University Magazine* put it in 1843. 'The first rate physician is a kind of ambulatory conscience to which each man reveals his delinquencies and from which he looks for relief'. 'No other class', the *DUM* declared, 'whose minds are trained by a long and arduous course of labour have so many opportunities of mixing with their fellow-men of every grade of life.' With this came an almost superhuman self-control—'fatigue, pre-occupation, illness itself are luxuries which the medical man must conceal'. Medical practice was potentially well-rewarded, but also dangerous which added a sheen of comfortable martyrdom.

Young Catholic doctors were taught a slightly more restrictive self-image. In a lecture to the medical students of Cecilia Street, Newman laid down that the proper province of the profession was simply 'the physical nature of man'. They must, however, be aware that minds and souls were more important and with these doctors had no legitimate business. To illustrate his point, he set a scene: 'A patient is [very sick]; the priest wishes to be introduced, lest he should die without due preparation; the medical man says that the thought of religion will disturb his mind and imperil his recovery.' Whose decision should prevail? Newman was clear: the final decision should be the priest's. He clinched his view with a statement that he took as a truism: 'Who will deny that health must give way to duty?'[27]

Choosing and using medical advice

At the top end of the medical market were the consultants with their (unpaid) hospital appointments and their rooms in Merrion Square. Although it is unlikely that these men earned as much as their legal counterparts, they were certainly well off. Less well paid were surgeons and consulting apothecaries, who would themselves have earned considerably more than the humble dispensary doctor.

There was as yet no formal referral system from GP to consultant. Families could pick and choose as they thought appropriate. We can see this in operation in the personal cash records of John Findlater, of the grocery family. In 1854 John married Mary Johnston, whose family ran a bakery (later part of Johnston, Mooney & O'Brien). Medical costs (consultation and medicines) represented an apparently modest 3 per cent of his expenditure; though from another perspective, the average annual £16 spent represents one-third of the yearly wages of a skilled labourer of the day. Over the eight-year period (1855–62) that John Findlater kept detailed records, the visits of Dr Charles Johnson, ex-Master of the Rotunda (1840–7), 'attending Mrs F in her confinement' were a regular item. Johnson, an honorary Fellow of the College, was by now in his seventies. He charged £5 for each such occasion. His great contribution had been to insist that every woman had a maternity nurse to herself for her confinement, so there was an additional £2 for the nurse-tender. There is no record of a wet-nurse. A month or two after the birth Johnson would come again to vaccinate the child for an extra £1. Dr Johnson was probably the most mentioned medical name, for he would also give advice on paediatric matters. Between August and October 1855, for instance, he was consulted on no fewer than eight occasions, in addition to the vaccination in April.

In this frequency of consultation, he was the nearest approach to a modern GP, but there is no sense that he would refer patients on to colleagues. So, as well as Johnson, the Findlaters consulted directly with a wide variety of medical men. They were evidently discriminating buyers of medical services, though there is no indication as to their sources of information—they did not subscribe to any medical publications.

Ten other doctors appear, namely Surgeons Rynd and Wilde and Drs Adams, Blythe, Stokes, Duncan, Dwyer, Quinlan, Wyse and Walsh. They were a distinguished group: the names Wilde, Rynd and Stokes are instantly recognisable. James Duncan was a Fellow of the College, and George Wyse, a graduate of St Andrew's, had rooms in Upper Sackville Street. Albert Walsh (FRCSI), of St Stephen's Green, was a former surgeon of the Adelaide who had written on erysipelas. The *Medical Directory* lists two Dr Adams: Robert (FRCS) of St Stephen's Green and William, a Fellow of the College, of Kingstown. Three dentists, curtly referred to by their surnames only, appear—McClean, Moore

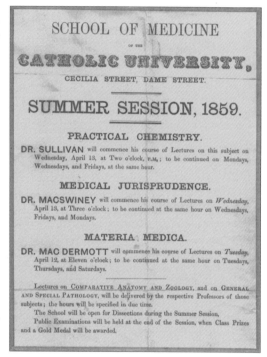

SCHOOL OF MEDICINE

OF THE

CATHOLIC UNIVERSITY,

CECILIA STREET, DAME STREET.

SUMMER SESSION, 1859.

PRACTICAL CHEMISTRY.

DR. SULLIVAN will commence his course of Lectures on this subject on Wednesday, April 13, at Two o'clock, P.M.; to be continued on Mondays, Wednesdays, and Fridays, at the same hour.

MEDICAL JURISPRUDENCE.

DR. MACSWINEY will commence his course of Lectures on Wednesday, April 13, at Three o'clock; to be continued at the same hour on Wednesdays, Fridays, and Mondays.

MATERIA MEDICA.

DR. MAC DERMOTT will commence his course of Lectures on Tuesday, April 12, at Eleven o'clock; to be continued at the same hour on Tuesdays, Thursdays, and Saturdays.

Lectures on COMPARATIVE ANATOMY AND ZOOLOGY, and on GENERAL AND SPECIAL PATHOLOGY, will be delivered by the respective Professors of those subjects; the hours will be specified in due time.

The School will be open for Dissections during the Summer Session.

Public Examinations will be held at the end of the Session, when Class Prizes and a Gold Medal will be awarded.

and Langford. 'Mrs F' evidently had some trouble with her teeth, for the charges seem high, presumably covering a number of sessions.

In any one year three or four doctors (apart from Johnson) might be consulted. Occasionally doctors were consulted once and never again—Stokes in 1855 and Quinlan in 1858 for instance. More usually the doctors were consulted year after year—Francis Rynd was consulted for four successive years before his death in 1861; Wilde in 1856, 1857, 1860 and 1861; Duncan was consulted in 1856 and again in 1859 and 1860; Walsh two or three times a year between 1857 and 1861. Virtually all of the Findlater consultations are charged at £1—in one case only does the traditional guinea appear 'fee Dr Wylde [sic] 20s & gratuity to manservant 1s'. Occasionally larger sums appear, as for instance £5 'paid Dr Walsh as agreed surgical treatment of self for this year' in February 1861.

Courses offered at the School of Medicine, Catholic University Dublin, Summer 1859.

THE OLD STYLE.

MEATH HOSPITAL NURSES, 20 YEARS AGO, 1872.

FEVER NURSE	NIGHT NURSE	SURGICAL NURSE	ACCIDENT NURSE
HODGENS.	SPRING.	MURRAY.	BRAZIL.

Old-style nurses from the Meath Hospital. These ladies could well have been in the Crimea with Florence Nightingale.

In the country the small but crowded market forced doctors to charge much less. Even in Dublin less successful doctors chafed under the *de facto* necessity to charge £1 (lest they lose face), and would supply dressings and medicines free of charge. In the summer of 1853 a Dr Smith of the Mountrath dispensary issued his scale of fees, prefacing the scale with the comment that on account of the depressed state of the country the fees listed were 'much below what was hereto-fore paid him'.[28]

	£	s	d
For one visit within three miles of Mountrath	0	5	0
For all calls at night lowest fee	1	0	0
For one consultation, fee	1	0	0
For all engaged attendances on midwifery cases, and upwards	3	0	0
For all important surgical operations and upwards	1	0	0

The Findlaters' medicines were usually purchased at Bewley & Evans, at the bottom of Sackville (not yet O'Connell) Street, which was convenient for John's place of work at the top of the street. Just occasionally a doctor would provide his own, as Dr Wyse did in 1854, and Dr Dwyer (a Fellow and Censor of the College) in 1855, when he charged £2 for 'medicine and attendance on baby when ill'. We cannot tell from the record which medicines were medically prescribed and which self-prescribed, but the names of those bought indicate a prevalence of digestive problems which suggests self-medication. There were solution of magnesium, Gregory's powder, Epsom salts, Siedlitz powder, sulphur ointment, sulphur baths, sulphuret of potash, cough lozenges, Dr Jongh's cod liver oil, castor oil, salts of senna, tincture of rhubarb and essence of peppermint. In December 1858 6d was spent on a bottle of 'prepared chloriform'; this was a month after Mrs Findlater's latest confinement, so presumably it was not related to that but perhaps to treat incipient asthma.

Elizabeth Smith's diaries, which are full of her own and other people's illnesses, record a similar profusion of medical advice. In 1851, for instance, Drs Eckford, Graves, McMunn, Stokes and Robinson were all consulted. In 1853 she began to fear for her husband's life, such was the confusion of things wrong with him. 'Asthma for years has affected his chest, one lung is gone, a rupture on each side, a tenderness where he sits, kidneys wrong, and now a complicated stricture.'[29] In August Colonel Smith had written to summon the doctor about the latter, but had been too embarrassed at first to explain to his wife what was wrong, except by hints. 'Soon after the pain he was suffering from became so violent he had to go to bed. We put him in a hot hip bath with little effect. The Doctor came with the proper instruments—he was not able to use them.' Next day Dr Porter came from Kildare Street with 'plenty of instruments—again unsuccessful'. So they try Surgeon Cusack of Merrion Square, 'the cleverest operator they say in Europe, on a par with Brodie. He accomplished the business, it was a wonderful relief, at the same time painful and exhausting.'

The case now settled down to the classic sickroom vigil, a role in which Elizabeth Smith felt comfortable. She had firm beliefs in the woman's place in the sickroom, having no truck with any ladylike squeamishness about bedpans and catheters. As a girl in Scotland she said, she

> . . . used to faint when I saw blood, so Grandpapa made me attend the Doctor whenever he had to bleed anyone and very soon I could hold the cups and even assist him in many surgical operations. It is mere selfishness that prevents women from being thus useful. Nature intends them for nurses and if they thought more of the sufferings they could relieve than of the unpleasantness to themselves, they would soon lose their nervousness.[30]

She did not, however, approve of nurse-tenders, for she had no good opinion of what she called 'that evil branch of the profession'.[31] Certainly the reputation of the average lay nurse was not good, drunkenness being generally perceived as the least of her defects. (This was only a few years before Florence Nightingale's successes in the Crimea, and her influential *Notes on Nursing* (1859) began to replace the idea that women had a natural gift for nursing with a sense that nursing was a skilled profession to be learned and, furthermore, practised with an austerity approaching the vocational.)

Now, 'all that remained to be done', for Colonel Smith, 'was to sooth his torture by the only means in our power, doses of morphine, and watch him, his moans for a few hours were most distressing. The Doctor sat up by him till one in the morning, [when] I exchanged to the easy chair which at six I gave up to Marianne.' (Watching all night was particularly important, for it was in the small hours that most deaths occurred.[32])

Despite the relief provided by Surgeon Cusack's technical skill, all was not over. Dr Porter continued to visit 'twice, sometimes thrice, daily, but as I have learned to administer the necessary relief and have done so several times quite surgically he will probably come but once after Tuesday, which will be a crisis. Should no fever or inflammation come on then, I believe the present danger will be over.'[33]

Obviously the kind of care that the Smiths or the Findlaters could afford, with two or three visits a day, and multiple practitioners in attendance, was a long way from the service that Dr Edmundson's patients could expect. All this medicine was expensive, but 'the fees [were] not quite so high as I expected' Elizabeth Smith recorded in August 1852. 'Mr Porter takes but one [fee] a day—£10 and expenses for going down to Baltiboys, Mr Cusack but £2—no medicines—and not much expense of any other kind.' Although the immediate crisis was over, the patient was still very weak. A few days later Dr Cusack 'gave him but five days of life. Dr Robinson says weeks'. As it happened, Smith recovered and lived for another ten years, suffering regular asthma attacks after bibulous evenings in the Kildare Street Club.

Not every household was in such capable hands as the Smiths'. More typical was the well-meaning incompetence described by Dominic Corrigan. Two nurses would usually be employed to look after a private patient with fever, and then, as he put it, it was a cardinal rule of this school of nursing that the patient be not left alone, day or night. 'A continued noise of whispering is perpetually kept going', which the patient naturally tormented himself to hear. The patient's ability to sleep was constantly disturbed by 'the perpetual motion of the nurse or some member of the family about the room'. Corrigan complained also of professional and other attendants 'forcing [the patient] to swallow drinks every other minute' to a quantity that would be too much even in a healthy state.[34]

Like the Lennox sisters, Elizabeth Smith prided herself on her medical acuteness. On one occasion, visiting her son at school, she became convinced he was sickening for measles. 'I dosed the little fellow with grey powder and senna draught, so all was ready for other measure without loss of more time . . . I nurse him myself, so that all is done that is ordered, and nothing else. I wish [her daughters] could be removed from the infection but none of them heed me. I keep quite apart from them. Still the air of the house is tainted.' More intractable was the case of her relative Arabella who suffered from what were described as fainting fits. At first Dr Stokes thought they were 'aggravated hysteria', but after he 'examined and questioned her very minutely', and was called in at night to witness a fit, he confirmed suspicions that the girl was epileptic. This was a serious matter: the fits were dangerous and incurable, not to mention 'the disadvantage it would be to her sisters to have them talked of'.[35]

Sometimes patients or their relatives would reject orthodox medicine altogether. Ireland at that time was relatively free of irregular practitioners. 'The truth is', wrote Arthur Jacob in the *Dublin Medical Press* (27 July 1853), 'the English are quack-fanciers by nature . . . here in Ireland we really suffer little from the unlicensed quack. The country bone-setter or cancer-curer does mischief now and then, but we have few of the race of obscene advertisers amongst us; the disgusting panderers to the wretched taste for medical mysteries by newspaper overtures all come from England.' The experience of fifty years later, discussed in the next chapter, suggests that this was no more than a function of the underdeveloped nature of the Irish economy.

Homeopathy was the alternative medical system of choice among the upper classes (including the Royal family). It attracted a fanatical following. Elizabeth Smith records the case of poor Mr Cotton whose homeopathic wife and sister 'sent him over to Scotland to this quack and insisted on every direction being implicitly followed and he has not the nerve to say no'.[36] He did not dare take even the glass of wine and the small dose of Gregory's powder recommended by Dr Robinson (who incidentally refused to give him any further advice while he adhered to the homeopathic regime). Ten years later, Sheridan Le Fanu agonised over the contest between normal and homeopathic remedies as his thirty-five-year old wife lay dying in Merrion Square. Months after she died he wrote: 'I will not trouble myself with the faithless thought that errors of art or the misapprehensions of the beloved patient hastened her death.'[37]

The boundary between medical and non-medical was by no means tightly drawn. Hypnotism, hallucinations, premonitions and the newly fashionable spiritualism all clouded the distinction, not to mention the ordinary people's beliefs in the fairy folk. Elizabeth Smith vividly describes a drawing-room exhibition of mesmerism: 'Sir Philip [Crampton] came to disapprove'. When a woman was 'sent to sleep', Sir Philip 'went out and brought the strongest spirits of ammonia and held it under the nose of one victim. She held her breath which he hailed as a partial victory'. Elizabeth Smith herself could not decide if the phenomenon was real, concluding only 'if it be a true power, it is a fearful one'.[38] Many younger doctors, notably Francis Cruise (President of the College 1884–5), conscious of the power of the mind in curing, took an acute interest in such matters. During the 1859 evangelical Revival in the North, an outbreak of what we now call contagious psychogenic illness struck thousands of men and women, who collapsed

Opposite: To demonstrate that cholera was a function of miasma not contagion, Dominic Corrigan demonstrated that the uninfected towns (white) were nearest the ports and busiest trafficways where contagion might be expected; while the infected towns (black) are in the remote West.

with apparent total exhaustion, some remaining in that state for days. In other similar prostrations the victims seemed to be sleeping. For the devout this was simply the hand of God striking the victim down 'under an awful agonising sense of sin'.[39] Those who dismissed the religious significance of such events were inclined to attribute them to a kind of mesmerism or hysteria, but medical men, though evidently interested in the phenomena, were charily conscious of the religious sensibilities involved.[40]

'The all-important subject of fever'

In his report on deaths between 1841 and 1851 for the Census, William Wilde distinguished three main types of cause: zymotic disease (contagious, epidemic etc.) representing 45 per cent of all identified causes; sporadic diseases (everything from asthma to rheumatism, taking in lockjaw, insanity, gout, cancer, consumption and marasmus—51 per cent); and violent deaths (4 per cent). The most prominent sporadic diseases were consumption (12.5 per cent of all specified causes), marasmus (failure to thrive) and the catch-all category 'infirmity, debility and old age' (11 per cent). Sporadic diseases were grouped according to their 'seat'—'brain and nervous systems', 'circulating systems', 'digestive organs' and so on. A sad, but revealing, group labelled 'diseases of uncertain seat' included cancer, gout, scrofula, and 'mortification'.

By far the biggest individual killer was simply called 'fever', which accounted for nearly one in five of all deaths. The bundle of diseases included in this description had been a source of medical controversy and challenge since the days of Hippocrates. Like so many ailments, we now know they were caused by human activity, being a deleterious inheritance of the agricultural revolution of 10,000 years before. The new farming economy enabled people to live closer together and in ever larger conurbations thus presenting ready opportunities for mosquitoes (which breed in stagnant pools and puddles), lice, fleas and rodents to transmit disease, not to mention easy movement of amoebas, worms and other internal parasites. By living in close contact with dogs, cattle, pigs, rats and poultry, humans created an enormous Petri dish in which new viruses and bacteria could mutate, creating a whole range of diseases that our nomadic ancestors knew nothing of. Over the centuries smallpox (from cattle), measles (from dogs) and influenza (from poultry) have caused devastating plagues. Agriculture, finally, involved intimate contact with the soil and its teeming population of viruses, and bacteria carried by ticks, fleas and lice. Larger parasites such as roundworm and hookworm were also presented with a new range of victims.

Debate as to what fever really was, and therefore how to treat it, was still central in medical discourse in the mid nineteenth century. Virulent outbreaks of Asiatic cholera in 1832 and 1848 stimulated public debate. The new disease was a frighteningly fast killer which particularly attacked young adults, reducing to

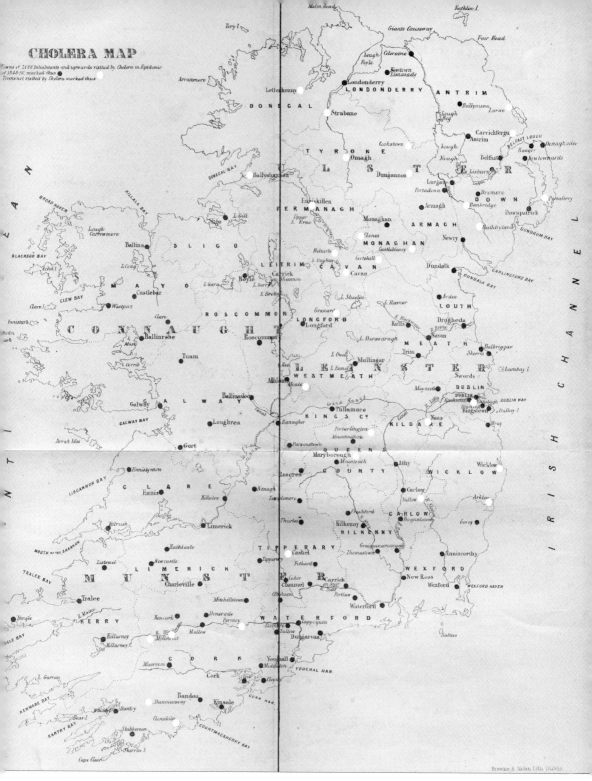

CHOLERA MAP

Towns of 2000 Inhabitants and upwards visited by Cholera in Epidemic
of 1848-55 marked thus
Towns not visited by Cholera marked thus

Browne & Nolan Lith Dublin

nothing 'often in a few short minutes—youth and health and strength'.[41] With a
case-mortality rate of 40 per cent, the first visit of cholera to Ireland claimed at
least 20,000 lives. The memory of the terror this outbreak caused was still fresh

when cholera revisited Ireland in the wake of the Famine.

In 1849 young Ellen Palmer witnessed its advent into her seaside village of Rush, County Dublin. 'Mrs Hoare', she records in her diary for 2 September, 'told us the cholera was raging in the town today, and poor Reed, the girl who cleared the walks died this morning after being in perfect health yesterday afternoon. Everyone about is perfectly panic-struck & the general gloom is awful to witness.' On 3 September she wrote 'there were ten deaths in Rush today. The village is quite heart-rending. We met three funerals on our way and at many doors the people were sitting outside crying, afraid to enter their own houses. In some of these houses as many as four people had died.' A couple of weeks later, she herself was suspected:

After dinner I was seized with diarrhoea which increased considerably, accompanied with spasmodic pains in the stomach & shivering. Dr Graves [kinsman to the famous physician] was sent for & I was put to bed with hot water bottles to my stomach and feet. Dr Graves gave me a powder & ordered me to take pills every 1/4 of an hour in case the symptoms did not abate. There was happily no reason for this but I passed a miserable restless night.

The following morning however she was able to record that 'I was a good deal better, but Dr Graves would not let me up, indeed he was greatly surprised to find me so well'.[42] Rush, which had just over 2,000 inhabitants in 1851, recorded 824 victims of cholera in 1849, of whom 176 died.

There were broadly two theories of how cholera was propagated. Some still believed that it was contagious, i.e. passed on person to person. Exactly how was never specified—was a touch or a breath sufficient or did one have to spend several hours in the company of a victim? The more fashionable view was that it was due to miasma, that is, 'a material substance distributed through the air and undergoing increase in the air'.[43] Dr George Robinson explained to Elizabeth Smith that cholera was caused by 'positive properties in the air acting on the nervous system affecting those otherwise prepared by accident or neglect to receive them'.[44] 'The symptoms', he said, 'are exactly those following some deadly poison taken internally.'

Robert Graves, on the other hand, rejected the miasma theory, proving that the disease never travelled from its homeland in Bengal more quickly than human transport. But once it arrived in a susceptible spot, it seemed evident that the local environment propagated the poison regardless of human activity. Despite Graves' arguments, contagion theory had many objections against it. Why for instance did the disease die down in areas where there were still plenty of unaf-

Sir Dominic Corrigan (1802–1880). A Catholic of Scottish origin, Corrigan was one of the leaders of Irish medicine, and one of the most influential physicians of his day. He was instrumental in the building of the College hall in the early 1860s.

fected potential victims? How did the disease so easily leap over the elaborate continental quarantine procedures? How did it sweep so rapidly and yet so partially through a town, by contrast, for instance, with the slower but comprehensive pace of influenza? Why did outbreaks seem to be so closely related to rivers and damp unhealthy times and places? Since the disease could clearly be traced moving up rivers, not to mention that 'many facts prove that the disease can spread through towns without the aid of contaminated water', the idea that the infection was largely water-borne got short shrift.[45] As with most medical debate, there was no neat bundle of stipulated facts—what facts were regarded as critical depended on the underlying theory adopted by the arguer.

In December 1852 the *Dublin University Magazine* quoted three of the most distinguished doctors in Dublin, Sir Philip Crampton, Dominic Corrigan and Sir Henry Marsh, in a report from the Central Board of Health, as declaring that 'the weight of evidence is decidedly in favour of the opinion that contagion has little if any influence in its propagation'. 'Doctors differ,' the article went on, 'but they all unite in ascribing if not the origin, at least the spread of epidemics to some impure state of the atmosphere'. By way of further proof, the 1851 Census made it clear that in Dublin damp, noisome areas such as the Wood Quay, Arran Quay and Merchant's Quay wards, and so-called second- and third- class shop districts were very significantly more susceptible to fevers than better districts. Naturally, people acted on this understanding. Dubliners who could afford to do so steadily moved out of the city to the healthy areas of Pembroke and Rathmines; and for their holidays they went to the sea, where the ozone was believed to be active in destroying the impurities in the air.

Apart from addressing most of the obvious facts the miasma theory had one huge human advantage in that it allowed the archetypal Victorian deathbed farewells—with the children and relatives gathered round—to take place without fear of infection. The *DUM* article noted:

> If cholera be not contagious, the inconveniences and pain of separating friends and relatives at a time when friendship is tested and fidelity found most grateful will be spared to many a sufferer. The children will be allowed to approach the bedside of a dying parent and the parent will be permitted to receive their caresses unalloyed by the fear that such proofs of endearing affection may be followed by danger of death.

As well as debate about how cholera was promulgated, there was enormous discussion as to how to cure it. Noticing the absence of bile in the stools, one school wanted to stimulate the liver with calomel (mercury) tablets; but others said this absence was an effect, not a cause. Separation of cause and consequence has been a perennial problem in medical debate. As John Neligan, editor of the *Dublin Quarterly Journal of Medical Science*, underlined, recovery does not necessarily imply cure. This did not prevent men such as Dr Toland, a Fellow of the RCSI,

The College's new hall in Kildare Street, opened in 1864, near Trinity and close to the two leading scientific bodies of the day, the Royal Dublin Society and the Royal Irish Academy.

declaring that he cured nineteen cases out of twenty by applying wetted towels to the stomach and feet. And he was by no means alone in claiming what Neligan sarcastically called 'the most convincing proofs of astonishing cures'. The debate was urgent and the public were not inhibited from contributing. There were, wrote John Neligan, plenty of 'kind-hearted, soft-headed, good-natured, worthy old folk, who hearing that something once did a great deal of good to someone' instantly felt it their duty to make this important information public by writing to the papers. This was bad enough, 'but', as he more severely went on, 'how individuals pretending to medical knowledge could pen half the sheer nonsense that has appeared about this disease, we know not.'[46]

Going further, in his *Lectures on Fever* William Stokes remembered that in his student days in the 1820s, at the height of the fashion for bleeding revived by Broussais, 'there was hardly a morning that some twenty or thirty sufferers from acute local disease were not phlebotomised. The floor was running with blood.' By the middle of the century bleeding was so seldom done that students would crowd round to witness such an unusual treatment. Conscious of the shifts of therapeutic fashion, Stokes was tempted to cast doubt on the whole armamentarium. 'Venesection, blistering, mercury, opium, bark, alkalies, acids have all had their advocates, whose statements are supported by genuine cases, and yet the question remains unsolved: would not the disease have subsided of itself and as quickly as under specific treatment?'[47]

In the country, on the other hand, bleeding was still fashionable. Dr Babbington, writing in 1836, noted 'the very free abstraction of blood too often had recourse to by village practitioners.' The anonymous *Medical Hints for Plain*

People (1840) confirms that 'a bleeder may be found in almost every village . . . blood letting is the favourite remedy with the poor, they practice it with very little regard to age, sex or symptoms.'

The great difficulty, as with any such debate, was to isolate the signal from the noise. What significance could be read for instance, into the idea that epidemic disease of this sort was, in the *Dublin University Magazine's* view at least, a cosmic event? There was, it was argued, 'the undoubted fact that epidemics are almost invariably accompanied by an extraordinary development of insect life and seldom fail to produce most remarkable effects upon the lower creatures' and instancing cases of dogs, cats, goats, horses all dying unexpectedly during epidemics. (The same phenomenon had been noticed during outbreaks of plague and justified the prophylactic slaughter of cats.) The debate was not simply of academic interest. Being inexplicable and a sudden killer, cholera was profoundly frightening. As George Robinson, Elizabeth Smith's doctor friend, admitted, he was 'much afraid of the cholera, which is the worst part of it, as all one's nervous energy is wanted to resist it'.

The last years of the heroic age

Although the Irish profession seemed to be thriving, with the College's splendid new hall (built on the ashes of the clubhouse of the Kildare Street Club) and its five-term President Dominic Corrigan being awarded a baronetcy (in 1866), it is arguable that an important trend in the development of medicine was being missed.

The future was in the biomedical model of medicine being nurtured in laboratories in Germany and France. In Germany, ironically the original source of Graves' and Stokes' world-famous concept of clinical education, medical education was increasingly university- and laboratory-based. But the English-speaking world, especially Ireland, clung to the idea that medicine was an art, not a science, and was best taught at the bedside. In a lecture in the Meath Hospital in 1847 William Stokes was clear where he stood. 'Do not suppose for a moment,' he told the students, 'that I would decry the importance of anatomical and physiological investigations which now occupy so much attention in different parts of the world . . . [but] our great object is to be practical men and we have laboured to make our pupils practical men also.'[48] In 'Apology for the Microscope', a lecture delivered in 1854 to medical students in Dublin,[49] Robert Lyons deplored the fact that there was no one teaching or carrying out original research in histology and pathology by the use of the microscope in Ireland, despite good work in Britain and on the Continent for twenty years or more. That year the College of Surgeons bought 'a mace and a handsome gown for the President'—eight years later they bought a microscope.[50]

The Irish school was therefore not well placed to respond to Virchow's theory of cellular pathology (his seminal book *Die Cellularpathologie* was published in 1858) or Koch's bacteriology. (The only Irish exception, John Houston of the Baggot Street Hospital, died in 1845.) This loss of the high seriousness of the pre-Famine years is symbolised by the fate of the Dublin Medical Philosophical Society, which was revived in 1856. A generation before it had been the vehicle for serious medical work— Wilde's first paper, on spina bifida, had been read to the society in the 1830s—now, as Wilde's biographer put it, the members spent their evenings 'in arguing on the merits of boned turkey, how to serve snipe, or how a saddle of mutton should be carved'.[51] Writing of the 1870s, O'Donel Browne bluntly states in his history of the Rotunda, 'there was no notable medical activity in Dublin at this time', and records that when Lombe Atthill wrote about puerperal fever he was obliged to deal with the subject from the clinical aspect 'no microscopical work being available'. Despite theses by Thomas Compton and T. W. Grimshaw in 1866 and 1867 respectively, it was not until Wunderlich's great work was translated into English in 1871 that 'the clinical thermometer became an auxiliary to the surgeon as essential as the use of light'.[52] And even when they were used regularly the tools were not always appreciated.

Mr Butcher on Excision of the Knee Joint

The real vulnerability, humanity and modesty of this image illustrating a knee operation makes a quite different impact from a modern scientific plate.

O'Donel Browne tells the story of a ward sister who 'would not allow the nurses to chart [temperatures] accurately as, whether the temperature was normal or not she entered it as normal, thus saving herself much trouble'.[53]

The resolutely clinical rather than laboratory focus of the Dublin school was to remain a characteristic of Irish medicine. By the middle of the twentieth century this individualised, personal approach had become a doctrine. Unfortunately for the fame of the Dublin school it was not one that was shared by the rest of the world, as we shall see.

Chapter Six
The 1900s

'We know the germ—the cause'

RADICALLY NEW IDEAS about disease do not appear often. This is perhaps just as well, since when they do they undermine the whole ecology of treatments, symptom analysis and ways of looking after patients. There had been, as we have seen, a constant ebb and flow of ideas about disease since the foundation of the College in 1654, but the generation that came to maturity around 1900 had to wrestle with the implications of the most far-reaching of such changes—from versions of humoural theory to the germ theory of disease.

The new theory finally rendered obsolete debility and miasma and a thousand other terms of art. Therapeutic standbys such as leeches, emetics and purgatives (at least for fevers) went the same way. It declared, astonishingly, that the necessary and sufficient cause of those diseases on which so much ink had been spilt, so many subtle theories had been spun and, frankly, as Neligan had said, so much undisciplined nonsense proposed, was likely to be one of a series of micro-parasites. Initially the medical profession had great difficulty in discarding the ancient wisdom that diseases were always multi-caused, and that to adduce a single cause smacked of lack of sophistication at best and quackery at worst.

We can see physicians struggling to incorporate the new and the old at a meeting in 1905 of the State Medicine Section of the Royal Academy of Medicine in Ireland. Sir John Moore (President of the College 1898–9) presented a paper linking the rise in soil temperature to the incidence of mortality from diarrhoea, a favourite theme of his for 30 years. In the discussion, doctor after doctor adverted to multiple causation. Dr Kirkpatrick commented that 'epidemic diarrhoea was probably caused by organisms capable of producing decomposition in foodstuffs, and not by any specific bacillus'. Dr Langford Symes thought that 'a multiple series of factors' produced these diseases, including food, milk, soil temperature and bacilli. Only Dr James Craig (President of the College 1919–21) took a completely modern line, clearly stating that 'this very fatal affection was due to micro-organisms'. Summing up, Sir John, loath to abandon his favourite study of meteorology, noted that he had carefully

Dr T. Percy Kirkpatrick (1869–1954) was in 1899 the first anaesthetist appointed to any Dublin hospital (Dr Steevens). He remained on the staff of the hospital into his eighties. Historian and bibliophile, he was Registrar of the College 1903–54.

not committed himself to the view that earth temperature was the absolute cause of the epidemic . . . 'he agreed that various organisms might cause the diseases'.[1]

The great medical textbook author William Osler was a convert to the new theory, but even he did not succumb instantly. In the 1892 edition of his *Principles and Practice of Medicine* he simply noted that, in respect of typhoid, 'the bacillus of Eberth is constantly present'. By the time a new edition was required in 1901, typhoid fever was unambiguously described as 'a general infection caused by *bacillus typhosus*'. In dealing with tuberculosis he identified bad food, bad air in 'wretched habitations and miserable cabins' and, with a typical hint of social control, 'bad drink, alcohol' as the elements preparing the 'body-soil' for consumption. But these comments on the relative importance of 'soil' rather than 'seed', in the metaphor of the day, were only fifth in a list of

The outdoor treatment—TB patients were encouraged to live and sleep in sheds like this, often located in private gardens, for months at a time.

eight 'things we know about tuberculosis' which started with the triumphant 'we know the germ—the cause'.[2]

The 'Crusade against Tuberculosis'

The growing incidence of tuberculosis was the great worry of the day. Half of all the deaths between the ages of fifteen and thirty-five were caused by tuberculous diseases.[3] Unlike countries such as Scotland, Germany or England, the incidence was actually increasing in Ireland. Some clung to the belief that 'the delicacy', as it was often called, had hereditary or racial origins and that Celts were particularly susceptible. Others more robustly blamed poor diet and living conditions, and regarded the tuberculosis mortality rate as a reproach and a disgrace to

Ireland. Sir Robert Matheson, Registrar-General, pointed out that of the 1,694 tuberculosis deaths in 1906 only 11 came from the 'professional and independent classes', and 1,049 came from labourers and workhouse inmates: the less well fed, housed and clothed, the more likely to succumb (see table below). Sir Robert quoted Dr Bermingham, the medical officer of Westport, in his description of the 'English cold' that plagued the young men returning from the harvest in England. 'It is sometimes a simple bronchitis, but most commonly incipient phthisis. It is easily traced to the wretched sleeping places called "Paddy-houses" in which Irish farm labourers are permitted to be housed in England. These "Paddy-houses" are often regular death-traps, dark, unventilated barns, in which men have to sleep in coarse bags on the floors.'[4]

Table 6.1: Deaths from tuberculosis in 1906

Class	Deaths	Rate per 1,000
Professional & independent (clergy, doctors, lawyers, 'persons of rank and property')	11	0.63
Middle (clerks, managers, civil servants etc.)	243	2.79
Artisans and petty shopkeepers	391	3.54
General service (unskilled labourers etc.)	635	4.12
Workhouse inmates	414	n/a
Total deaths	**1,694**	**4.50**

Source: *Ireland's Crusade against Tuberculosis* Vol. 1, 38–9.

One of the instruments by which the new germ theory of disease percolated to the public was the so-called 'Crusade against Tuberculosis' launched in 1907 at the Irish International Exhibition by the Women's National Health Association, led by the Lord Lieutenant's wife, the Countess of Aberdeen. A roving exhibition followed, complete with displays (blown-up images of bacilli, photographs of infected lungs etc.) and lecturers. This travelled round Ireland, visiting, as claimed, 135 places in two years. In order to make the people understand that tuberculosis was not the result of hereditary taint or moral turpitude they had to be introduced to what was, in effect, a whole new order of being.

Lady Aberdeen's lecturers used humour and homely metaphors to express the scale of the unbelievably tiny 'plants' that caused tuberculosis: 400 million of these (about a quarter of the entire human population of the world) could comfortably sit on a penny stamp, said one. Another noted that the 'monster steamship the *Lusitania*' was 'just as many times larger than this matchstick as this match exceeds in size a tubercle bacillus'. What was more, they multiplied alarmingly: 'an enterprising bacillus who may wake up in the morning to find no child about him to fetch his slippers, at sundown may have a tidy little family of twelve or fifteen millions of young germs to minister to his evening comfort'.[5]

Christmas morning in the children's ward of the Belfast City Hospital (1906). The medical profession is the only one routinely expected to attend on Christmas morning.

Not everyone was convinced. Surgeon Tobin of St Vincent's reported a lady saying to him 'I don't believe a bit about what you men see through your microscopes'[6] and Lady Aberdeen recorded a conversation between country women after a lecture about TB and germs. 'One said all that talk about germs was just a lot of nonsense, but she was overwhelmingly discredited when another . . . declared there was a power of truth in it, so there was, for when she washed out a room after a girl had died in a decline there was germs in it as big as a young babby's finger!'[7]

The implications had to be spelled out against a background in which personal hygiene was nothing like as easy as it is today. Some medical men even warned against washing excessively with soap, lest the skin's natural oils be depleted. In 1907 Surgeon Tobin, on the other hand, (whose nickname was 'Daddy') urged the medical students at Vincent's to adopt two rules: 'firstly cleanliness of body . . . secondly self-restraint in regulating his appetites'. Jewish women, who for ritual reasons had a bath once a month, had a reputation for exceptional cleanliness.

Furthermore, as William Osler put it, consumption was 'a house disease'— infection occurred where microbes could accumulate, so domestic customs and practices had to be changed radically. Under penalty of allowing their families to become sick, women were urged to force open windows; to burn bedding that had been in the family for generations; to provide nutritious food; to avoid dubious milk; and above all to keep the home scrupulously clean. 'We must educate the people', wrote Sir John Byers of Belfast, somewhat unrealistically, 'as to the importance of keeping their homes clean and sanitary, well ventilated, not over-crowded, and so situated as to be properly lighted by the sun'.[8] By the 1920s these messages amounted to a duty laid squarely on the woman of the house. A Catholic Truth Society pamphlet *Woman in the Home* published at that time declared: 'Once disease germs find access to dust it acts as a veritable hot-house or breeding-ground for them and for this reason it is absolutely necessary that dust should be removed from our homes daily.'

The Crusade focused especially on the widespread habit of spitting. According to the lectures reprinted in *Ireland's Crusade against Tuberculosis* people spat on the floors of churches, offices, shops and pubs, in trams and, of course, on the pavement. Lecturers gave frighteningly vivid descriptions of how a consumptive was

> . . . capable of coughing up millions of tubercle bacilli even during a sin-gle hour . . . as long as the phlegm remains moist the tubercle bacilli are as securely locked up in the sticky mass of phlegm as flies in amber; but let the phlegm once get thoroughly dried, then there is no longer any-thing to hold the bacilli and the first current of air which comes along floats them up and blows them about to the common danger.[9]

To ram home their points, well-meaning medical commentators deliberately stimulated fear. Infectivity could lurk in pocket-handkerchiefs, in second-hand clothes and furniture, in an innocent kiss, in wallpaper, in the pages of a library book, even in the dust on a shop floor. As in the early days of AIDS, vivid sto-ries were told of infection lurking everywhere: 'Who can be certain', asked one lecturer, 'in ordering a cup of tea in a public eating-house that the individual who drank from that cup a few minutes before was not a consumptive with microbes in his sputum and on his lips and moustache?'[10] Stories told of 'the schoolboy, for instance, who drops his apple on the floor of a railway carriage and eats it after merely brushing off the visible dust may some day swallow a dose of tuberculous poison'. The same writer cited cases of a heavily infected midwife whose practice it was to breath heavily down the throats of new-born babies, thus unwittingly infecting them, or of infection by a cut from a broken glass spittoon used by a consumptive.[11]

Medical men differed as to whether one could properly talk of 'curing' con-sumption. Some used the term freely, especially about cases caught early; others would talk of no more than what the Germans called 'economic cure'—sufficient to allow the patient to go back to work. There was no magic bullet, so the best that could be done was to establish conditions in which the patients could fight the disease themselves. The preferred solution was the so-called 'fresh air' treat-ment in special sanatoria, which had been revived in Germany in the 1880s (the plan had been proposed by a Belfast doctor in the 1850s). The first Irish version of these was established in County Wicklow in 1896, followed by public sanatoria in Belfast, Cork and Dublin. Lady Aberdeen's Peamount was established in 1912. Since there were less than a thousand beds in such sanatoria by 1914, most consumptives were treated at home, ideally in a chalet or separation area apart from the house, so they could not infect other family members. Relatives were warned not to spend more than fifteen minutes in the same room as a sufferer.

The strange world of the sanatorium, where patients were neither acutely ill, nor well, became a theme in world literature. For months patients would lie exposed to as much fresh air as possible, just waiting for their bodies to heal. They were permitted to read, undertake light work, but little else except eat. In the stricter places patients were encouraged to remain alone, and avoid the excitement of 'discussions on social, religious and political questions'.[12]

A substantial diet was a key part of the curative process. In the sanatorium in Newcastle, County Wicklow the daily diet was 'milk 4.5 pints; butter 1 ounce; eggs 3; bread 7 ounces; potatoes 6.5 ounces; sugar 2 ounces; oatmeal 1.5 ounces; rice 1.5 ounces; meat (cooked) 8 ounces; bacon or ham 3 ounces.' The large portion of milk was explained by the fact that 'the average Irishman is not a cheese eater' and nor would he eat pulses, preferring cabbage and potatoes.[13]

Sanatoria were feared as focuses of infection in the neighbourhood. The first pavilion at Peamount was smashed by frightened locals, and a proposed TB unit in the Royal Hospital, Donnybrook was refused for fear of upsetting the local residents (not least in respect of their rents).[14] Potential patients feared the constant exposure to the air (compelled to sleep out all night in the rain without proper covers, went the rumour), or being mercilessly stuffed with food, or the overstrict discipline. Worst of all was the juggling of hope and fear of the future— from every ward there were enough deaths to make one very conscious that TB could be fatal, and at the same time there ever-beckoned the hope of cure— as the Bible put it, 'hope deferred maketh the heart sick'. It was particularly hard for a mature working man without welfare benefits to leave his family to spend months in such places; and for the young, anxious to explore the world, the sanatorium was a kind of grey limbo dominated by irksome rules. Even after months inside the outcome was very uncertain; a high proportion of patients were discharged merely as 'improved'.

Cancer

Apart from tuberculosis, which reached a peak around this time, the Irish people were undoubtedly healthier in the first decade of the century than their parents and grandparents had been. Decade after decade the Census had recorded a steady improvement in the health of the nation since the Famine. On Census night in 1851 there were 104,000 people recorded as sick (15 people per 1,000 living); ten years later there were 12 per 1,000. At the turn of the century the number of sick had dropped to 8 per 1,000 living, and ten years later the number had

*Dispensing medicine
and medical supplies in
the most fashionable
street in the city—
Fannin's shop at 41
Grafton Street in the
late nineteenth century.*

dropped again to 7 per 1,000.[15] 'Sick', obviously a highly imprecise category, was defined as bedridden or unable to perform normal duties. Nonetheless, the decade on decade drops reported by the Censuses do echo both the improvement in other indicators such as life expectancy, mortality rates etc. Impressed by these facts, John Moore, in his inaugural address of the Meath Hospital session of 1895, feared for the future of the students in front of him: 'The triumph of Hygiene means the passing away of Medicine . . . already there are signs which seem to indicate that at least in certain directions the doctor's occupation will be gone'.[16]

The general Europe-wide improvement in health has been variously ascribed to better nutrition, sanitation, housing and water quality and personal hygiene practices. A major contribution to the Irish phenomenon flowed from the fact that the country was no longer conspicuously poor. Historians estimate that average incomes had quadrupled since 1845, and were higher than in European countries such as Spain, Italy and Norway.[17] In the 1911 preface to *The Doctor's Dilemma* George Bernard Shaw confirmed a change: 'Ireland is certainly a transfigured country since my youth', he wrote, 'as far as clean faces and pinafores can transform it.' A similar improvement was noticeable in the quality of rural housing.

Even at the time, medical men did not claim that the quality of medical care had much to do with the improvement, though the sheer presence of ordinary dispensary doctors (not just attending the sick, but vaccinating and registering births, marriages and deaths) must have had some effect in promoting norms of cleanliness. Certainly, the activities of the Dublin Sanitary Association (founded in 1872), many of whose members were doctors, had a positive influence. The high-pressure Vartry water supply introduced in 1868 enabled one-third of the city's households to abandon the noisome 'ash-pit and privy' system of waste removal and to introduce water-closets by 1880. Ironically, the extra pressure put on the drains exposed many a middle-class Dubliner to enteric fever. The old drains, designed solely for water runaway, could not cope and drinking and washing water became contaminated. Frederick Pim of the Sanitary Association noted: 'Every autumn we have an outbreak of typhoid among our well-to-do classes, by which prominent citizens are struck down, some never to rise again . . . the proportion of deaths from this disease is nearly twice as great amongst the well-to-do middle classes as among the artisans and labouring classes'.[18] Although the tenements were still a running sore, by the end of the nineteenth century the scourges of previous generations—smallpox, cholera and typhus—had been largely eradicated.

The increase in cancer, however, was worrying. The disease, as Austin Meldon put it in his opening address to the 1901–2 session at Jervis Street 'cause[d] more deaths in Ireland than any other save pneumonia, heart disease, tuberculosis and bronchitis'.[19] It seemed to be increasing also: in 1871 deaths had been 3.2 per 10,000 living—by 1901 this rate had doubled to 6.5 per 10,000. Not everyone agreed that there was a real increase. William Dobbin, a dispensary doctor from Banbridge (who qualified from Queen's College, Belfast, in 1865), for instance argued that the apparent increase in cases was simply due to better diagnoses and 'the fact that medical advice and observation are more universal than formerly'.[20] Or perhaps it was simply that more people were now surviving into the so-called 'cancer age' of fifty-five to seventy-five. Similar increases in England (where cancers were responsible for 1 per cent of male deaths in 1871 and 4 per cent in 1901), and in Holland, Norway and Hungary made it clear that this was not just an Irish phenomenon.

The worst hit area of Ireland was Armagh, and in 1903 the Registrar-General ordered a special investigation of the disease there. The responses of the dispensary doctors reveal much about the medical cast of mind of the day—these were largely men who had completed their training before Koch's results became publicised. A few were fashionably convinced that microbes were the root cause, perhaps the 'recently discovered microscopical organisms so minute that they pass through fine porcelain' (i.e. viruses) as Meldon suggested. For most, to look for a single cause of this kind was naïve, so they sought to identify 'pre-disposing conditions' which might weakly combine to give rise to disease. Pre-disposing conditions might be environmental (as, for instance, in the damp, airless, crowded rooms of the Dublin tenements), psychological or physical (perhaps hereditary, or from a destructive habit of life etc.).

Unconstrained by an agreed theory, observations swirled like leaves in the wind. Cancer, the doctors thought, was probably hereditary and it was somehow connected to TB. It seemed to be related to damp areas, especially woodlands and river banks; a Professor Loffler pointed out that it was rarely seen in countries where malaria was prevalent (a thought which prompted the Professor to suggest that cancer tumours be injected with malaria). It seemed likely that there was an infectious element; Austin Meldon described a case in London where a lady died in 1884; the next occupant of the room also died of cancer to be followed by a third who also died of the disease. There was no blood relation between the ladies, and they all seemed in perfect health when they took the room. No more cases occurred after the bedding was burned and the room disinfected. The Armagh study identified other specific causes including the custom of both farmers and labourers of smoking constantly from short clay pipes, giving rise to cancers of the lips and mouth, and 'general use of indigestible food such as insufficiently baked bread and strong tea'. The labouring man's fondness for strong drink was, as usual, identified as a predisposing factor. Everyone, however, was clear that the old tale that raw tomatoes caused cancer was nonsense, and the previously suspected 'unsound fruit' was also in the clear.

When it came to cure there was the usual inverse relationship between the number of remedies proposed and their effectiveness. Ideally surgery might be possible, though patients did tend to leave tumours growing until dangerously late. If surgery was not available different physicians proposed attacking the tumour with arsenous acid, turpentine, cobra venom, methyl violet, electrified mercury, carbide of calcium or, as we have seen, malaria. Others proposed x-ray treatment or internal application of thyroid or lymph gland extract. Not surprisingly, as Austin Meldon put it, 'the victim of cancer felt that his doom was cast and his days numbered.'

Other medical beliefs

The range of beliefs about disease among patients, many echoing the opinions of long-dead medical men, was as always much wider than orthodoxy would allow. The country belief in fairies and fairy doctors was still widespread, as the shocking, if exceptional, case of Brigid Cleary of County Tipperary, who was burned

The country cure for whooping cough—passing the child several times under the belly of a donkey. This practice was still prevalent in country areas in the early twentieth century.

to death because her family believed she was a fairy changeling, confirms. However, in his study of his dispensary district in Wicklow Langford Symes reported that superstitious remedies and practices were much less prevalent in Wicklow than in the south-west. 'Modern school-teaching, the better housing of the labouring classes and the railway and telegraph communication' had combined greatly to reduce such beliefs. Of course, a few such remedies survived: for jaundice, for instance, earthworms were boiled in milk, and then, as he puts it, 'administered to the patient with great solemnity'; children with whooping cough were made to walk under a donkey; and a basin of cold water placed under the bed was specific against erysipelas and bedsores.[21] For shingles the blood of a Keogh married to a Keogh was rubbed on to the skin. 'Water from holy wells [was] largely made use of'—holy wells and their associated thorn bushes hung with rags were all over the country, and many were linked with particular ailments. 'Fairy doctors' could be consulted about men or beasts, and particularly about children suffering from a variety of wasting diseases. Individuals in the locality often gained a reputation for being able to cure particular diseases such as migraine or external cancers.

Also on the fringes were continuing work on hypnosis and fashionable exploration of extra-sensory perception. Charcot's work in Paris on hysteria had put the well-known power of the mind over the body on a new basis, one that Freud was to build on. Charcot was elected an Honorary Fellow of the College in 1887. After two years' study of the subject, in 1891 Francis Cruise, consulting physician to the Mater Misericordiae, Dublin, reported himself convinced that 'hypnotism is a reality—a most extraordinary and interesting development of neurological and psychological science and in certain cases a potent aid to therapeusis'. He had

Knock in the 1880s— the orderly array of ex voto offerings of crutches hanging on the wall advertises the effectiveness of the shrine, at least for certain complaints. Despite episcopal disapproval, Knock was very popular.

visited the opposing schools of Nancy and Paris, and had returned from France a convert, though conscious that his reports would be received 'with incredulity and even derision'. It was not only his fellow-professionals who had doubts. To traditional religious the procedure smacked of diabolism. Sir Francis related that one old countrywoman, watching askance as he treated some patients by hypno-tism in his clinic in the Mater, finally said to the sister in charge of the ward: 'I think he might try it on me, so I will go to the chapel.' With his colleague Joseph Redmond (President of the College 1906–7), he relieved by hypnotism and auto-suggestion a neuralgia of long duration in a young girl—'after five repetitions of the hypnosis a full week's perfect relief ensued, and the girl went home'.[22]

This power of auto-suggestion was typically adduced by sceptics to explain the 3,962 miraculous cures that had been recorded from the shrine at Lourdes since 1858.[23] Dr Gustave Boissarie, head of the Medical Bureau at the shrine (1892–1913), claimed that there were between 1,000 and 1,500 cures every year. Faced with the challenge of medical scepticism, from 1883 this Medical Bureau (from the 1890s partly staffed by visiting doctors) documented in exacting detail cases such as that of Gabriel Gargam of Bordeaux. He had been paralysed from the waist down in a railway accident. After years without the use of his legs, he dra-matically rose from his stretcher during the blessing of the sick. Even the *British Medical Journal* was obliged to admit that the Gargam case was as well authenti-cated as anything could be. The (Protestant-edited) *Dublin Journal of Medical Science* was less broad-minded, and the index for these years contains references to Vichy and Sicily as health resorts, but none to Lourdes, despite its importance to the overwhelming majority of Irish patients. To some, Lourdes was a supersti-tious affront; to others it was a curious revelation of the forces in the human mind that were also responsible for mediumship and extra-sensory perception; for most in Ireland it simply challenged materialistic ideas about the relationship between the physical and the spiritual.

In County Mayo, Knock, where the Virgin and her companions had been seen in 1879, was attracting an increasing number of visitors. People would scrape away the plaster from the church wall and mix it with holy water. This was then used as an embrocation for sores and bruises. The miraculous virtue of the shrine was assiduously promoted by the local parish priest, Archdeacon Cavanagh; as he told the *Daily Telegraph*, 'some while ago I received a sick-call late at night to a man who was said to be vomiting blood and in extreme danger . . . after ministering to him I called for a glass of water, sprinkled on it a few particles of the mortar from the gable walls of the chapel and bade him drink. He did so; at once he began to recover and is now well.'[24]

The medical marketplace

According to the 1901 Census there were 2,221 physicians and surgeons in Ireland, supported by 1,920 chemists and druggists. By comparison, there were 2,200 barristers and 5,300 Catholic and Church of Ireland clergymen. The count of doctors included 20 women practitioners, noted for the first time, although the very first women to qualify had been admitted as Licentiates of the College as long ago as 1877, when five women, including the redoubtable Sophia Jex-Blake, were added to the list. Not that they were particularly popular with their male colleagues, except in special niche roles, especially gynaecology. As Foster Reaney put it in his 1905 Carmichael Prize Essay, 'the whole position of the female sex in the social economy of the world—passive as opposed to the active male, makes it extremely undesirable that a woman should engage in ordinary general practice, or should include men among her patients'.[25] There was not much more scope in the hospitals—when the resident medical officer of the Royal Hospital, Donnybrook resigned in 1900 there were six applicants for the £100 a year job, four women and two men. Neither of the men succeeded, so a new advertisement was posted specifying 'only gentlemen to apply'.[26]

Together with village practitioners, herbalists, wise women and fairy doctors (invisible to the official Census), these doctors looked after the 35,600 people who were recorded as seriously sick on Census night of 31 March 1901. These did not include the pregnant, or the blind, deaf or lunatic. Nor did they include the staples of the GPs' waiting rooms, those suffering from bronchitis or influenza, or back pain, or sore eyes, or 'bad blood', or the results of chronic self-indulgence, or 'slipped wombs' (a favourite if vague diagnosis of internal unease)—not to mention those whose symptoms betrayed no more than anxiety, unhappiness and the loss of youth.

Although all of the 2,200 doctors practising in Ireland had their registration

Sir Andrew Horne, the first Master of Holles Street and President of the College 1908–09 — the formal presentation of a prosperous Catholic Edwardian physician and his family.

under the General Medical Council Act of 1858 in common, that was where equality stopped. On becoming qualified, a young doctor had broadly three choices. The lucky ones found hospital work in Dublin; the next most favoured found jobs in the Empire, where, as William Smyly once put it, 'the best men' were to be found. The rest generally looked for work in the state service, in the dispensaries or county infirmaries. To land the top jobs it helped to be of the right family and religion. As Dr Bob Collis remarked: 'My father was a surgeon of some renown. He inherited the position of Surgeon to the Meath Hospital and County Dublin Infirmary from his uncle, another well-known Dublin doctor'.[27]

In appointing doctors to the country dispensary jobs a similar gross bias prevailed, as one contemporary commentator confirmed: 'Professional qualifications [were] ignored, and political opinions, religious beliefs and local influence [were] the only questions considered'.[28] In large population centres there was the possibility of 'club' work. Oddfellows, Rechabites, Foresters and numerous similar groups would contract a doctor in advance to look after their medical needs for so much a head. In principle this seemed attractive to the doctors, particularly since attendance on the (male) club member would usually bring the women and children of his family in as well. In practice, the medical marketplace was so oversupplied with doctors that committees were able to exploit the lack of solidarity among applicants and recruit medical attendants at knock-down rates.

When bankers and well-off merchants joined these organisations for the cut-price medical care, the so-called 'battle of the clubs' was joined. Starting in Cork in the 1890s the doctors of a town would refuse to treat on a club basis anyone earning more than a certain amount. This idea quickly spread to similar towns throughout the British Isles. Club administrators would then attempt to sack their refusing doctors and hire replacements. The results of this long-drawn-out struggle, which differed from town to town, were regularly reported in the medical journals. If the doctors remained 'solid' all was well, but sometimes the temptations offered to 'blacklegs' were too great. For men aspiring to the social status of learned professionals, it was bitter to discover that a decent salary was dependent on the tactics of the despised trade unions. After this experience of the ruthless bargaining of the clubs and the corruption of the local political system, it is perhaps no wonder that the next generations of practitioners treasured so highly independence from paymasters.

A notable feature of the system of pricing for medical service was the large discretion doctors practised in assessing charges. The profession prized its private system of progressive fees, by which the richer you were, the more you paid. The *Irish Times Almanac* of 1898 recorded a carefully graduated fee system based on the annual rental of the house. Thus for a visit to a house of less than £25 annual rental the cost would be between 2s 6d and 3s 6d; for a house with a rental over £50 the fee jumped to between 5s and 10s 6d. If more than one member of the family was sick at the same time 'half a fee is charged for each patient beyond the first'. Fees for midwifery, attendance on servants or the charge for being detained in the house for more than half an hour, were graduated accordingly. The Findlaters, whom we saw in the 1850s paying £1 for a doctor's visit, paid rent of £52 for their house in Upper Leeson Street, which indicates that medical costs may have drifted down in the second half of the nineteenth century in line with prices generally. On the other hand the *Almanac* noted that a visit to a consultant physician, which used to cost one guinea, was now more likely to cost two.[29] This suggests the possibility that in a crowded market ordinary GPs' fees had fallen since the 1850s, but the top men had been able to differentiate themselves and increase their charges.

In the medical profession 43 per cent of practitioners were Catholic in 1901 (rising to 48 per cent in 1911), and in the top Dublin hospital positions the ratio was much more skewed. Only two out of the nine medical knights were Catholic. The Catholic Sir Christopher Nixon was the first President of the College of the century and was followed by two Protestants, Sir Arthur Macan and Sir William Smyly (who were in turn followed by two Catholics, Joseph Redmond and Andrew Horne.) Most of Dublin's great hospitals, the Rotunda, Jervis Street, the Meath and so on, were Protestant-founded and, although theoretically nondenominational, were predominantly so staffed.

At the very top of the heap were the residents of Merrion Square, where 44 houses out of 95 were occupied by medical men. (At this time Fitzwilliam Square was more remarkable for lawyers than doctors.) With large practices and their hospital appointments these men might earn £3,000 or more a year. Although a more than comfortable living (a labourer could hope for about £50 a year), this was much less than the top lawyers could earn—the Lord Chancellor, for

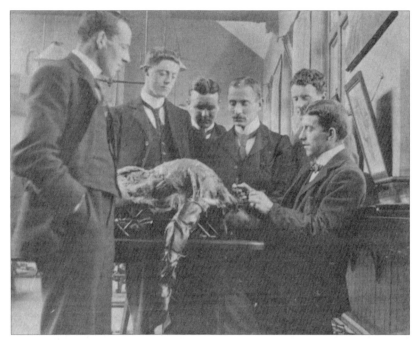

Students of the Catholic
University at anatomy
class at the beginning of
the twentieth century
attentively watching the
Demonstrator at work.

instance, was paid £8,000 a year. A political commentator of the day, Michael
McCarthy, wrote, 'with the exception of Sir George Porter, I, in my own experience, cannot just now call to mind any medical men who died recently in Ireland
possessed of a considerable fortune. But we can all count scores of legal men who
have accumulated large fortunes'.[30] Kinkead's 1889 *Guide for Irish Medical
Practitioners* likewise deplored the state's niggardliness to the profession: 'The
Church, the law, the naval, military and civil services and trade have rich pecu-
niary prizes and are rewarded with peerages, patronage and honours. Medicine
has few prizes, the State appointments are poorly paid, and the entire profession
is placed outside the pale of the peerage'.[31]

There were 26 ordinary hospitals in Dublin (including 3 lying-in, and 2 specialising in children's diseases); these provided a total of 228 staff and consultancy posts, although some posts were held plurally. Sir John Moore, for instance,
(as well as being Editor of the *Dublin Journal of Medical Science*) was consultant
physician to the Cork Street Fever Hospital (total 270 beds), the Coombe (65
beds), the Dental Hospital of Dublin and the Drumcondra Hospital (35 beds).
Sir Francis Cruise was consultant physician to the Mater, the City Hospital for
diseases of the skin, St Michael's in Kingstown and the tuberculosis sanatorium
in Newcastle, County Wicklow (66 beds). Most of these jobs were unpaid. A
consultant earned his keep by his private patients (for whom the hospital role
constituted an attraction) and significantly from fees paid by students.

To fill their shoes when they died (for few retired) there were, according to the

1901 Census, 1,331 medical students, of whom 46 were female. Normally the medical course took five years, the first of which was spent in the study of physics, chemistry and biology before moving on to more medical subjects. These included anatomy, physiology and *materia medica*, but also midwifery (recorded attendance at 30 cases required) and 'Theory and Practice of Vaccination'. There were five university medical schools in Ireland: Trinity, the Catholic University school in Cecilia Street, and the Queen's Colleges of Belfast, Cork and Galway. (The two last private schools, the Carmichael and the Ledwich, had recently amalgamated with the College of Surgeons.) The Royal Colleges of Physicians and Surgeons also provided fully registerable qualifications in medicine, surgery and midwifery, though the College of Physicians offered no teaching. Because there were rather more than 260 newly-qualified medical graduates looking for jobs in any year, a large proportion of students expected to spend their lives overseas.

For some, such as Sir Philip Smyly, a member of one of Dublin's medical dynasties, advancement came rapidly: he graduated at the College of Surgeons in 1861, having spent some time in Berlin and then Vienna, quickly became surgeon at the Meath and was elected President of the Royal College of Surgeons in Ireland when aged only forty. His brother, Sir William, also became a doctor and became Master of the Rotunda aged thirty-nine and President of the College 1904–5.

Less well-connected men sometimes progressed from the state sector to a consultancy practice, as did Lombe Atthill who preceded William Smyly as Master of the Rotunda and President of the College. His was a long and laborious rise. Born in 1824, the youngest of ten surviving children of an impecunious Church of Ireland rector, he completed his surgical training in the days before anaesthesia. His first job was with the Fleet Street dispensary during the winter of 1847–8, where he struggled to help the penniless refugees from the country, many living in cellars, or several families to a room 'without a stick of furniture amongst them'.[32] In 1849 he was elected to a dispensary district in Offaly 'which was situated in such a poor and uninviting district that no medical man would remain there a day longer than he could help'. In 1851 he became Assistant Master of the Rotunda. But despite professional advancement 'the years that followed were full of anxiety. I married young, children came, but my income remained miserably small . . . so slow was my progress in gaining patients that after being in Dublin seven or eight years I on two occasions entered into negotiations with the view of joining as partner gentlemen in practice in England'.[33] Eighteen years after coming to Dublin he was appointed to the Adelaide, and began to attract stu-

The red dispensary ticket which entitled the holder to free 'medical assistance and advice' in his or her home. It was distributed by the Poor Law Guardians to the sick poor (and sometimes to their friends).

FORM No. 2.—Ticket for Attendance at the Patient's Home.

Public Assistance Authority.

To Dr.
Medical Officer,

of
Dispensary District,

in the
Public Assistance District.

You are hereby directed to visit and afford medical assistance and advice to
aged

residing at
in the above-

mentioned Dispensary District, who is by occupation a

Dated this   day of   19   .

(Signed)...

* ....

*Member of Public Assistance Authority, Assistance Officer, or Warden, as the case may be.

[See the back of this Ticket for instructions as to presenting it.]

dents. In 1878 he was elected Master of the Rotunda, and his future was secure.

Towards the end of the century more and more medical knighthoods elevated the profession. Page Dickinson recorded that in his time (the 1890s in particular) Dublin doctors were prominent social figures. 'They contributed very largely to the activities of Dublin society, and were to be found engaged in all sorts of activities, from literature to hunting'.[34] However, for the great majority of doctors practising in Ireland, employed as salaried doctors in the dispensary service, there was little opportunity for scientific work or social elevation. George Birmingham's irrepressible Dr O'Grady was typical.

He enjoyed, as a dispensary doctor, a salary of £120 a year. He received from Lord Menton an additional £30 a year for looking after the health of the gardeners, grooms, indoor servants and others employed about Clonmore Castle. He would have been paid extra guineas for attending Lord Menton himself if the old gentleman had ever been ill. He could count with tolerable certainty on two pounds a year for ushering into the world young O'Loughlins. Nobody else in the district ever paid him anything.[35]

Although normally welcome, he was not invited to dinner, luncheon or even afternoon tea by Lord Menton at that season of the year when Clonmore Castle was full of visitors—'they were not the sort of people who would associate with a dispensary doctor'.[36]

Popular fiction tended to show doctors as slight oddities, but with depths of kindness and courage. H. A. Hinkson's Dr Finucane was 'a short, thick-set man dressed in a frock-coat and baggy trousers'[37] who was inclined to boast of the feats of his student days. George Moore's Dr Reed was described as 'an unpolished and somewhat commonplace man'. Both, however, behaved with a kind of calm heroism in the end. 'A doctor', as Edith Somerville put it some years later, 'is a dedicated man. He accepts risks with a laugh, and toil with perhaps a grumble but he does not flinch'.[38] Social aspiration by doctors was touched on by more than one novelist. In Moore's *Drama in Muslin* the doctor aspires to marry the daughter of the house. 'My darling child,' remonstrates her mother, 'wait a few years before you throw yourself away on such a man as Dr Reed.'

One reason for this attitude was that many doctors had ended their general education very early. 'It has long been an axiom in practically all professions', wrote Foster Reaney in the 1905 Carmichael Prize Essay, 'that a man should, theoretically speaking, be in a position to earn his living by the time he has reached his majority. Medical education has now been fixed at a minimum of five years'

The doctor as social hero—in October 1901 Dr William Smyth dispensary doctor at Burtonport, Donegal, found the Gallagher family on Arranmore suffering from typhus; in the course of treatment he contracted the disease himself and died on 19 November.

study. This means, therefore, that the lowest standard of general education that shall be accepted shall be that which can be reached by the average lad by the age of sixteen.'[39] Some started younger still—in the 1850s Alex MacAlister, later Professor of Anatomy at Cambridge, started anatomy in the College of Surgeons at the age of fourteen.[40]

Behaving like a doctor

As the concept of the family doctor became established, books were written to help the young practitioner (who had not, as in the past, served an apprenticeship) fill out into this new role. In his 1889 *Guide for Irish Medical Practitioners* Professor Kinkead, ex-President of the IMA, carefully detailed the formal behaviour expected—don't undercut fees; don't disparage fellow-practitioners; don't boast about your triumphs or gossip about patients' diseases; don't become involved in your patients' private affairs such as wills; be cautious about volunteering technical information; if called in his absence to attend someone else's patient don't immediately change the treatment; and so on. The 1890 publication *The Young Practitioner* by Jukes de Styrap, Licentiate of the College, described as 'practical hints and instructive suggestions for his guidance on entering into private practice', contains a fascinating mixture of advice on the day-to-day problems of running a practice, from dealing with patients' often bizarre medical beliefs to handling slow payers.[41]

The tone is sometimes elevated, as when the young practitioner is told that to give directions for the prevention of conception is 'derogatory and degrading to the medical profession and a gross abuse of his professional knowledge'. At other times the advice is more worldly: keep the patients in ignorance of what you prescribe (particularly if you suspect the presence of 'self-important sickroom critics'); never declare the patient's sickness feigned or trifling; certainly never guarantee a cure; on subsequent visits always re-examine the patient's tongue, pulse etc. (the patients like it); always check whether the medicine previously prescribed has actually been used (lest you expose yourself and your medicine to ridicule); identify as quickly as possible the 'ruling spirits' in a family and cultivate them; do not take your wife on visits (patients will assume you discuss the cases with her) and so on.

A constant theme is the necessity of the cultivation by the young doctor of a grave and discreet demeanour—in this way the new profession of 'family doctor' was being forged. 'Study so to efform [sic] your manner and address that patients will not hesitate to impart to you their secrets and the nature and seat of the disease'. There was a practical side to this also, for doctors who failed to inspire confidence would never be told the 'troubles and anxieties that give rise to feelings of hesitancy or shame'. The young doctor, who a few months before no doubt had larked in music halls and pubs and on sports fields, was adjured to maintain a calm and courteously impressive dignity, not to drink, smoke or eat with patients, nor to accept presents or 'allow patients to call you by your Christian name', nor to appear, even at home, in shirt sleeves, or in creaking boots, or engaged in household chores, lest you 'diminish your prestige, detract from your dignity and lessen yourself in public esteem by impressing people with the idea that after all you are but an ordinary person and not up to their ideal standard'.[42] 'Bear in mind that you are gentlemen', as William Smyly told the students in the opening session of the Meath in 1903.[43]

The average Irish dispensary practice covered a population of just over 6,000 people of whom (if Langford Symes' experience is typical) perhaps 600 might require attention during the year. There would generally not be a nurse, so the doctor might have to remain with a patient for hours or rely on the family or handy-women for assistance. If surgery was required there was generally no time to get to a hospital, so the kitchen table was called into use.[44] In his sentimental memoir *My Uncle Frank* Thomas Bodkin recalled how the dispensary doctor's work called him out 'at all hours of the day and night, often on emergency cases of the gravest kind. Many a thrilling story have I heard from the peasants of drastic operations successfully performed on bare wooden tables in lonely cottages, while the agonized wife or husband of the patient held up the pony-trap lamp to light the surgeon at his gruesome task'.[45]

Weather 'fit only for a snipe or a dispensary doctor' (Somerville and Ross). The dispensary doctor in his dog cart was an essential part of rural Ireland before 1914. The profession became early adopters of motoring thereafter.

There would probably be 130 births in the district during the year, but most of these would be looked after by local birth attenders. Langford Symes recorded that he was called in to only 6 of the 72 confinements in his district in 1895. Two patients a day is not a full demand and, although no doubt duties as the district's medical officer of health could have filled up the time, it is not surprising that there were complaints that many dispensary doctors allowed themselves to be distracted by 'farming, horse dealing and other pursuits' as one report put it, adding, 'the standard of sobriety is below what it ought to be'.[46] More sympathetically, the drunken dispensary doctor in *The Night Nurse* warned: 'Never be tempted to settle in a small place where you're the only doctor, where the only educated men you have to talk to are the parson and the priest, and you can't afford to be too friendly with either. You can stand it all right at first, but present-ly the hard laborious days, the broken nights get upon your nerves. Then you take to whiskey occasionally to tide you over an emergency.'[47]

The hospitals

At the other end of the profession were the prestigious voluntary hospitals, notably those in Dublin, Belfast, Cork, Waterford and Limerick, some of which were now over a hundred years old. Established and maintained by private char-ity, they operated as great colleges of advanced medicine. A constant stream of patients allowed intense scrutiny of disease. The up-to-date equipment (Ireland's first radiography department was set up in the Meath, in 1897, a mere two years after the announcement of Röntgen's discovery, St Vincent's followed in 1905) and the support of trained nurses provided the best possible conditions for such study.

As time went on the middle class began to recognise that they were missing out on the special facilities and skills in these hospitals. Obviously they could not be expected to use the public wards, so private (paying) rooms began to be attached to voluntary hospitals. To meet the increasing middle-class demand for spe-cialised hospital attention, particularly for patients from the country, several 'home hospitals' sprang up, often established as a private speculation by a doctor or group of doctors (the early-twentieth-century equivalent of the Blackrock Clinic). This was an important moment in the development of the delivery of medical care. Even if you were rich, the place to be seriously sick was increasing-ly in a hospital, no longer a private home. The working class had by now become thoroughly reconciled to the use of hospitals, and hospital outpatients' clinics were well attended (Since the urban dispensary service was notoriously under-staffed, this was just as well.)

Nurses

A new feature of the dramatis personae in the late-nineteenth-century hospital was the trained nurse. Before the 1870s Irish nursing had been done by nuns (during the day only) or nurse-tenders (whose reputation was not the highest) and neither of these had much formal training. In the Mater in Dublin, for instance, there were no trained nurses employed until about 1890; before that date nursing was done by nuns and night nursing by ordinary maids.[48] Since nuns were not allowed by their profession to undertake certain tasks, notably in the operating theatre, this effectively limited their role. The first formal training school for lay nurses was founded in the Adelaide in 1858, followed by the Institute of Nursing (established by the Archbishop of Dublin and his wife for Protestants only) in 1866. The developments in surgical technique made possible

The accident ward in the Meath (1900): the consultant addresses a patient while his houseman takes notes; note the new-style nurses and touches of middle-class domesticity, such as the patterned bed covers and the potted plants.

by antisepsis, introduced into the hospital in the 1880s, gave rise to the need for more sophisticated nursing.[49] Gradually, more and more hospitals established their own nurse training schools to meet this need. By the 1911 Census there were around a thousand hospital-certified nurses. The concatenation of medical students and nurses added a new flavour to hospital life (and a new theme for popular literature). Despite Matron's best efforts to maintain a conventual discipline, as the centenary history of St Vincent's put it, 'romance lived and throve even in the watches of the night. How could one expect otherwise?'[50]

A few hospitals, such as St Vincent's (founded 1834), the Mater (1861) and the still tiny Holles Street (1895), were as Catholic as they could be—or 'National' as the euphemism had it. In the early days of Holles Street there was a determined attempt to be exclusively Catholic—no Protestant nursing students were to be allowed, and 'no amount of subscription by a Protestant should entitle them to a vote on the [managing] committee'.[51] However, only the Adelaide discriminated as to patients. Except in obstetric matters, which were always sensitive, the Catholic/Protestant gulf does not seem to have interfered with the doctor-patient relationship. Catholic patients went to Protestant doctors for their ailments just as they went to Findlaters for their bacon and eggs.

Surgery

The first practical outcome of germ theory was the practice of antiseptic surgery. Sir Joseph Lister had proclaimed its benefits at a Dublin meeting of the British Medical Association in August 1867, but the Irish profession was not immediately convinced. 'Listerism' and the then unproven germ theory were inevitably linked, and this perhaps delayed the introduction of antiseptic techniques into

Dublin operating theatres. In the Adelaide, for instance, a new operating theatre
was built in 1879, and 'antiseptic surgery was only then beginning to be adopted'
for the 80 or so operations a year carried out.[52] In his history of the Rotunda,
O'Donel Browne confirms that in the 1880s 'the whole idea of antisepsis was a
complete novelty, and the era of asepsis had not dawned'.[53] The contrast with the
speed with which anaesthesia was introduced is striking. By 1913, however, a popular novel (by a doctor) described the 'rigid discipline of asepsis', and a young
surgeon in Dr Steevens' Hospital 'in the theatre scrubbing his hands, with a nurse
waiting to help him with his operating coat. Quickly he ran his eye over the
instruments laid out, in their white glazed trays awaiting his use'.[54] The public ritual of the operating theatre began to be established. Surgeons in their sterile operating robes, the bright electric lights; the 'neat-waisted nurse' arranging the
instruments 'with a faint metallic rattle on the instrument tables', the anaesthetist
at the head of the operating table; the senior surgeon gossiping about horses; the
patient swathed in mask and gowns; then the quick neat knife movement opening the body, swabs, commands barked out —'"knife"; he said abruptly', '"scissors" he barked' and finally the relief at the end and the moment of self-congrat-
ulation.[55]

The new pharmacy

By 1900 much of the old *materia medica* had gone quite out of use, and the scep-

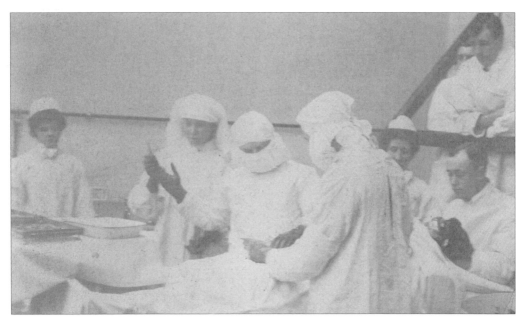

ticism that we have seen William Stokes expressing towards the medical armamentarium was becoming general. 'Throw out opium,' advised Oliver Wendell
Holmes in the 1860s, 'throw out a few specifics . . . throw out wine . . . and the
vapours which produce the miracle of anaesthesia, and I firmly believe that if the
whole *materia medica*, as now used, could be sunk to the bottom of the sea, it
would be all the better for mankind,—and all the worse for the fishes'.[56]

In this new atmosphere many doctors (later dubbed 'therapeutic nihilists') felt
that explanation and prognosis were nearly the best that could be done. When
Oliver St John Gogarty studied in the Allgemeines Krankenhaus in Vienna in
1907, as his biographer J. B. Lyons put it, 'the ideal and sufficient objective [of
medicine] seemed to be an exact diagnosis confirmed by a post-mortem examination'.[57] In *The Night Nurse* Dr Joyce, a dispensary doctor in the West, put it
thus: 'It's my belief if a patient's goin' to get well from typhus the divil himself
can't stop him; but if he's goin' to die, all the medicine in the world won't save
him'.[58] This approach, however, was hardly going to appeal to a mother pleading
that something be done for her sick child. So, in his advice to young practitioners de Styrap goes only some of the way. 'Avoid poly-pharmacy', he urges.' 'Drs
Diet, Quiet, Faith and Hope are excellent assistants, whose aid you should constantly evoke. Dr Time also is in some cases very successful, but he is slow and
unreliable.' He recommends becoming familiar with a small range of effective
medicines, to learn how they worked and in what doses. It was, furthermore,
important that patients felt that whatever was prescribed was tailored especially
to their personal needs and ailments. Indeed, successful treatment of one family

*An operation in the
same hospital as the
picture opposite, some
ten years later with
full precautions,
watched by students
from the gallery.*

member often led to others of the same family consulting you in the belief that you had understood the special subtleties of the family temperament and constitution.

Pharmacy had travelled a long way since the pharmacopoeias of previous centuries with their ponderous multi-ingredient nostrums including viper's flesh, honey, digitalis, opium and so on. The first step had been towards more precise specification of the active ingredients. From the 1830s alkaloids and other chem-

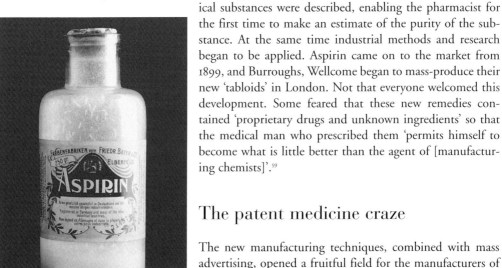

ical substances were described, enabling the pharmacist for the first time to make an estimate of the purity of the substance. At the same time industrial methods and research began to be applied. Aspirin came on to the market from 1899, and Burroughs, Wellcome began to mass-produce their new 'tabloids' in London. Not that everyone welcomed this development. Some feared that these new remedies contained 'proprietary drugs and unknown ingredients' so that the medical man who prescribed them 'permits himself to become what is little better than the agent of [manufacturing chemists]'.[59]

The patent medicine craze

The new manufacturing techniques, combined with mass advertising, opened a fruitful field for the manufacturers of patent medicines. As therapeutic nihilism increasingly became orthodoxy, entrepreneurs (both inside and outside the profession) quickly filled the void. It would be difficult

A bottle of Bayer's Aspirin, in 1885. This was one the first and ultimately most versatile of the new pharmaceutical products.

to overstate the importance of patent medicines in the ordinary medical experience at the beginning of the twentieth century. Indeed, to discuss medicine without referring to them would be like writing a history of food dealing only with restaurants and great chefs. Self-dosing after all was an old pastime. 'Most patients', wrote Foster Reaney in 1905, tried 'the effect of domestic, if not quack, treatment, before consulting the qualified doctor'.[60]

Stimulated by growing newspaper circulations and increasingly flamboyant advertising, the trade grew rapidly in the late nineteenth century. Figures covering the whole of Britain and Ireland show that receipts from stamp duty (typically 12 per cent *ad valorem*) went from £43,000 in 1860 to £324,000 in 1906. Over 42 million stamps (one per box or bottle sold) were issued in 1908—the equivalent of almost 1,100 prescriptions a year for every doctor in Ireland and Britain.[61] Two quirks of the law made this an underestimate of the true position: where no ailment, but merely a part of the body was mentioned, no duty was payable—so a cough mixture paid tax, but a throat lozenge did not—thus Carter's widely advertised Little Liver Pills paid nothing. Also, because the original legislation predated the Act of Union, patent medicines manufactured and sold in Ireland did not have to pay duty.

The attractions of patent medicine to the user were its low cost, the retention of control by the sick person and the well-touted possibility of a cure for cases more honest doctors despaired of. Professional medical attention was both expensive and fraught with uncertainties and possible humiliations. In his preface to *The Doctor's Dilemma* (1911), George Bernard Shaw pointed out in his exaggerated way the ambivalence with which doctors were regarded: despite mutterings about 'the noble character of the profession and the honour and conscience of its members, . . . the tragedy of illness at present is that it delivers you helplessly into the hands of a profession you deeply mistrust.' In his novel about Dr Steevens' Hospital already quoted, J. J. Abraham describes how, when a houseman prescribes an operation for a diphtheria case, the mother protests: '"Och, docther jewel, docther darlin", she cried, "Wud ye be after hurtin' me poor innocent darlin? Couldn't ye be givin's her somethin' to aise her like, an' let me take her home?"' The mother is coolly described, through the eyes of the staff nurse, as having a 'tear-washed face, draggled skirts, and mud-splashed, shapeless boots'.[62] 'Something to aise her', without a supercilious nurse, was exactly what the patent medicine promoter offered.

Increased literacy, prosperity and the expanded railway network enabled a boom in sales of weekly and monthly newspapers and magazines to take place in the late nineteenth century. Leading the field was the *Weekly Freeman's Journal* of which Louis Cullen has written: 'No other newspaper, Irish or English, equalled it in circulation, and in particular no other newspaper could match its rural readership'.[63] Patent medicine promoters tended to advertise in weekly and monthly publications rather than dailies. Although some of the advertisements were in the 'small ads' section, many were prominent full column or quarter pages in the body of the text.[64] As much as three-quarters of the advertising space in the *Weekly Freeman's* was taken up by proprietary medicines. Altogether its readers were offered no fewer than 25 different proprietary medicines in January 1905 alone—mostly for chest, stomach and internal disorders (see Appendix).

The way patent medicines were promoted gives us an insight into the medical world of their purchasers. There is much more of miasma than germ theory. The advertisements promoted or perhaps responded to a particular view of the body in which organs would become jaded ('indigestion means jaded stomach', say the producers of Bile Beans,) or perhaps 'torpid' (Carter's Little Liver Pills). Torpid kidneys were held responsible for many ailments. Grape nuts were recommended as preventing the souring and fermenting of starchy foods which created an

Consumption Can be Cured

Derk P. Yonkerman, specialist, discoverer of a remarkable Cure for Consumption.

Derk P. Yonkerman was by origin an American vet. He was a prodigious advertiser of his cure for consumption which the BMA analysed as being mostly glycerine, colouring, flavouring and water.

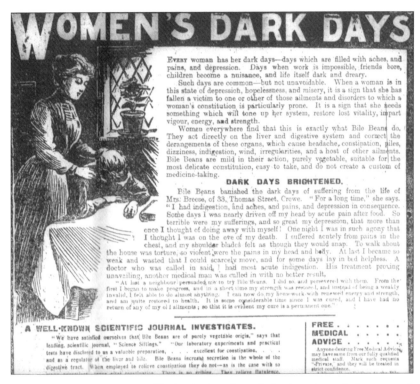

'Every woman has her dark days' runs the text. The solution?— Bile Beans.

WOMEN'S DARK DAYS

Every woman has her dark days—days which are filled with aches, and pains, and depression. Days when work is impossible, friends bore, children become a nuisance, and life itself dark and dreary.

Such days are common—but not unavoidable. When a woman is in this state of depression, hopelessness, and misery, it is a sign that she has fallen a victim to one or other of those ailments and disorders to which a woman's constitution is particularly prone. It is a sign that she needs something which will tone up her system, restore lost vitality, impart vigour, energy, and strength.

Women everywhere find that this is exactly what Bile Beans do. They act directly on the liver and digestive system and correct the derangements of these organs, which cause headache, constipation, piles, dizziness, indigestion, wind, irregularities, and a host of other ailments. Bile Beans are mild in their action, purely vegetable, suitable for the most delicate constitution, easy to take, and do not create a custom of medicine-taking.

DARK DAYS BRIGHTENED.

Bile Beans banished the dark days of suffering from the life of Mrs. Breese, of 33, Thomas Street, Crewe. "For a long time," she says. "I had indigestion, and aches, and pains, and depression in consequence. Some days I was nearly driven off my head by acute pain after food. So terrible were my sufferings, and so great my depression, that more than once I thought of doing away with myself! One night I was in such agony that I thought I was on the eve of my death. I suffered acutely from pains in the chest, and my shoulder blades felt as though they would snap. To walk about the house was torture, so violent were the pains in my head and body. At last I became so weak and wasted that I could scarcely move, and for some days lay in bed helpless. A doctor who was called in said I had most acute indigestion. His treatment proving unavailing, another medical man was called in with no better result.

"At last a neighbour persuaded me to try Bile Beans. I did so, and persevered with them. From the first I began to make progress, and in a short time my strength was restored, and instead of being a weakly invalid, I felt able to do almost anything. I can now do my housework with renewed energy and strength, and am quite restored to health. It is some considerable time since I was cured, and I have had no return of any of my old ailments; so that it is evident my cure is a permanent one."

A WELL-KNOWN SCIENTIFIC JOURNAL INVESTIGATES.

"We have satisfied ourselves that Bile Beans are of purely vegetable origin," says that leading scientific journal, "Science Siftings." "Our laboratory experiments and practical tests have disclosed to us a valuable preparation, . . . excellent for constipation, . . . and as a regulator of the liver and bile. Bile Beans increase secretion in the whole of the digestive tract. When employed to relieve constipation they do not—as is the case with so

**FREE . . . .
MEDICAL . . . . .
ADVICE . . . . .**

Anyone desiring Free Medical Advice may have same from our fully qualified medical staff. Mark such requests "Private, and they will be treated in strict confidence.

internal gas (a miasma, in effect) which inflamed the bowels, and thus caused constipation, peritonitis and appendicitis. A similar line was taken by the promoter of Veno's Lightning Cough Cure who darkly suspected that you had 'catarrh'—after all 'every fourth person you meet has it'. This 'insidious and dangerous disease' started as an ordinary cold, and then the mucus settled into the stomach and other regions where it rotted (another miasma), causing catarrh of the stomach and intestines, followed by catarrhal deafness, bronchitis and consumption.

Not surprisingly, cures for consumption were prominent. The American Derk P. Yonkerman (a vet by training) declared in large letters *Consumption Can Be Cured* and *Consumptives There is Hope For You*. His remedy was Tuberculozyne, which retailed at £2 10s for a month's supply (mostly glycerine and water, costing 2s 5d, said the British Medical Association). With it, he announced, 'startling cures [had been] effected, physicians mystified, sceptics convinced', and 'even sufferers given up to die have been by it restored to perfect health'. Yonkerman did not explain how Tuberculozyne worked, but cleverly insisted that the patient continue the treatment even after benefit had been felt. If no benefit was seen, that simply proved how serious the case was. Another prominent anti-consumptive was the Weidhaas Hygiene Institute whose 'Nature' cure 'permanently and absolutely' eradicated asthma, bronchitis and consumption. They claimed to have treated 90,000 cases, which 'included hundreds of so-called "incurables" who had been given up by eminent Physicians and Hospitals'.

These advertisements were repeated month after month, so we can be sure that they successfully entrapped hundreds of tuberculosis sufferers and their families, whose choices after all were not many. It was believed that there were 80–100,000 people with tuberculosis in Ireland. As we have seen, the preferred medical response was rest in a sanatorium but of course only a tiny number could afford to go to Switzerland for six months, and not many more could find beds in Ireland.[65] Most sufferers could not even afford to take time off work. Yonkerman's tablets at least offered hope, at a price.

Over a twenty-year period discovery after discovery had focused the medical mind on the germ theory. One by one bacteria were found that were at the bottom of major diseases—typhoid (1880), tuberculosis (1882), cholera (1884), enteritis (1888), plague (1894) and dysentery (1898). Eventually, as we have seen, doctors began to assume that micro-parasites were at the root of virtually all disease, even cancer. At the same time, faith in the traditional *materia medica* had waned, a movement that can be traced to the middle of the nineteenth century. The new understanding of disease represented by germ theory required new medicines. Unfortunately, as Koch found out with his premature announcement of the virtues of 'tuberculin', it was much easier to identify *mycobacterium tuberculosis* than to find a way of killing it inside the body. The search for ways to repress bacteria was on, and the anti-syphilitic Salvarsan (1909) was an early success. Antitoxins for diphtheria and tetanus came later, but it was to be a whole generation before broad-spectrum antibiotics became available. In the meantime the profession began to enjoy an ever increasing prestige, as we shall see when we examine the 1920s.

Appendix: Proprietary medicines advertised in *The Weekly Freeman's Journal* January 1905

Angier's Emulsion For troublesome coughs, bronchitis, lung troubles.

Beecham's Pills Described as 'without equal in dispelling all disorders of the Stomach, Liver, Bowels and Kidneys'. Advertised in England as a 'reliable, searching, cleansing' medicine for syphilis.

California's Syrup of Figs 'Nature's pleasant laxative' (but contained no figs).

Congreve's Elixir For asthma, bronchitis, consumption (28 per cent alcohol).

Cuticura Soap, Ointment and Pills For psoriasis and eczema (retailing at 2s 6d per box, contents cost 1/2d).

Dean's Pills For kidney and backache.

Doan's Pills An American remedy against the creeping onset of Bright's disease and dropsy—bread pills with a small quantity of juniper oil.

Grasshopper Ointment For leg sores, pills 2s 6d a box.

Keating's Lozenges 'Easily cures the worst cough'.

Keye's Worsdell Pills 'For ladies of all ages they are invaluable' also for indigestion, biliousness.

Mother Seigel's Syrup 'Half dead people gain new life'. Cures liver and stomach disorders. 'Mother Siegel's cures are permanent cures'. American in origin: made of 40 per cent treacle, 8 per cent vegetable extract and 50 per cent water. The firm was said to employ 300 people in London.

Ozerine Fits cured 'cured permanently the very worst cases of epilepsy when every other remedy had failed'; made in Ireland.

Paris Medicine Company 'A guaranteed cure for piles'.

Plasmon Recommended for dyspepsia by Mark Twain.

Potter's Asthma Cure Sold by all chemists and herbalists at 1s per tin.

Scott's Emulsion For 'all round health at home, the perfect "bringer-back" of strength, the great "thrower-out" of disease'.

St Jacob's Oil American: Cures rheumatism, neuralgia, lumbago.

Vaughan's Bronchial Cure From Kiloh & Co., Cork.

Vegeler's Curative Compound Cures indigestion, nervousness and constipation. '"Nervous patients" that means habitual drunkards—it's put that way to save unpleasantness', said George Birmingham's Dr Whitty.

Veno's Lightning Cough Cure 'How the lungs become diseased—it is the hawking and coughing that destroys the lungs'. So stop the cough with Veno's and you will nip consumption in the bud. Made of 8 per cent glycerine with small quantities of alcohol, chloroform and resin.

Ward Chemical Co. 'Drunkards can be cured without their knowledge.'

Note: The comments are based upon the BMA's *Secret Remedies—What they cost and what they contain* London: BMA, 1909.

Chapter Seven
The 1920s

'Go to a kind doctor and tell him about it'

THE IRELAND OF THE 1920s was an anxious, uneasy place. The aftershocks of the troubles of 1916 to 1921 left a ravaged economy and an uncertain civil society. Armed robberies were daily occurrences—in just one issue of the *Weekly Freeman's* (2 February 1924), for instance, there were reports of a farmer in Dungarvan beaten by an armed raider; a young servant stripped and robbed in Kenilworth Square, Dublin, by a twenty-four-year-old unemployed clerk wearing Free State uniform trousers and leggings; a bookmaker held up at gunpoint in Mountjoy Street; a hold-up in Rathmines staged by two armed men; and a Jewish merchant robbed in Greenville Terrace by a man with a Colt revolver. Casual shootings were also common. In October 1924 a young woman was accidentally shot dead after a dance in Kerry, by a Free State officer, and a farmer was shot after a quarrel.

Marlborough Street en fête for the Eucharistic Congress in 1932—the Catholic Church's influence on social and medical life for the next generation was unassailable.

In June 1925 Dr Purcell, from the dispensary district in Blessington, was accused of shooting one Honour Bright (a girl 'of the unfortunate class') in the Dublin mountains. He was found not guilty, but no one queried what he, a Peace Commissioner, was doing with a gun. Like the body of Major Geoffrey Smith, which in July 1925 re-emerged from the bog hole near Blarney into which it had been flung, the shadows of the violent past were close. So, when a special *Irish Times* supplement looked back over the state's first decade, the very first article in the 60 page retrospect was about law, order and policing.[1]

In other aspects, too, civil society was slow to re-establish itself. There were accusations of profiteering in milk and vegetable selling in Dublin, and of bribes in connection with the establishment of the new Irish radio station. In April 1924 it was reported that unionists had wasted no time in establishing gerrymandering in Tyrone and Fermanagh—it took 1,562 Catholic votes to elect a councillor, but only 500 Protestant votes. In July the newly elected dispensary doctor from Kiltoon, County Roscommon, lately house surgeon in St Vincent's, was displaced after it was found that several of his electors had 'offered their votes to the highest bidder'. (They were only following an old practice. In South Tipperary before the First World War, as Dr Dowling remembered, 'during some elections as much as £50 was paid for a vote . . . one Guardian who called on me said that he would like to see me elected and he would be very pleased to vote for me if I gave him a cheque for £20.'[2] Before the war £50 was a labourer's annual wage.)

Although for socio-economic reasons the island's population declined for more than a century after the Famine the same factors that had dramatically reduced both mortality and morbidity throughout Europe (improved nutrition, sanitation, public health etc.) were present in Ireland. By every indicator, the new generation of 1925 were, once again, healthier than their parents. The crude mortality rate for the Free State area had fallen from 17.6 in 1891–1900 to 13.3 in 1923, a drop of 24 per cent. Infant mortality showed a similar drop, from 99 per 1,000 births in 1891–1900 to 66 in 1923.

"Fellow Irishmen, are we to lie down an' see a man from another parish appointed as our Dispensary Doctor?" The election of a dispensary doctor was rarely on medical merit alone.

The infant mortality figures, however, concealed a worrying trend. Across Europe infant mortality had come down significantly between 1900 and 1925. In England and Wales, Germany, Belgium, and the Netherlands the rates had more than halved. Norway, which had started in 1900 as the safest place in Europe to be born, had managed to halve its infant mortality rate and was still the safest place to be born. The improvement in the whole island of Ireland had not been so impressive, with the 32 county rate dropping from 109 deaths per 1,000 births to 83. Given the improvement in the Free State figures quoted above, it seems that worsening conditions caused by industrialisation in the North were responsible for this relatively poor performance.[3]

For children were still vulnerable. One in six deaths were of children under the age of ten, as infectious diseases continued to take their toll. Illegitimate children were particularly vulnerable. Of the 554 registered in the state in 1923, one-third were dead by the end of the year, a rate of 375 deaths per 1,000 for infant boys and 318 for girls. 'These rates', as the Registrar-General put it, 'must be regarded as excessive.' Forty per cent of deaths of illegitimate children occurred in orphanages and other institutions in Dublin city and county.

In the absence of antibiotics infectious diseases hit all ages. The great influenza epidemic of 1918–19 had killed at least 18,000 people, causing the Registrar-General to comment that 'no disease of an epidemic nature [had] created so much havoc in any one year' since the Famine.[4] Recent epidemics he noted were the scarlet fever outbreak of 1878 in which 4,034 people died and the smallpox epidemic which killed 3,248 in 1872. There had also been an influenza outbreak in 1900 to which 4,677 deaths were attributed. In 1924 there were 2,073 deaths from influenza, 4,600 tuberculosis victims and numerous deaths from various infectious diseases including diphtheria, enteric fever and measles. Pneumonia and bronchitis registered 5,500 deaths between them and heart disease 4,800. Just 6 per cent of deaths were attributed to cancer (the modern figure is over 20 per cent).

Partition, *de facto*, if not quite yet *de jure* pending the decision of the Boundary Commission, focused attention on the six counties of Northern Ireland, where the overall mortality rate was worse than in the Free State, and so were the death rates from heart disease, cancer, diabetes and tuberculosis. The fact that the rural infant mortality rate in the Free State was half that of the urban, suggested that the cause of the worse rates in Northern Ireland was its greater degree of urbanisation.[5] The country was still notably healthier than the city.

A new code

The Free State hurried on with the task of establishing a new social and moral code. An Act setting up film censorship was quickly passed, as was one limiting the opening hours of public houses. The campaign against Evil Literature (by which was typically meant racy Sunday newspapers from Britain) gathered pace. The ideas behind these social controls were ultimately those of the Catholic Church, but middle-class Protestants did not necessarily dissent. Social class was, as usual, a potent influence in such matters. In practice the social controls were to be exercised by the class from which most doctors came over the class from which most patients came. So, in the debates leading to the control of, firstly, contraceptive information (1929) and then the sale of contraceptive devices (1935) there was no real expectation that the professional class could be prevented from access to both—but since they could be trusted to preserve the values of society this did not matter. Oliver St John Gogarty, surgeon and senator, had three children, more or less the average (mean) number for his class, but about half the national average per married couple. This did not prevent him declaring in the Senate in April 1929: 'No one who has any care for a nation's welfare can for one moment countenance contraceptive practices, which are a contradiction of a nation's life.' Farms, factories and armies needed men. Even when the rhythm method of contraception had been given a grudging papal approval, Irish priests restricted information about it as far as they could, on the grounds of the 'calamitous social consequences' of 'indiscriminate' use.[6] (Emigration was not alluded to in these debates.) Statistics from the 1940s confirm that not only did the middle classes live longer and healthier lives, but on average they contrived to have notably fewer children per family than the labouring classes.[7]

Particularly in obstetric matters, the Catholic Church's hand could be heavy, preventing a range of medical interventions that might otherwise have been indicated. This did give rise to some disquiet. For instance, as Dr Rowlette (President of the College 1941–2) pointed out in the Dáil debate on prohibiting the importation of contraceptive devices, an absolute ban even where a woman's life would be endangered by a further pregnancy could cause difficulties. For cases where the couple did not regard contraception in those circumstances as immoral, the clause was, he said, an ill-advised attempt to impose (Catholic) morality by statute.[8] The education of medical students was another sensitive area, with the Hierarchy's ban on Trinity ensuring that the natural rivalry between institutions would be sharpened by a religious divide. As it happened, many older Catholics, such as Gogarty, had gone to Trinity. When Andrew Horne, son of the first Master of Holles Street, was proposed to succeed his father in 1931, his application was vetoed by Archbishop Byrne of Dublin, the *ex-officio* chairman of the hospital, solely because of his Trinity degree. Ironically, young Horne had been recommended to study at Trinity by his Jesuit teachers at Belvedere.[9]

Being a doctor

The first Free State Census, in 1926, showed that there were just over 2,000 doctors practising in the state, of whom 10 per cent were women. Supporting them were 5,300 nurses and 500 midwives. At the top of the professional tree were the consultants, with their hospital appointments and their private consulting rooms in Fitzwilliam and Merrion Squares. Their position depended on the curiously organised voluntary hospital system. Originally these hospitals had been purely charitable institutions offering free treatment to the poor, supported by the great and good of society, who themselves were doctored at home. Technical developments in the late nineteenth and early twentieth centuries (including asepsis, radiography and a wide range of specialised measuring instruments) had resulted in an enormous increase in equipment that was both expensive to buy and required skill to operate.

Hospitals had ceased to be simple hostels for the sick, and had become highly specialised (and increasingly costly) places for the study and cure of disease. They were also the central institutions of the medical profession, of more importance to individual doctors than the Royal Colleges or the Irish Medical Association. Here students first encountered real patients and undertook their first faltering

steps into care. Here they were induct-
ed, if they were lucky, into the practical
mysteries of their profession by charis-
matic and even brilliant teachers.
Hospitals were the locus for the prestigious (though still unpaid) consultancy
jobs, and also of loyalties sometimes so
complete that a Vincent's man would
not seek a job in the Mater, or a
Coombe trainee be given a job in
Holles Street. For historical reasons
there were too many hospitals, but it
was hardly practical politics to propose,
as Gogarty once did in the Senate, to
eliminate duplication of staff and
equipment by closing them all down
and building one giant hospital on the
model of the Allgemeines Krankenhaus in Vienna.[10]

The Land Acts and income tax
(whose impact was particularly felt during and after the Boer War) had
between them drastically reduced the
ability of the traditional supporters to
pay for the growing costs. Before the Hospitals Sweepstakes were established, the
future of these once-great hospitals seemed bleak. Long years of financial strin-
gency had severely embarrassed many of them, and as a result (as the Hospitals
Commission reported in 1936)

*Dr Kathleen Lynn
(1874–1955) a daugh-
ter of the rectory, she
combined social
republicanism with
pioneering ideas for
the care of children.
Co-founder of St
Ultan's Childrens'
Hospital.*

> . . . the administration and management of the Irish hospitals, generally,
> leaves much to be desired . . . in the vast majority of cases, the small size
> of the hospitals rendered the provision of a well-organised administrative
> staff uneconomic, and the financial position of the hospitals before the
> Sweepstakes did not permit of a very great expenditure on administra-
> tion.[11]

At the same time a certain ineffable cosiness had settled on the Dublin voluntary hospitals. Bob Collis memorably described his first introduction to the staff
room of the Meath (founded in 1753).

> There the Matron dispensed coffee like a *grande dame* before the French
> Revolution. As I entered the first time the Matron was handing Mr
> Henry Stokes a cup: 'Can I press two lumps on you today, Mr Stokes?',

The Portobello Nursing Home, originally a canal hotel, acted as a half-way house between medicine at home and the hospital wards, which were still mainly providing free treatment for the working class.

while holding up one in a pair of silver sugar tongs. Sir John Moore seemed to be explaining to Dr Murphy, one of the younger doctors, something important in the construction of Greek irregular verbs . . . at that moment Gogarty entered and everybody turned towards him. He made some Wildean kind of brilliant quip and everybody laughed.[12]

In between the very rich and the poor lay a large middle class, for whom the necessity to pay the high costs of ordinary hospital accommodation was recognised as potentially involving real hardship. The continuing boom in private nursing homes was partly to address this problem. In these homes a wide range of medical procedures was performed, including operations. The nature of private enterprise meant that the standard of these homes varied considerably. On her visit to Portobello Nursing Home (one of Dublin's most prestigious), in November 1929, the Danish writer Signe Toksvig, who was living in County Wicklow at the time, casually records: 'the close-stool was by the bedside and I slew a cockroach in the breakfast tray'.[13]

The previous ten years had introduced Irish doctors and nurses to considerable military training. Many served in the British army, following a long tradition—of the eight men who served as President of the College between 1925 and 1945 six had served in the RAMC. Medicine in the hospitals behind the trenches was, of course, very different—an endless supply of horrific wounds, gas gangrene and infestation. Some even had to re-create the skills of operating without anaesthetic. Thomas Moorhead, a Fellow of the College, went from Sir Patrick Dun's to

the military hospitals of Alexandria, where he found the officer in command and the matron were both Irish. Moorhead, who became Professor of Medicine in the College of Surgeons, was particularly struck by the time saved in a military hospital by not having to provide long explanations of treatments![14] Another notable soldier was the obstetrician Henry Jellett, then Master of the Rotunda. Jellett joined up in 1914, and was decorated several times. In fact he might have served the Empire better by staying at home, for a 1917 report noted sensationally that you were more likely to die as a baby in Dublin than as a soldier in the trenches.[15]

Many Irish doctors served in the trenches; in brutal circumstances some even found they had to rediscover the skills of operating without anaesthesia.

One thing learned during the war was the technique of blood transfusion. The discovery of blood types in 1900, and in November 1914 of the use of sodium citrate to prevent coagulation of collected blood, led to increasing use during the Great War. After the war the practice emerged slowly in Dublin, constrained by the scarcity of donors. Rumours had suggested that donors had suffered various ailments after giving blood, which discouraged others. Reporting that he had kept track of fourteen donors himself, none of whom had come to any harm, Henry Stokes of the Meath proposed that donors be paid at £5 5s the dose (a considerable sum, but he had heard of people being paid £20!)[16] Despite the tech-

Male surgical ward in St Vincent's in the 1930s. Clinical notes are kept above the patients' heads; the Catholic atmosphere is represented by the nun and the large crucifix and religious picture at the end of the ward.

nique's recognised utility, it was not to be until 1942 that a National Blood Transfusion Council was established. Even after that hospitals such as Holles Street maintained their own blood banks as a cost-saving measure. To keep up supply, 'during evening visiting hours the Assistant Masters used to prowl the wards and corridors, shaming fathers and other male visitors into giving blood. Donors got a pint of Guinness to revive them afterwards'.[17] In the Rotunda (male) medical students got Guinness, nurses who gave blood only got tea.

Many of the professionals who did not go to war found similar excitement at home. J. D. MacCormack, medical inspector for Munster and three Leinster counties, recalled spending six dangerous weeks hunting a suspected typhoid carrier across Kerry during the Civil War, the man himself being on the run; on another occasion he was escorted across 27 trenches by a troop of Irregulars; on another he was threatened by 'three enormous and enraged' IRA men, all speaking Irish (of which he had not a word).[18]

During the 1919–22 period there were regular curfews in Dublin between nine p.m. and five a.m., and, despite special passes and ostentatious wearing of white coats, students and doctors were at real risk. The paediatrician Dr Colman Saunders, who was at UCD with the most famous medical victim of those years, Kevin Barry, recalled the constant moving across the perilous central streets of Dublin. Science subjects were studied in Earlsfort Terrace, zoology in 86 St Stephen's Green, and medical subjects in Cecilia Street. Ambushes and shootings were frequent: 'If you went out of, say, Grafton Street into Stephen's Green and saw the place deserted with the pedestrians hiding in doorways or lying down behind lamp-posts, you picked your lamp-post or gutter with a high pavement and lay there until the fun was over.'[19] Most hated were the Black and Tans, though being a medical student had its advantages:

Even while walking along the street you would have to take your hands out of your pockets if a lorry-load of them passed or they might put a bullet into you. They didn't seem to worry much about death or injury to themselves, but they had a horror of disease, and we soon learned if arrested after curfew and thrown into a lorry to say that we were only students from Cork Street Fever Hospital, on which we were immediately kicked out into the street.

Less dramatically Saunders remembered his first hospital experiences, in his third year of study:

In Vincent's when I was there, there were only two housemen, no registrars, a house physician and a house surgeon and eleven students, so that we had to undertake almost the same duties as the present house officer. We had to do dressings, collect all specimens, blood CSF, catheterisations and so on. Examine our patients daily, supervise all treatments and be available for 24 hours a day . . . just after I entered Vincent's as a resident student, insulin came on the scene, and I was expected to care for several diabetics in addition to my ordinary work.

Since insulin had only been discovered in 1921 the techniques for its use were still a novelty.

For historical reasons there were still far more medical students in Ireland than the country could accommodate. The technical and commercial structure of the country was small, leaving the sons of the middle classes limited choices. Business opportunities were few, and usually restricted to family connections. Other professional openings (outside the clergy) were equally limited. According to the 1926 Census there were only 1,356 lawyers in the new state, 382 accountants, 978 engineers and 567 journalists. There were some 1,200 medical students who paid fees for the basic MB, BCh. and BAO courses totalling £247 in Trinity and £168 in UCD at a time when the average worker in industry earned £118 a year.[20] As many as 80 per cent of the newly qualified had to seek employment in Britain or in the British services.

When Ireland was part of the Empire, these newly qualified doctors had naturally taken their place on the British-run General Medical Register, side by side with the products of the great London hospitals. As part of the independence project, in 1924 the Cumann na nGaedheal government proposed to establish a separate and independent medical register. This would have condemned Irish qualified doctors to, at best, an appendix in the British register along with Canadians, Australians, etc., and it was widely expected that the change would deter potential students from studying in Dublin. A large question mark was suddenly raised over the survival of the medical schools, and by implication over other parts of the structure of medicine. Many senior doctors gained income and prestige from their teaching posts (every student paid £55 for the privilege of 'walking the wards'). Even those not directly benefiting were intensely loyal to their old medical schools and hospitals and often their old 'Chief'. The loyalty had been intensified by sporting encounters and by the fact that for religious reasons these educational facilities were in effect duplicated—Trinity and UCD, the Meath and Vincent's, the Rotunda and Holles Street. In the end a compromise was cobbled together allowing Irish-qualified doctors to retain their position in the British register.

It would have taken a very much more aggressively radical government than that led by William Cosgrave to amalgamate forcibly the medical schools of Trinity, the College of Surgeons and Cecilia Street, or even to combine the resources of the smaller hospitals. Moreover, it was clear that Irish medical education was far from the laboratory-based ideal represented by the Johns Hopkins Hospital and University in Baltimore. This model had been assiduously promoted since 1910 by the influential educator Abraham Flexner, backed by the Carnegie and Rockefeller foundations, and had led to a complete reform of American medical education. Flexner's magisterial 1925 comparative survey of medical education in America and Europe had, to the dismay of the College, ignored Ireland (even referring to Graves and Stokes as English). The Rockefeller Foundation was equally scathing, describing Queen's University Belfast as 'the best of its kind in Ireland' but still no more than a respectable provincial school. There were, said the Foundation, too many students, too many schools, and the teaching was done by practitioners not academic specialists.[21] Furthermore, there was a growing tendency for students to attend any hospital as fancy took them, with the implied lack of supervision: 'Dr A at such a hospital, and on Tuesday Mr B at another.' This was bad for the students, and worse for the popular teachers who, faced with large audiences, became 'stagey and emotional'.[22] Generally the schools were criticised for setting themselves low targets, attempting to teach 'no more than the ordinary general practitioner would need of the various preliminary and essential disciplines such as physiology, bacteriology and pathology'. On the other hand, since the vast bulk of the students were destined for general practice, it could be argued that this aspiration was both realistic and reasonable.

Dr R. J. Rowlette agreed that in Dublin 'provision for research apart from teaching is absent, and . . . our teachers are fully occupied in teaching'.[23] (This attitude to research of any sort was common in the contemporary Free State university system as a whole, as Professor Joe Lee has recorded.[24]) A mixture of complacency and preoccupation kept Irish medicine firmly on the traditional side in the 'clinic versus laboratory' debate. There was even a kind of pride in the isolation this implied. When Bob Collis went for his Membership of the College (in the 1930s), he was presented with a case of childhood rheumatic fever, a subject he had studied intensively in London. After he had given his examiners the full benefit of his up-to-date information, they failed him, saying 'in Dublin we pride ourselves on our clinical acumen. Perhaps we are a little old-fashioned, but honestly all this semi-scientific stuff that seems to be the thing now is not what we feel will make a good doctor of you.'[25] 'A little old-fashioned' meant, for instance, that in accordance with practice established when fevers were thought of as different presentations of the same underlying ailment, itself a function of the atmosphere, in the Meath 'all kinds of infectious patients [were put] into beds beside each other and the ordinary patients'. When a child with kidney disease caught diphtheria, Collis protested, and Matron explained: 'Sir John calls it "hospital throat"'.[26] (Sir John, who was in charge of the ward, had been born just before the Famine, and was then in his eighties.)

St Vincent's outpatient department in the 1930s. In 1936 42,000 patients shuffled patiently along these benches, overlooked by a statue of St Vincent. The outpatients clinic was behind the hospital in a side street off Leeson Street.

Fully a quarter of the doctors were Protestant, and a chill must have run down their collective spines as they read of de Valera's comments in the Dáil in 1931 to the effect that 'the Catholic community does want to be assured that the doctors appointed locally to minister to their people, who will be at their side at the most critical moment, at the time of death, shall be members of the same religious faith as themselves'. Was the Fianna Fáil party going to choose its doctors by religion and insist that in majority Catholic areas (virtually the whole country) only Catholic doctors need apply for official positions?

In the North this polarisation had already been effected. James Deeny, later Chief Medical Advisor to the Department of Health and a Fellow of the College, qualified in Belfast in the late 1920s, after seven years of training. His first thought was to look for a dispensary doctor appointment, 'but these were generally to be got only by political influence and in the North of Ireland Catholic doctors did not have much chance of such posts or of appointments to the local hospitals'.[27] There was also no chance of an appointment at the Royal Victoria Hospital where he had been a student. 'In those days, in that vast hospital there was not a single Catholic medical on the staff'.[28]

Frustrated of any chance of an official position, Deeny decided in the late 1920s to 'put up his plate'. He found a house, furnished a waiting room and surgery, and equipped himself with instruments and a display of textbooks to represent learning. He decided to do his own dispensing. This was an important decision implying targeting the less well-off section of the population, for those catering for the rich always worked through a pharmacist. He laid in 'stock' mixtures which

. . . you would dilute to make up cough bottles, digitalis for heart disease, antacids for stomach troubles and so on. You had 'Tabloid Products B. W. & Co.' for injection and splints and bandages and things like needles and sutures for sewing up cuts. There was a lot of thought given to fitting out the midwifery bag. . . . The first patients were mostly the local hypochondriacs 'trying' the new doctor . . . there are always people who have persistent complaints for which the existing men have had no cures. The new doctor, by finding a new dimension, might cure the odd one. The word is spread that the 'new man' is good, and so it goes on.[29]

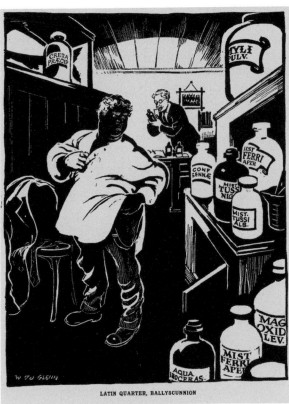

LATIN QUARTER, BALLYSCUNNION

A dispensary doctor of the 1930s and his favourite remedies, masked in the learned obscurity of Latin.

James Deeny shared his father Donnell's very busy practice. There were three surgeries a day, with a special morning one on Sundays for difficult cases. There was a lot of midwifery, mostly home deliveries, of which there might be several in a night. Although by now it was considered appropriate to have a doctor even at normal births, none of the mothers would have had any ante-natal care—'the young ladies' mothers usually regarded this as "interfering" and not natural'. Although midwifery practice was an essential part of the practice, it was fraught with perils. Calls invariably came at night, when the doctor was tired after a busy day, and ill-equipped to deal with anything but a normal delivery. There were no blood transfusions, and knowledge of how to deal with shock was rudimentary. Caesareans were 'highly dangerous because of the risk of sepsis or of pulmonary embolism'; midwifery assistance was not good, since midwives had only been put under regulation since 1911, and those practising at that time had been allowed to enter the register without examination. 'Some had traditional skills and were wise women, but some were "shockers", real Sarah Gamps'.[30] 'Luckily', Deeny commented, 'childbirth is a natural process, and most women survived it.'

As there were no antibiotics [he wrote] practice included a very large element of abscesses, pleurisies, chronic bone disease and septic infections.

There seem to have been more fractures: more people rode bicycles, there were always accidents with horses, the roads and footpaths were not so well paved and people seemed to fall about a lot. Most fractures were set by the family doctor and people like my father had wonderful hands and a feel for bones.

In the country few people thought of going into a hospital or seeing a specialist, so the GP was always close to the community. It was only with the advent of the motor ambulance in the 1920s, as Dr Dowling remembers from his time in South Tipperary, that if necessary patients could be brought into hospitals or one of the five nursing homes in the town, so except for dire emergencies farmhouse surgery came to an end.[31] Deeny continued: 'You were always on the look-out for fevers such as typhoid and an epidemic of measles meant a lot of very sick children and some deaths. Acute pneumonias often struck people suddenly; they gasped for breath for days, bringing up large quantities of "rusty" sputum and trying to hold on till the crisis occurred and then suddenly recovered.'[32] And occasionally he would be summoned to a lonely hilltop to provide first aid to an IRA man injured in training.

From Tallaght in the 1920s Rory Doyle (the novelist Roddy's father) remembered that

> . . . Dr Lydon was the dispensary doctor and he had been in the British Army during the War and he'd picked up strange habits, like drinking excessively. Medicine wasn't practised as an exact science in those days, if you went to him with something, you got a blue bottle or a green bottle. But invariably old Lydon was jarred. Katie Coombes was his factotum: cleaning the place was in fact, her job. But she gradually took upon herself the role of dispenser, and when you went to the doctor, she'd ask 'What do you want the doctor for?' and you had to describe your symptoms to her. 'Oh', she says, 'the doctor gives a blue bottle for that'.

There was no getting past Katie Coombes.[33] The alternative was the neighbourhood chemist. 'You never seen doctors', said one old man from the Dublin tenements, describing the 1930s, 'You could go to a chemist and even if your throat was cut he'd give you a cure for it! . . . People really believed in them, swore by them'. Harry Mushatt worked as a chemist in Francis Street in Dublin. 'We made our own medicines in the shop. My brother and I made up 44 different preparations, from skin ointments, psoriasis ointments, foot pastes, stomach bottles, skin creams, tablets for kidneys, headaches, neuralgia.'[34] The people's belief was not always justified. Dr Ethna MacCarthy recorded one Dublin chemist who evidently held the common belief that lice came from water, having told two girls that 'they had got lice from washing their hair too often'.[35]

The status of the profession

In the 1880s, as Ruth Barrington put it, 'it was a source of disappointment to medical practitioners that their profession ranked below the church, the law, the naval, military and civil services and trade in terms of income and social status'.[36] But gradually this changed, until for most of the twentieth century the medical profession enjoyed a special esteem, as the then current joke about the elderly couple underlines. The doctor examines the woman in the bed and declares she is dead. 'No, I'm not,' whispers the old woman. 'Bridget!' says her husband, 'don't contradict the Doctor.' This attitude partly reflected the profession's estimate of itself. The *Irish Journal of Medical Science*, the official organ of the Royal Academy of Medicine in Ireland, promoted in the 1920s a high attitude to 'Medicine' (with a capital) and its practitioners. Its obituaries record the deaths of men of 'the highest culture and keenest intellect' (E. McWeeney) or 'wide learning and of the very highest integrity' (A. Blayney); a volume of essays published after the death of Sir Clifford Allbutt is 'invested with the solemn dignity of a great teacher's last words'. There was, of course, a class aspiration to this boosterism. A book of surgical aphorisms reviewed in 1925 included the recommendation that surgeons should avoid operating 'for what may be got out of the case'. The anonymous reviewer commented: 'The avoidance of these things is natural to surgeons who have the instincts of gentlemen, and the advice is wasted on those who do not.'[37]

By the early twentieth century, despite the medical armamentarium still generally shooting blanks, and the relative somnolence of the College, the prestige of the medical profession had reached a high point. In literature the local doctor had previously been a figure of slight fun, as typified by the cheerful lightweights of George Birmingham or *The Irish RM* stories. But a change was in the wind; in the 1919 novel *Mount Music* by Edith OE Somerville, Dr Francis Aloysius Mangan is a man of personal power. He was 'one of the leading doctors in the district' who, by his skill at doctoring, with 'his power of sympathy, good nature, intuition, adroitness, discernment of character, and a gift for taking every man in his humour', had found a house in the 'most fashionable quarter of Cluhir', and now schemed and plotted to marry his daughter to the son of a nearby Big House.[38] 'A doctor', writes Edith Somerville, 'is a dedicated man. He accepts risks with a laugh and toil with perhaps a grumble, but he does not flinch.' At the end of the novel Dr Mangan is drowned attempting, in the course of a violent storm, to reach a patient. 'In his last act he took his life in his hand and gave it for another.' The theological echo is not accidental. In 1932 Signe Toksvig (writing about Bethel Solomons, President of the College 1946–8, for whom she had a very soft spot), recorded 'the clean gravity of a priest about him on operation morning. Keen, quick and kind in waiting on his guests at breakfast, but silent and rather withdrawn as if concentrating his whole being, gathering up his sparkles of energy to the one thing. . . . that chill, fresh awesome remoteness. The doctorial face.'[39]

There had been a crucial change in the way the profession approached a diseased person. Traditional medical theory clung to the essentially Galenic idea that how a disease presented itself was dependent on the idiosyncrasies of the sick person—including age, sex, usual diet, living conditions and way of life. When Hippocrates wrote that 'one man's meat is another man's poison' it was not a metaphor for the diversity of taste but a literal fact. So the family doctor was not just the doctor normally consulted, but one who had a unique insight into the physical balances, responses and peculiarities of the patient's family.

The germ theory of disease, on the other hand, implied that a duchess with TB should be treated in exactly the same way as a dustman. The duchess may get cream rather than skimmed milk in her tea, and some more exotic massaging, but ultimately what works in her case works for the dustman. This understanding of medicine is at the root of the welfare state. The disease process rather than the individual sick person became the focus of the physician's attention. This was, of course, a theory highly suitable to the increasingly important hospital wards, in which patients were not even named, but referred to as 'the PUO in bed 14', or, as in the fictional A&E room based on Dr Steevens' Hospital, 'a Colles' fracture arriving just then . . . he examined and set it with the aid of the accident nurse'.[40] In his memoir *Drums under the Window* Sean O'Casey recalls his time as patient 23 in St Laurence's Ward in Vincent's Hospital: 'Well, 23,' [said Sr Paul] 'your wound's healing splendidly, and there is little more that we can do for you here.' Others were less lucky: the night nurse sharply told a patient moaning 'You'll have to stick it, 18, . . . You've had your morphia, and you'll get no more.'[41]

Dr Bethel Solomons, ex-Master of the Rotunda, in his robes as President of the College, by his daughter the noted artist Estella.

The infantilising of the sick was another, related, part of the hospital 'script'. During her stay in Portobello Nursing Home in 1927 Signe Toksvig records: 'Nurses pleasant. One, however, always called me "naughty girl" or "good girl"'. In hospital again for a hysterectomy in 1931 'the nurse talk[s] to me as if I were seven years of age, "now dear, now dearie, be a good girl, now"—but they are all more or less given that way'.[42] The mechanism seems to be that the intimate services provided by nurses, and to a lesser extent doctors, infringe the normal distance between adult strangers, but much more is permitted between an adult and a child.

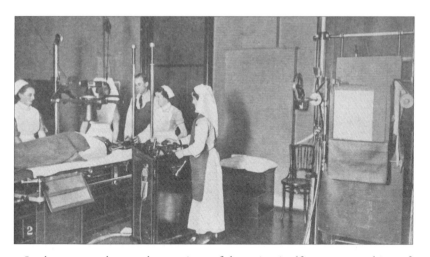

The x-ray treatment room of St Vincent's in the 1930s. Four nurses and a doctor attend.

In the 1920s and 1930s the mystique of doctoring itself was a new subject of great popular interest. Two bestselling British novelists, themselves trained as doctors, gave the public vivid images of the medical life. Perhaps the most popular was *The Citadel* by A. J. Cronin, which sold 100,000 copies in ten weeks. The theme of the novel was the sensitive relationship between the various driving forces in doctoring. Since Hippocrates (and no doubt before) the medical profession has been driven by three desires: the desire to cure, the desire to understand the human body for its own sake, and the desire to make money. As long as these three urges are kept in reasonable balance, all is well—but if one predominates disaster follows. An excessive desire to make money leads to quackery, an excessive desire to cure to the bullying of 'heroic medicine', an exclusive interest in science to the cruelties of human experimentation.

The Citadel was initially fiercely denounced by the medical profession for its portrayal of cynical consultants milking rich hypochondriacs. One such was pictured charging three guineas for injections of sterilised water, saying: 'And why not? It all boils down to faith and the bottle of coloured water.'[43] Other characters in the book supported the Irish surgeon Sir William Wheeler's jaundiced remark that one could tell a wealthy patient by the number of scars on her abdomen. There was no question but that these books affected the way people looked at doctoring, and, conversely, the way doctors looked at their own lives. Bethel Solomons tells how a woman who had read *The Citadel* when told she must have an operation for acute appendicitis responded 'No, you're not going to "citadel" me.' She was dead in 24 hours. Nonetheless, in the end the novel's hero, a passionate, caring doctor, continued to inspire many. Solomons himself always recommended the book to his students.[44] Another popular writer was Francis Brett Young whose novels *The Young Physician* (1919) *Portrait of Clare* (1927) and *My Brother Jonathan* (1928) also explored the profession. William Doolin, Editor of the *Irish Journal of Medical Science*, described one scene Brett

Young wrote as 'far and away the best and most truthful description of medical life . . . a scene in the panel surgery is so true to life that we can almost imagine a shorthand writer having taken it down'.[45]

These books and other media references consolidated the feeling that doctors were carriers of secret knowledge, and this gave spice to the popular moral parlour game: 'Should a doctor tell?' There were several dimensions to this conundrum. Firstly, there was the question of patient confidence: could a doctor ever reveal secrets of the consulting room, for instance, in the witness box? or, should a doctor tell a young bride that her husband-to-be has a venereal disease? Then there was the vexed question of how much information the patient should be given about his or her condition. It was believed, particularly in cases of heart disease and cancer, that the patient would at once lose hope and die if told the diagnosis. Older practitioners were often unashamedly economical with the truth, as an anecdote about Sir Dominic Corrigan demonstrates. A nervous lady suffering from a minor gastric ailment demanded to be told what was wrong with her. 'Oh! The matter with you, madam,' said Sir Dominic and paused and looked through the window (where he saw across the road a painter putting the finishing touches to a shop sign); he pointed to the region of her stomach and said: 'You've got a little emporium there.' The lady thanked him and seemed quite satisfied. 'It is a great mistake', concluded Sir Dominic, 'to give that kind of person too much information.'[46] The Vincent's surgeon R. F. Tobin told his students in 1900 that 'in the practice of medicine the truth needs careful handling. I have known a patient's pulse intermit one beat in five on being told the truth'.[47] The patient's relatives would of course be informed, and this imbalance of information was a stock element of the sickbed 'script', as was the strong-minded patient who refused to be infantilised and demanded to be 'told, honestly'.

The sickroom scene

Although the underlying theory of medicine had definitively changed, during a sickness, carers and patients brought a long-established series of expectations as to how their respective roles might be played out. The historian and novelist Dorothy MacArdle described how the

> . . . smells of bread-and-milk and iodine brought back her childhood illnesses to Nan. Her mother had told her stories and fed her and sung to her. You had to sit up all night with a sick child. Her mother had sat up alone. Some fathers would watch too . . . she thought of all the women down the centuries who had sat like this, putting a child to sleep, and of all who would do it before the world came to an end. This was the first time, for her, and it had come to her as naturally as if she had done it always. It gave her a strange restful sense of being carried on the main stream of life.[48]

A sick-room scene in St Vincent's private nursing home—both the patient and his visitor are smoking, the bed table is typical; the scene itself retains a domesticity that has vanished from hospital wards.

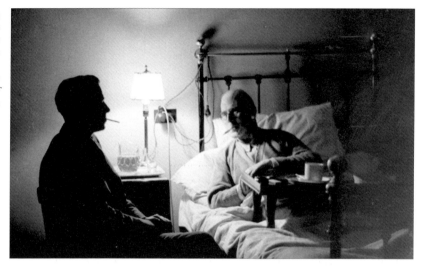

In Matthias Bodkin's novel *Floodtide*, the Jesuit author describes clearly the roles to be played at a sickbed in a well-off Dublin Catholic family in the 1920s. The young hero's mother has caught a chill which quickly develops into pneumonia (then responsible for 1 in 15 deaths in Ireland every year). He is rushed home from his boarding school (Clongowes) and is greeted by his sister, Clare. She tells him that "'the doctor expects the crisis to develop very soon, . . . and he says that mother has such a good constitution that she may pull through'". The patient lies, at home, in her darkened room looked after by nurses, with the daughter in attendance: "'She's got two nurses and I stay with her most of the time.'"

The son's role is to distract the anxious father, who waits "'sitting huddled up in the study armchair just staring at the empty grate. You must take him out for a walk somewhere this evening.'" Although the nurses provide some comfort— "'Mother's holding her own well, Nurse O'Keeffe says'"—the doctor is the crucial oracle: "'We won't know until the doctor comes how she really is.'" The doctor's early visit confirms that "'the crisis will be today'". Then there is, for the men downstairs simply the waiting—'only the nurses and Clare watched in the darkened room. . . . In a couple of hours perhaps, the height of the crisis would be reached. Then life and death would be balanced, and after that, if she came through, her strength would return slowly but safely.' Downstairs they try to distract themselves with chess and newspapers, but their strained ears hear only 'at long intervals doors open and shut softly, a tinkle of running water, or the faint clink of smitten glass,. . . once a nurse speeding all but soundlessly downstairs on some errand.' At four o'clock the doctor comes again, with Fr O'Dwyer, and they both go up to the sickroom. The doctor gives the patient a cursory examination, feels her pulse then tells her that she has given them all a great fright. All will be well.[49]

The things people believed

Few households, even of practitioners, have only the very latest concepts in their store of medical ideas. Some of the notions (a few) may be quite up-to-date; but others are apparently justified by day-to-day medical practice (perhaps of the previous generation); and a few are ideas from traditional custom and practice. Like superstitions, medical beliefs have an extraordinary 'half-life'. Long after the intellectual framework in which they were nurtured has been abandoned, old practices linger, often cheek by jowl with ideas of quite different provenance.

Evidence is easy to find of such different ideas. The persistence, for instance, of the use of red flannel next to the skin derives from the theory of signatures. The beliefs that one should 'feed a cold, starve a fever', or that washing was 'weakening' and could lead to tuberculosis are obscure, but common. Ethna MacCarthy noted in 1947 how, as a result of well-meaning ignorance, 'mothers frequently bring ill children in a filthy condition, with resultant secondary infection such as impetigo, simply because a sick child must not be washed or have its clothes changed'.[50] Behind this theory was a sense of an almost eighteenth-century vulnerability to ill-health. Doctors were expected to applaud their 'prudence and sagacity' when women ceased to wash because they were 'sick'. 'Sick' in this context might mean 'menstruation or any minor indisposition such as a cold'. Perhaps the belief lingers still: 'I've had this dose for over a week, doctor', GP Nuala O'Farrell was told in 1994, 'and I've been afraid to wash myself.'[51] In 1928 the newly launched Irish women's magazine *Model Housekeeping* told its readers that 'over indulgence of such foods as meat, sugar and fats encourages a choleric, domineering, fiery disposition'—the vocabulary is pure Galenic humour theory, abandoned by the medical profession in the early eighteenth century.[52]

The formally qualified medical profession was certainly not the only source of medical information and advice in the 1920s. A robust self-help was common. In 1927, for instance, Signe Toksvig recorded that her husband vaccinated her against flu. 'The antiseptic, the spilling of the vaccine, the pushing of the needle, the consequent sore arm, still sore. How mysterious a hypodermic syringe and needle seem! How amateur we felt!'[53] For those just too far up the social scale to be given dispensary tickets, medical advice was expensive. So every week both the *Weekly Freeman's* and the *Weekly Irish Times* had health columns, in which specific remedies were offered on foot of a correspondent's description of symptoms (which were not printed). This consultation was of course very much on the correspondents' terms—on one occasion the advisor in the *Weekly Freeman's* complained gently that 'Leitrim' had revealed neither sex nor age, though this did not prevent prescription.

In the answers patients might be given detailed recipes to take to their local chemist, or perhaps told to consult a doctor as soon as possible. The most frequent responses were variants on (a) this is quite normal at your age or (b) take more exercise, eat less fatty bacon and cabbage, drink less tea and wash regularly. The *Weekly Freeman's* medical advisor was more inclined to give general health advice than specific prescriptions. Often the paper responded to correspondents who had hoped their own doctor had made a mistake, for example writing to 'County Meath': 'If it is what your doctor says, we are afraid there is little hope of a cure' or to correspondents hoping that they would not need to incur the expense of medical help: 'This is serious, you should see a doctor immediately.' Control of diet is frequently advised. To a correspondent in Castleisland the advisor writes: 'The moral is not to eat foods of a greasy or heavy sort. The usual Irish dinner of bacon and cabbage is responsible for a lot of indigestions and "bad stomach" in the country.'

A woman in Ballinasloe exposes a world of distress with origins far beyond the medical sphere: 'You poor woman, it is just a case of "nerves" with you and heaps of people suffer from that especially anxious young mothers like yourself. Give up thinking about the dead child and think only of those you have. Go to a kind doctor and tell him about it and get a nerve tonic . . . the great thing is to keep occupied and give up thinking and worrying. Just leave yourself in God's hands.' The role the 'kind doctor' is expected to play is clear—that of a calm, sympathetic ear; the nerve tonic is almost an afterthought. It is notable that this woman was not recommended to consult a 'kind priest' about her evidently non-medical problems.

In addition to the answers to correspondents, for six 1d stamps and a stamped addressed envelope the *Weekly Irish Times* offered prescriptions for a range of ailments including asthma, bald spots, bronchitis, gout, flat chest, influenza, obesity, rheumatism, 'tobacco nerves' and wrinkles. Patent remedies were still the mainstay of the advertising columns of the weeklies. The American vet 'Dr' Yonkerman continued to proclaim that 'A remedy for Consumption has been found' and Beecham's Pills were still 'prompt and pure, safe and sure'.

Nervous complaints (such as we have seen with the woman from Ballinasloe) were often linked with ideas of strain and overwork, and with ideas such as 'tired blood' and 'nerve fag'—Signe Toksvig describes Bethel Solomons as 'utterly nerve-tired' towards the end of his seven-year term as Master of the Rotunda.[54] Dr Hommel's Haematogen was good for 'anaemic conditions and nervous breakdowns'. Phosferine 'invigorates the brain and body naturally' against a host of ailments including influenza, nervous debility, malaria, lassitude, premature decay and nerve shock. With Clarke's Blood Mixture you could 'start cleansing your blood today'. The *Weekly Irish Times* readers were regularly told in large striking ads how Dr Cassell's Tablets had cured one victim of 'spinal nerve trouble', and how another 'after twelve years of suffering' was restored to complete health by a course of the tablets. For other complaints there was the perennial Dr J. Collis Browne's Chlorodyne (first marketed in 1855 at the height of the chloroform craze), and for skin problems Zam-Buk and Budden's Skin Ointment, which was good for itching, eczema, wounds and sores, 'bad legs', piles and ring-

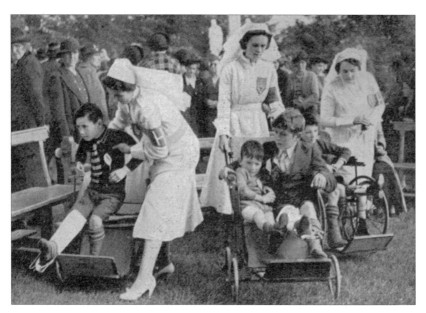

Young patients dressed in their best for a visit to Knock in the 1930s.

worm, as was Germolene. Pain relief as such, the staple of today's patent medi-cine advertising, is mentioned only glancingly, as in the ads for Martin's Pills—'sure and certain for all Female complaints'.

Because religion was of central importance to people's lives, the attitudes springing from belief were very influential. Both evangelical Protestants and the Catholic Church actively encouraged a culture in which intense prayer for favours of all sorts was normal (one prayed for exam success, for jobs, for family happiness and for health). Faith-healing by laying on of hands, during which the celebrant would encourage the sick to show their faith in Jesus by throwing away crutches, was common in evangelical environments. Catholic priests were cred-ited with access to a darker magic. Signe Toksvig records her servant Katie relat-ing how

> . . . a friend of me mother's had a child and it near dying, the doctor had given it up, but she went down on her two knees and embraced the priest's knees and begged of him to save it, for she knew he could. And he gave in to her. The child lived. But he said afterwards that all the chil-dren in the world could die, he'd never be after taking a child from the Blessed Virgin again; seems he had some awful penance to do for it.[55]

On another occasion Katie recommended that her friend take her toothache to the local parish priest. 'It'll be alright if he'll draw the sign across it. Priests can do a lot if they want to.'

Pilgrimages for the sick to Knock or Lourdes, often perceived as a last resort, were sponsored by the Church. The return in October 1924 of the National Pilgrimage to Lourdes, in which over 5,000 had taken part, was greeted with great enthusiasm. Although this was formally a pilgrimage to a shrine, the *Weekly Freeman's* reporter knew what his readers wanted to discover—had there been a miracle? Officials made no comment, referring to the Medical Bureau in Lourdes. The doctors were equally tight-lipped: 'Dr Walsh, the chief medical officer, in obedience to the wishes of the Bishop of Lourdes, was silent on the subject of miraculous cures', the *Weekly Times* readers were told. Others were not so reticent. Fr McSweeney, Diocesan Secretary to the pilgrimages, admitted he had no authority to say there had been cures, but he said that at Lourdes 'it was a very frequent occurrence to witness miracles, and some had been seen by the present pilgrimage'. In fact the pilgrims themselves claimed that eleven invalids had been cured or greatly improved in health, including William O'Connor of Mabel Street, Dublin (paralysis of the right hand) and Joseph Fitzpatrick of Botanic Avenue, Dublin (tubercular leg). Numerous others had received significant amelioration, and even the reticent Dr Walsh conceded that 'on the whole the invalids showed a marked improvement in their conditions'. The pilgrimage worked.

Although the religious force had long gone out of such ideas, more ancient beliefs were visible throughout Ireland at the mysterious holy wells. The ancient Celtic association of water, tree and rock still held a powerful magic. Particular wells were associated with particular ailments, with a whole subset devoted to infertility. One famous holy well, dedicated to St Brigid, was described by Dr Patrick Logan MRCPI. Near Liscannor, County Clare, the well was traditionally visited on the last Sunday in July (the festival of Lughnasa). Once there, the ritual consisted of 'recitation of six Our Fathers and six Hail Marys while going round an outer ring of stations'. This was repeated six times and then the same prayers were said around the inner ring before the water was drunk and an ancient crucifix kissed. 'The votive offerings, crutches, holy pictures, rosaries left inside the well house testify to the faith of the pilgrims and to the belief that diseases are cured there'.[56] The associated practice of tying a piece of cloth belonging to a patient to a 'clooty tree', which was common throughout Ireland, is unlikely to have had a Christian origin.

The shadow of medicalisation

The effects of the growing prestige of the medical profession and therefore the importance ascribed to what it did will be seen in more detail in the next chapter. But the process of 'medicalisation', whereby the techniques and concerns of medicine become generalised can already be seen in motion in the 1920s. In *The Young Physician* Francis Brett Young gives a dramatic example of the focus that unconsciously claims a higher reality for the view from the sickroom. He tells of

The National Maternity Hospital was the first major investment of Sweep money, built to accommodate the rising trend of mothers wishing to have their babies in hospital rather than at home.

the hero's medical training where, at the price of a certain cold objectivity in the face of pain and death, he feels himself 'richly learned in human nature', so much so that 'it seemed to him that people who were not doctors could never really know anything about life'.[57] In his autobiography the paediatrician Dr Bob Collis, who had no doubt read his Brett Young, showed how these ideas were internalised in the profession. Doctors, he wrote, with no air of presenting an extreme or radical view, 'enjoy a position unique in its power for good. For they really know. They know all about the people. They see the man hard pressed by the tensions of the world. They see the woman as she really is. They watch the child growing up. They see society without its mask.'[58] In reality it is only in a rather specialised sense that, for instance, a craftworker is more 'really himself' when he or she is in the often humiliating and squalid environment of the sickbed than when creating a satisfyingly useful object—yet the Collis line has become so ingrained in our worldview that it is difficult not to assent to it.

Parallel to the acceptance of these ideas by profession and public alike, there seems to have been an increased medical presence at times of birth and death. The normal place of birth from time immemorial had been the home, and the normal attendant a midwife or wise woman. In the eighteenth century upper-class women began to call on the services of male *accoucheurs*, and this spread down the class system. For her births in the 1850s, at home, Mrs Findlater had the attention both of a nurse and an ex-Master of the Rotunda. But in the contemporary dispensary districts we have seen that the doctor was only called in if special problems had arisen. By James Deeny's time, although there was little or no ante-natal care, the doctor's presence at the birth had become normal. (No doubt this trend was encouraged by GPs themselves. It had long been a commonplace of medical lore that assiduous care to mother and baby at birth inevitably led to being called in for childish ailments and so to an established position as the household's medical attendant.) However, the deliveries were still at home. Only the poorest women in Dublin took advantage of the facilities offered by the three lying-in hospitals and for most in the country there was little choice.

From the 1920s, however, echoing an international trend, women increasingly abandoned home birth for the comfort and security of hospitals or nursing homes. The latter boomed in this period. In 1921 *Thom's Directory* listed five such homes in Dublin—by 1931 there were 36, and more were added in the subsequent decade. By 1925, 57 per cent of births looked after by the National Maternity Hospital in Holles Street were in the hospital itself—before the First World War two-thirds had been 'on the district' i.e. in the mother's home. The same trend was reported by the other Dublin maternity hospitals. By 1942 half of all births in the Free State were in hospital, a figure reached in urban USA in 1922, New Zealand in 1926, and Sweden by 1940.[59] *Post hoc*, but by no means certainly *propter hoc*, by 1942 maternal mortality in the 26 counties had sunk to 24.7 per 10,000 births, compared to 62 in 1900 and 47 in 1925.

Scanty evidence suggests that there was through the twentieth century an increasing tendency for doctors to be, as de Valera put it, at their patient's side 'at the most critical moment, at the time of death'. In 1911, at the end of a long medical career (which included presidency of the College), Lombe Atthill had noted in his autobiography that 'the doctor is seldom present when the soul departs . . . when that event is evidently in hand he can do no good and his presence is seldom desired.'[60] This was certainly, as we have seen, how Cardinal Newman would have wished it. However, it seems that over time a change occurred in practice and doctors were more likely to be present, if not at the very last, certainly quite soon before that, as can be seen in the literature. In Francis Brett Young's *Portrait of Clare*, the old doctor on his deathbed is described as having seen death too often to be afraid of it. And another doctor consoles a relative by saying 'Do you know, I have never seen an unhappy deathbed? Pain, yes. But spiritual unhappiness never. At the very last there's a sort of . . . clearing.'[61] In practice it is of course

A Holy Well (photographed in the 1990s) showing echoes of a very ancient healing magic combining earth and water, and the tokens attached to the tree. Courtesy Irish Image Collection.

impossible to quantify exactly how many deaths occurred in the presence of a doctor, but it seems at least that people now perceived this presence as an accepted part of the 'script'. It was merely a continuation of this practice that in due course death itself was moved out of the home into the medical arena of hospital and hospice.

The next stage of the process of medicalisation came when it was realised that medicine had finally became too important to be left to doctors, a development that escalated in the 1950s, as we shall see in the next chapter.

Chapter Eight
The 1950s

'Medicine at the crossroads'

Dr W . R . F. 'Bob' Collis (1900–75), pioneer paediatrician and play-wright of Marrowbone Lane, *he was one of the first doctors to enter Belsen; he later worked in Nigeria for ten years.*

ONLY TWENTY-FIVE YEARS on from the era of the previous chapter, the physical fears and dangers of the immediate post-Troubles era had long evaporated—but so had the excitement. Ireland was now proverbially law-abiding. In 1949, for instance, there was just one murder and two cases of armed robbery. In 1956 the horrible Nurse Cadden was convicted of dumping the victim of a failed abortion on the pavement in Hume Street, but this was a startling exception. It appears that only during the restricted travel times of the war was there any kind of local abortion practice.[1] Indictable offences in general were a fraction of what they are now—'larceny of pedal cycles' is virtually the only indictable offence to be less common now than then.

The Church had replaced the national project as the source of authenticity. Political leaders of all hues regularly reiterated in various words de Valera's 1932 mantra: 'If all comes to all, I am a Catholic first'. So when, in 1948, the bishops protested against a proposed extension of Sunday licensing hours, their 'guidance' in this matter was accepted by the political system, the public and the publicans. The response to the acceptance of similar 'guidance' in respect of the Mother and Child scheme two years later was, to the bishops' surprise, considerably more controversial.

In business circles, as a visiting team of Americans found in 1952, there was 'extreme caution and pronounced lack of enterprise, and an overwhelming desire to consolidate whatever gains had been achieved . . . and generally a conviction that what served the ancient Irish fathers might be retained and perhaps adapted—very cautiously—to present day demands.'[2] Perhaps, like the Sicilians in Giuseppe di Lampedusa's *The Leopard*, the Irish secretly thought themselves incapable of significant improvement. As an etiquette book published in the 1960s put it, one always had to remember 'the aristocratic stamp of the Irish, their innate refinement, delicacy of feeling, artistic sense, their interest in culture and learning, . . . and side by side with these, their manliness, physical vigour and courage.'[3]

In his Carmichael Prize Essay of 1944 Bob Collis hit the same self-satisfied note.

> There is something distinctive about Irish medicine as a whole [he wrote]. The difference is difficult to express. We have here something we might call 'personal medicine' an intimacy between doctor and patient, between teacher and student which is unique in the world. It has been built up by long tradition and is part of the atmosphere of Ireland and the soul of the people. At its best it raises medicine to the highest vocation, and even with all our shortcomings it has given us a place in the hearts of the Irish people which no others possess.[4]

Equally, in 1953 when the American Medical Association criticised the quality of the Irish clinical education, the RCSI responded that 'if this [American approach] means spending time on endless note-taking and the performance *ad nauseam* of unnecessary tests and examinations, the College authorities prefer the Irish to the American ways'.[5]

Ireland saw itself as very much on the spiritual flank of the anti-Communist alliance, deploring communism, but not forbearing to denounce the liberal excesses of its allies. From the profession's point of view, among these liberal excesses was the National Health Service which, after much bad-tempered argument, was finally initiated in Northern Ireland in July 1948.

In retrospect, we can see new foundations being quietly laid in the 1950s. The success of the reforms proposed in the 1958 publication *Economic Development* is legendary, but there was also: the return to the international stage signalled by Ireland's admission to the United Nations (1955), the development of an Aer Lingus service to North America (1958) and the establishment of Irish Defence Force officers as UN observers in the Lebanon (1959); the creation of agencies such as the Industrial Development Authority (1950), the Irish Management Institute (1952) and Bord Fáilte (1952); the abolition in 1958 of the ban on married women teachers; and the final retirement of Éamon de Valera and also General Richard Mulcahy, the leader of Fine Gael, from day-to-day politics. But

"Is this the new Ministry of Health?" Ireland was one of the last European countries to establish its Department of Health as a separate entity when it did so in 1947.

The missions exercised a strong call: an Irish Medical Missionary of Mary sister—Abakalki, Eastern Nigeria, 1957.

in no area perhaps was this renewal more evident than in medicine, both from the patients' and the doctors' points of view.

At the time, however, the emerging pattern was not so clear. Indeed, as 'Nichevo' (R. M. Smyllie) wrote in the *Irish Review and Annual 1951*, 'in some ways our little backwater has become yet stiller than it was before the Second World War'.[6] The German novelist Heinrich Böll, visiting Ireland in the mid 1950s, felt this remoteness as he frequently had to explain that the Nazi concentration camps were not merely British black propaganda, and there was more to Hitler than someone who just 'went a bit too far'.[7] Following the collapse of the Fine Gael-led coalition government in 1952 after the Mother and Child controversy, de Valera was once again in government, with his old 1919–22 comrades Seán Lemass, Gerry Boland, Seán MacEntee, Frank Aiken and Oscar Traynor. They had no idea of dynamic government; as one political correspondent put it: 'If anyone asks for a clear-cut answer on a particular subject, the reply usually given is that the subject has yet to be studied . . . yet nearly all appear to be satisfied with this rather dilatory approach to everyday problems.'[8]

Three hundred years after the first foundation of the College, the prestige of the profession had never been higher. 'I think', wrote the poet Padraig Colum's wife Mary, 'that doctors are the nearest approach to saints on earth; they devote themselves so wholeheartedly and disinterestedly to their patients.'[9] As the 1956 Irish Independent *Guide to Careers* put it: 'There is no finer profession a young person can enter. It offers high standing in the community and a wonderful opportunity to be helpful to others and to do great good . . . no other work gives such life-long satisfaction or rewards practitioners with such a feeling of contentment.'[10] Politicians, in their cynical way, tried to cash in on this image: when broadcasting, said Harold Macmillan to Seán Lemass, 'I always like to appear like the family doctor.' The respect was given to the profession as a whole rather than to any one figure. When *Hibernia* magazine canvassed its thoughtful but conservative readers in January 1963 for possible candidates for an Irish honours list, politicians and religious comfortably dominated the list, and the only medical person nominated was Mother Mary Martin, the founder of the Medical Missionaries of Mary, who was not a doctor.

One reason for the shining image of the profession, though by no means the whole of the story, was the astonishing effectiveness of the new antibiotic drugs, particularly against a background of improved housing, higher standards of living, better hygiene and safer water supply. Discussing a report by the Registrar-General, *The Irish Times* noted in January 1950: 'The year 1948 showed the cleanest bill of health for the nation on record to date—the lowest mortality and the lowest incidence of disease. The year 1949 was even better. For example, that year the number of deaths from tuberculosis was 2,645, which is almost 500 less than the figure for 1948.'[11] An important factor in this improvement was the availability of streptomycin. The discovery of antibiotics also had the happy effect of making hospitals much safer places for those working in them. A report for the 1946–51 period noted that only 3 per cent of sick-leave days taken by student nurses were caused by sepsis, compared to a pre-war figure of 25 per cent.[12]

Young victims of the summer plague— polio—also, for good reasons, called infantile paralysis (early 1950s). Although apparently cured, many of these patients were to suffer further debilities in middle age.

There was of course plenty still to do. A certain low level of discomfort or pain was accepted as a constant of life. Thus, in the very healthy household of General Mulcahy, as described by his son Risteárd, 'Dad was afflicted occasionally by attacks of lumbago . . . mother suffered from bunions and corns which were endemic among women at that time, almost certainly caused by improper footwear.'[13] The children suffered from chilblains and chapped hands in the usually cold houses. Part of the routine of growing up was acceptance of periods in bed with one or other of the so-called childhood diseases, with their homely traditional names—whooping cough, mumps, measles, chickenpox and German measles. They were ghosts of their former virulence, but still potentially lethal, whooping cough and measles taking nearly 200 lives between them in 1949. For most children a dose of one of these diseases was a rite of passage, a fortnight or so of coddling, constraint and undemanding boredom (missing school, if the timing was right). Much more frightening were diphtheria, TB, rheumatic fever and polio, all of which struck children and young people especially.

Diphtheria in particular was feared as so infectious that children were at once whisked into hospital. No parental visits were allowed during the course of the child's sickness. To provide parents with information about their children, the Cork Street Fever Hospital ran a system whereby each child was given a number and a progress report for that number was printed in the evening paper every day. So infectious was the disease thought to be that parents were not even allowed to see the dead child, which was sealed immediately in a coffin. Urban legend, fecund as ever, quickly responded. As a student, John O'Connell was told of one case.

> One little girl was brought to Cork Street with diphtheria and duly became a number. Her parents invested in the newspaper every day and one day learned the bad news. She was dead. As usual the parents never saw the body and they went on with their lives and tried to forget about their daughter.
>
> Except that she had not died. The number went into the paper by mistake. The administration in the hospital had wrongly confused her name with that of an orphan from Limerick who did die. The mix-up meant that the young Dublin child was despatched to an orphanage in Limerick, where she grew up. In her late teens, the orphanage found her a job as a maid in Dublin, around the corner from where she had lived as a child and where her parents still lived. Even though she had been only a toddler when she was taken into the Cork Street Fever Hospital, the location sparked memories. Things began to click in her mind and eventually she found her family, sixteen years after she had been taken from them.[14]

There was little chance that such errors would be disciplined. In December 1953 the wife of a garda, who presumably kept out of the matter for official reasons, brought an action for negligence against a Donnybrook doctor, alleging that her daughter had died as the result of a needle inserted in the abdomen which had pierced the girl's liver 'causing pulmonary air embolism and cardiac respiratory failure'. The defence was first of all denial and then the claim that as a married woman, Mrs Bradin had no legal right on her own to bring such an action. Somewhat embarrassed ('I hope this case will be brought to a higher tribunal'), the judge had to admit the point and the case was dismissed.[15]

Down the social scale, as the chemist Harry Mushatt from Dublin's Liberties recalled, people would come to him 'complaining they had stomach trouble or a skin rash or a toothache or scabies. So we made up different preparations from skin ointments, psoriasis ointments to foot pastes for removing corns and calluses and warts to stomach bottles, tablets for kidneys and headaches'.[16] In the outpatient departments of Dublin's voluntary hospitals the patients would complain of

> . . . boils, blanes, sebaceous cysts, maculopapular rashes, cheiropompholyx and varieties of eczema; lice, tapeworms, bed bugs, scabies and fleas; continued diarrhoea, enormous pustular tonsils, flaming conjunctivitis, galloping tuberculosis and heroic syphilis. They would stagger in with double pneumonia or warts; fall off lamp-posts, get jammed under lifts and brewers drays, scalped by machinery, gassed by geysers and half drowned in canals or malting vats. They would achieve extraordinary dislocations under mysterious circumstances and suffer fabulous burns and scalds.[17]

Pain endured gave a kind of individuality ('my' lumbago, one might say, though not 'my' cancer) and a perverse nobility in an otherwise dull life—even becoming an index and marker of character.

Sanitary conditions, especially in rural areas, were not good. The 1961 Census recorded that more than half of the houses outside the urban areas had no fixed lavatory facilities, and in County Longford there were only 1,600 indoor toilets for 30,000 people. Typhoid was still present until the late 1950s, a threat not least to the nascent tourist industry. Most of the water- and milk-borne foci of infection had been dealt with over the previous twenty years, and now the main problems related to carriers. They were surprisingly difficult to find and control—one Irish outbreak was finally chased down to a carrier working in a guest house in the south of England. Carriers usually infected their own families, but the most dangerous worked in food or food-related industries. One man, who had been infected originally during the Boer War, was found working in a creamery, forming the centre of his own 'little nest of infection'. Once identified, carriers were naturally suspicious of the men from the Department, and some went so far as to substitute samples from other family members.[18] James Deeny tells the story of one who had taken a job as a cook in a fashionable seaside hotel. The Chief Medical Officer for the area, conscious that there were many staying in the hotel, had her dismissed. She

Patent medicine advertising in the Coombe (1950s).

NOTICE.

DO NOT SPIT.

The practice is OFFENSIVE and DANGEROUS. It favours the spread of

CONSUMPTION

through the scattering of the germs of the disease.

NATIONAL ASSOCIATION FOR THE PREVENTION OF TUBERCULOSIS
DUBLIN BRANCH.

promptly sued, and was awarded handsome damages. Deeny's unrivalled medical expertise was dismissed by the judge since he was 'only a civil servant from the Custom House'.

Other evidence points to widespread poor personal hygiene. In the 1940s, because of fears of typhus, Irish men and women wishing to emigrate to Britain had first to be inspected and if necessary decontaminated in Dublin. At the inspection station Ethna MacCarthy found as many as 70 per cent of young women from some western counties had body lice (an indication of much more severe infestation than head lice). So common was such infestation that victims were desensitised; 'Sure,' said one, 'no one can help having those things'. By comparison, Dr MacCarthy feelingly reported her own *nuit blanche* suffered after a single infestation. The Dublin poor were not much better off. Students in Baggot Street Hospital found that 'fleas were a menace, especially to fair skinned students, and lice infestation was so common that the smell of oil of Sassifras pervaded the ward as most new patients had to be deloused'.[19]

Dr MacCarthy blamed the lack of facilities for, or a tradition of, full-body washing (indeed it was widely regarded as weakening and leading to tuberculosis). 'Washing' generally referred to face and hands—'one girl boasted that she "washed once a fortnight", a statement that was meant to impress'.[20] The hygiene of de Valera's 'comely maidens' can be inferred from Dr MacCarthy's comment that 'people who have their clothes laundered once a week automatically disinfest themselves because the eggs are killed before their hatching time of nine days'. In the middle-class Mulcahy household in Rathmines daily baths or showers 'would have been considered a gross extravagance'. A bath once a week and washing of face and hands morning and night was quite sufficient.[21]

Medicine at the crossroads

As Dr John Fleetwood, pioneer historian of Irish medicine, put it in 1951, 'medicine is at the crossroads' had become a hackneyed phrase.[22] Although the Hospitals Commission had surveyed the medical field as a whole, and the Department had drawn up a plan, in practice the basic structure of the proposed service was not much different to what it had been a hundred years before. The bulk of the people were served by the 650 doctors of the dispensary service; in selected spots in town and country there were also private doctors tending to the middle classes. In the country there were the county hospitals (workhouse hospitals) and for the middle class there were nursing homes. In Dublin and a few other cities such as Belfast, Cork and Limerick, there were voluntary hospitals, some owned and run by the Catholic Church, others by boards of governors. These establishments ranged from the early-eighteenth-century foundations of Jervis Street, Dr Steevens' and the Rotunda to the nineteenth-century Catholic-dominated foundations of the Mater, St Vincent's and the National Maternity Hospital.

There were Catholic hospitals and Protestant hospitals, each with an atmosphere mildly repellent to the other. In medical terms this mattered little, except in the controversial areas of obstetrics and the right to life.[23] The Catholic hospitals in particular were explicitly focused on spiritual matters, following the teaching of Pius XI who, in a speech to a conference of Catholic nurses in 1935, had said: 'Bring health to bodies, but above all and before all bring salvation to souls. Look through the bodies of your patients and keep their souls before your eyes.'[24] In his moving description of his time in Our Lady of Lourdes TB sanatorium in Dun Laoghaire, William Heaney described how 'each morning there was 7.30 Mass . . . a little after eight o'clock the chaplain, preceded by a Sister or a nurse who tinkled a small silver bell, came round and distributed Holy Communion . . . at eight-thirty and six pm the Sister came along and recited prayers, with the midday Angelus in between'. At ten, just before lights-out, there was the Rosary, and the men of the ward took it in turn to give out the prayers.[25] What the solitary Protestant in the ward thought of all this is not recorded.

On both sides, feelings ran deep. Recalling his student days in the Coombe in the 1950s Dr John O'Connell (a daily Mass-goer throughout his student days) recalled how he went out to take care of a woman who had just had a miscarriage. 'On the windowsill', he wrote, 'was a condom. My immediate reaction was that the miscarriage served her right, because she had been flying in the face of God.'[26] 'I still', he adds, 'had a great deal to learn.' When in 1972 the first Catholic surgeon was appointed to the Royal Victoria Hospital in Belfast, deep objections were expressed, not so much as to his professional competence as to the fact that he wasn't 'one of us'. Maura Donohoe, the first Catholic theatre sister appointed to the Adelaide, experienced similar reactions. Recruited in 1963 she was constantly made aware that she was 'our little Catholic' as one matron put it. At certain moments, such as when Nelson's Pillar was blown up, or during the Pope's visit, there would be snide remarks and uncomfortable incidents. She was never part of the social circle, even being refused membership of the Adelaide Nurses' League. (She did however stay 35 years in the post, doing work she loved.)

The Royal Colleges were not of course exempt from this divisiveness. Edward Freeman, who was President of the College from 1952 to 1955, was the first Catholic in the post since 1925, and the first UCD graduate, following eleven successive Trinity alumni. The next UCD man was Bryan Alton (1974–7). As a result of this Trinity hegemony, for nearly two generations it was not customary for the senior men in Vincent's to become Members or Fellows of the College, a situation which came to an end only in the 1970s.

The end of independence for the voluntary hospitals

Though they were at the very top of the medical tree in the South, the Dublin voluntary hospitals were, by modern standards, generally small. The Adelaide had a mere 154 beds, while the Meath, perhaps the most famous, had only 144. Their elaborate boardrooms were hung with portraits of former staff, some of whom were genuinely world famous, and their successors were fiercely tenacious of tradition. Here the senior men of Irish medicine operated as consultants. They were unpaid, at least until 1953 when a complicated enterprise-based payment scheme was introduced. It is striking, from an organisational point of view, that the model chosen was that of partnership schemes operated by law and accountancy firms, in which the senior partners have more 'points' than the junior and so receive more of the profits.

These men were at the pinnacle of their profession, their success was envied and their attitudes were emulated by generations of students. Some revelled in their reputations as 'characters'. John O'Connell remembered one such from Baggot Street hospital, without much affection:

> [His] progress through a ward was witnessed by as many open mouths as

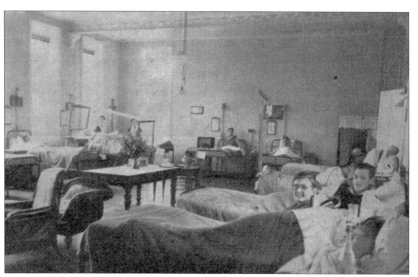

there were people there. He had a massive personality and a great swooping voice, and his gestures were wide, generous and calculated. I particularly remember how he related the incident of the patient with the full and obstructed bladder—the prize story in his repertoire. 'I was called to the house of an unfortunate fellow who was in agony because he couldn't urinate. I was therefore compelled to insert a catheter into his bladder to relieve his distress. Can you imagine my dismay when, within seconds, he expired before my very eyes.' A long sorrowful pause. 'The tragedy, gentlemen, was not that the patient died, but that my cheque lay unsigned on his mantelpiece.'[27]

Supporting the consultants was the stern sisterhood from matron to ward sisters who could intimidate a junior surgeon as decisively as a student, and perhaps restrained themselves with difficulty at the eccentricities of senior consultants. In her penetrating book for Catholic nurses, *At the Bedside of the Sick*, M. Catherine de Jésus-Christ, ex-Superior of the Pasteur Hospital in Paris, is more blunt than her Irish colleagues were wont to be, at least in public. She instructs her readers that

> . . . it would be tactless to draw attention to the failure of a treatment which [a consultant] has adopted—a misfortune that might happen to any doctor; to hint that more patients die under his hands than other doctors; to suggest that patients are nervous at his approach etc. . . . If something slips his memory, or he mistakes one patient for another, or omits to give a treatment, etc., come to his assistance in a skilful way.' [As to the younger doctors] older nurses in particular must be careful how

Nurses studying in the 1950s. The establishment of An Bord Altranais in 1951 led to steady improvements in the quality and conditions of nursing training.

they behave towards these men . . . never laugh at a failure or a blunder, even though it may have its funny side.[28]

Below the ward sisters were staff nurses, and at the bottom of the heap the unfortunate probationers, who paid a significant training fee (almost half the average annual industrial wage), but very often found themselves doing the menial work of the ward, treated, as one Irish probationer training in Leeds, put it 'as less than dust'.

Our training [she continued] included all the hospital disciplines, ear nose and throat, eyes, children's diseases, medical and surgical cases and casualties. Optional courses included fevers and tropical diseases, and obstetrics and midwifery at the Women's Hospital. We took case histories, temperatures, blood pressures, blood; gave injections, dressed wounds, removed stitches from eyes and post-operative cuts of all descriptions. We administered medicines and filled in charts. We washed patients, gave them bed-pans and bed-baths, and dressed and fed them when necessary. We comforted them and bolstered their confidence.[29]

Many of these nurses came from the country, as a study of the student nurses of St Lawrence's (the Richmond) in 1950 confirms. The nurses came 'mainly from small towns and rural areas', and were 'of good bodily physique, likely to withstand the rigorous work'; their average height is 5 ft 3 ins—though at an average

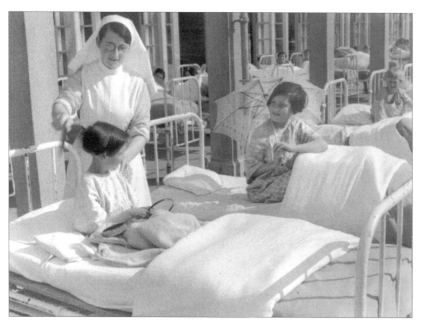

Cappagh 1950s. Fresh air and sunlight during continued to be regarded as important in treatment.

10 stone they were evidently not undernourished![30] One thing they did not do was to become emotionally involved. 'We answered their and their relatives' questions with discretion, telling them no more than they needed to know. And we kept our distance', wrote the Leeds trainee. This control of compassion was not easy. As M. Catherine put it, 'the heart of a woman is easily stirred, especially when she is surrounded by suffering' but a nurse could not do her job if she was not controlled.

> Be careful about your speech lest it be too soft and tender; let there be no emotional caresses, even with children. . . . [on the other hand] do not cultivate a scientific heart and concentrate on the contest between science and the microbe instead of that between suffering and an organism unable to retaliate. . . . Beware of an unfeeling heart, evinced by such remarks as 'nothing affects me; I've seen so much in my life'.[31]

Although the voluntary hospitals were the premier medical establishments in the country, the Department of Health had little to do with the running of them. Noel Browne confirmed this in the Dáil in 1951: 'So far as voluntary hospitals were concerned the Department of Health has no particular function and he [the Minister] had no control over them.' As with so many of Dr Browne's utterances, this was disingenuous, for in one critical aspect the Minister had every control.

Apart from small local authority grants, these hospitals had in the past been dependent on the charitable donations of their supporters, but since the Boer

War, a combination of the Land Acts and income tax had squeezed that source almost to non-existence. By the 1920s rising costs in equipment combined with falling incomes threatened some with partial closure. This was not a problem only for the Protestant or so-called 'interdenominational' hospitals. By the end of the 1920s the National Maternity Hospital in particular was in a desperate situation. Then came the Irish Hospital Sweepstakes, which initiated a prodigious flow of money. Naively, each of the 60 or so hospitals involved drew up elaborate expansion plans with no regard whatever to the existence or ambitions of other hospitals in the area. Money was frequently claimed almost as of right, with no attempt to justify the proposed expansion.[32] The total claims presented quickly amounted to three or four times what was historically a very large sum of money.

The official response to this flood of claims was to establish the Hospitals Commission to co-ordinate the Minister's disposition of the prize fund. It is interesting to speculate how different the structure of the health service could have been had it been possible for the voluntary hospitals to establish their own 'hospitals commission'. However, given the long history of rivalry between the hospitals, it would have required positively Napoleonic leadership from, for instance, the Royal Colleges, to engineer any such outcome. As money continued to pour into the fund other sources of income for the hospitals dried up and the hospital boards had no choice but to co-operate with the Minister more and more. In due course, they glumly accepted, though not without protest, that 'he who pays the piper, calls the tune'. Their cherished independence gone, the consultants' dismay was only increased when the Minister decided to spread some of the prize fund outside the golden circle and invest in local hospitals and tuberculosis sanatoria. As the governors and consultants saw it, this was no more than theft of what was rightfully theirs, motivated by what one medical writer of the time called 'the blind avarice of the modern State'.[33]

This result was probably inevitable. Given the Europe-wide trend towards the centralisation of medical systems, it was unlikely that such important institutions would have been able to maintain their independence. For 50 years or more European states had been taking the health of their people seriously. This was not, of course, solely for altruistic motives—the very poor physical quality of recruits for the Boer War had given the British élite a serious fright, and the fact that only two-thirds of conscripts during the Second World War were physically fit, reinforced the message.[34]

The process of medicalisation

Behind these political and social pressures was another, which gave them importance and force. This was the process of 'medicalisation', the process whereby medicine and health became an increasingly central public concern. Cardinal Newman had taken it for granted in the 1850s that duty would always come before health; but gradually his dictum was being reversed, and health was put above almost everything. As it happened, the medical profession exempted itself from this rule, and continued to work far too long hours, to accept sometimes intolerable pressures and to take great risks with their own health.

Medicalisation was a process that worked at various levels. We can envisage the individual engaging in four overlapping circles of life: the personal sphere is that of the individual, where pain and love and guilt are experienced, the private sphere is where the life of the family is led; then there is the economic and social sphere, and finally the public and cultural sphere. Throughout the twentieth century, in each of these spheres, in different ways medicine, health and the profession became increasingly visible.

For the individual, illness and pain continued to require interpretation. Sometimes, benignly, illness might also be construed as a period of privileged deviancy, when normally active participants in life were permitted to opt out for a while; as John D. Sheridan put it 'maybe the 'flu is a sort of spiritual retreat, a little interlude during which selfish, ungrateful people have time to count their blessings'.[35] But, either way, now doctors had evolved instruments to reveal details of the patient's conditions hidden from the patient. The interpreted 'readings' from such instruments superseded the patient's chaotic but intimate experience. In *The Magic Mountain* (1924), Thomas Mann tells how a patient 'continues to assert that she is actually feeling worse instead of better'. Her doctors are not pleased. 'They point out that only the physician can judge how she is—she herself only knows how she feels; which does not signify.'[36] Pain, especially where the symptoms reported by the patient could not be located in a specific lesion, was often contentious precisely because it rejected that premise. This has led the profession into down-grad-ing such unmeasurable symptoms—until the 1980s, for instance, it was commonly believed in the profession that children felt little or no pain, and analgesic regimes were delivered accordingly.[37]

In the slightly wider private sphere, that of the life of the family, the doctor had always been significant, but it is arguable that the increasing prestige given to the profession augmented that role. The family doctor, the loved and trusted GP, was, at least in middle-class households, a reassuring bulwark against all ills. In the Mulcahy household the GP was the 'well-known and respected' Dr Bill Cremin, who lived in a fine Georgian house in St Stephen's Green. 'He was a large, solid, portly and bespectacled man whose mature and professional appear-

Joe McGrath (1887–1966) the leading Director of the Hospitals Sweepstake who used his old IRA/IRB contacts to develop an international sales force with astonishing success.

ance inspired immediate confidence. . . . Cod liver oil, Parrish's food (containing iron), Friars' balsam, purgatives, cough medicines, poultices and camphorated applications for lumbago and other painful conditions, were the chief items in the pharmacopoeia.'[38]

The more people thought about health, the more fitness of body ousted fitness of soul, the higher it came up on the democratic agenda. Just as Talleyrand declared that 'war is much too serious a thing to be left to military men', control of the medical profession's activities became a concern of state. The instruments of bureaucratic control—reports, plans, budgets, returns and other documentation increasingly impinged. With the involvement of the state in national insurance, in health certification, in factory inspection and so on, the profession had taken an increasing presence in the economic and social sphere.

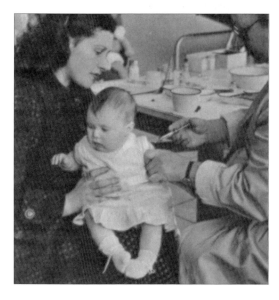

By the beginning of the twentieth century Ireland was one of the most thoroughly vaccinated countries in the world. The last case of smallpox recorded was in Athy in 1911.

And finally in the public and cultural sphere, where political, social, and moral issues were fought out, the increasing public expenditure on health and the strong views of the Church on such questions ensured that the issues relating to medicine were always prominent. More profoundly, acts that had previously been evidence of moral delinquency, and therefore subject to an individual's control and choice, such as drunkenness, gradually became medicalised, for example as alcoholism.

A potent symbol of this process of medicalisation can be seen in the long trend that resulted in the removal of doctoring in Ireland from the home to medical centres. In the 1850s almost all medical activity, including surgery, occurred in the patient's home. The therapeutic encounter was conducted in the patient's own sphere, in which the doctor was a visitor. A hundred years later all surgery, virtually all obstetrics, and most general medical procedures occurred in hospital. In the 1950s the GP still visited for minor ailments, and death typically occurred at home. Death soon followed birth into the hospitals and hospices.

Patients increasingly took their ailments to the medical centres whose rules and customs (clothing, visitors, times to eat, sleep, etc.) were designed to regulate the interests and activities of an increasingly complex organisation. In hospital, the archetype medical establishment, the patient became only one player jostling on a stage which included consultants pursuing careers, administrators balancing books and students trying to learn. The strangeness of the hospital environment was often exacerbated by a class division between doctors and patients. As the medical novelist Gabriel Fielding put it, 'the rules that obtained in the slums were denied to the hospital, whilst those of the hospital were Dutch to the slums'.[39]

The patient threatened in the 1950s with tuberculosis, for instance, was quickly left in no doubt of the system. One account described a first visit to the chest clinic, where after time in a crowded waiting room, the overworked tuberculosis officer snapped out a stream of questions: '"Name? Address? Age? Married? Employment? Rate of Pay?" and so on, meanwhile filling up a large form, adding "Nurse will give you a bottle, spit into it in the morning and send it back with this card. Take this other card to Blank St. and get an x-ray. Come back next week. Next, please."'[40] A middle-class family might consider nursing at home. Thus when in the 1960s the sixteen-year-old Brenda Fricker was diagnosed as having TB, 'there was an interesting social battle . . . my mother wanted to nurse me at home but my father said No and I ended up pretty quickly in Blanchardstown.'[41] Once in the sanatorium the daily routine for patients did not leave much space for individuality as the 1950s timetable in Peamount Sanatorium demonstrates:[42]

8	Rise.
9–10	Breakfast: porridge (obligatory), full fry, tea, bread and butter.
10	All allowed up must be fully dressed. Walking about in dressing-gowns is strictly forbidden.
10.15	Workshops, occupational therapy.
12.30	Dinner: meat, potatoes and vegetables, sweet.
1–2	Rest.
2.30	Workshops, occupational therapy.
6	Supper: potatoes (obligatory), fish or fish dish, salads, tea, bread and butter.
7	Music, cards, books, cinema etc.
8	Bedtime.
9	Lights out.

Treatment consisted, as the broadcaster John Quinn wrote (he was also in Blanchardstown—'the Blanch' as inmates called it) of 'rest, medication and fresh air . . . the regime was strict. Rest hours were hours of rest strictly policed by the sister-in-charge.'[43] The average stay of patients at this time was some 340 days; a year of isolation and boredom made worse by enforced inactivity. 'For the first few months', recalled Brenda Fricker, 'you had to lie still, there was a bell under the sheets and you had to ring for everything. . . . Every few weeks we were sent down by ambulance to the hospital block for a swab test'.[44] On the results of the test would depend one's progress through the various grades of treatment from complete immobility to being allowed to read, to walk about the hospital, and even take trips to the shops. Those less lucky, a quarter of inmates before the widespread use of the still-costly and, to a degree, experimental streptomycin and PAS treatment in the 1950s, died. 'Paddy, in the bed next to me', wrote John

Quinn, 'died four hours after we heard the bells ring in 1966 . . . it was the first of a succession of deaths I would witness over the next six months.'[45] This experience of isolation from the community was difficult to evaluate in normal terms particularly since there was a strong taint about the disease. As John O'Connell put it, 'at that time nobody admitted to having TB. Whatever else you had you didn't have TB. Nobody in your family, seed, breed or generation had TB.'[46]

Lying in bed as Claud Cockburn remembered, 'the drugs, or possibly simply the inevitably peculiar circumstances of hospital life had the effect of temporarily developing everyone's qualities or characteristics to slightly larger than life size.'[47] The less worldly William Heaney also felt that there was something special about his fellow-patients; as he put it, 'God spends an extra few minutes fashioning the hearts of those who would one day be afflicted with tuberculosis.'[48] This sense of the victim of serious illness as being or becoming 'special' was explored by Anna Farmar in her study of children with terminal cancer. As she found, 'because of all they had to endure the children were forced to confront the reality of sickness and death. They had had to submit to invasive and often painful treatment, to adapt to the strange world of hospital, to cope with baldness, obesity, the loss of a limb, the narrowing of their lives. Such trials called on their resources of courage, adaptability and acceptance . . . they sought and sometimes found their own answers to the great existential questions "Why?" and "Why me?".'[49]

The launch of the NHS in Northern Ireland

Before the advent of the National Health Service in 1948 there was little difference between the systems in the Free State and Northern Ireland. The dispensary doctors and GPs formed the base of the system and the voluntary hospitals the apex. We have seen Dr James Deeny's account of setting up his plate in Lurgan in the 1930s, and that experience could no doubt be echoed across the North. The great training hospitals such as the Royal Victoria (Protestant) and the Mater Infirmorum (Catholic) in Belfast were voluntary and between the poles was the City hospital (rather as among Dublin maternities the Coombe sat mid-way between the Protestant Rotunda and the Catholic Holles Street). Just as in Dublin, they were staffed by unpaid consultants whose incomes were earned from private patients and private nursing homes. In the depressed 1930s, without the benefit of the Sweep money, the hospital service in the North came under severe financial pressure.[50]

As in other aspects of Northern life, the religious divide was the basic fact of life. Most doctors studied at Queen's University Belfast and, as one authority has put it, 'many came to the university never having formed a friendship with a member of the other community, perhaps never even having met one.' As in Dublin, 'it was the custom for students to divide for their main clinical teaching . . . most Catholic students attended the Mater and most Protestants attended the Royal'.[51] The Belfast Infirmary, now the Belfast City Hospital, was much less polarised and drew staff, students and patients from both religious communities. The City Hospital was one of the first to appoint senior medical staff on a full-time basis. Most postgraduate qualifications were sought from British colleges rather than those of the Free State.

Although there was no conscription, many doctors (from both dispensations) joined up for war service, and became full-time paid medical officers. For a while the dispensary service struggled to cope. An emergency medical system was created to help co-ordinate hospital services in the likely event of mass air-raid casualties. After the war special funding was established to enable ex-service doctors to take up hospital training posts as registrars. All of these factors provided a preparatory taste of the centralised medical service that was to come within a few years.

On 5 July 1948 the National Health Service introduced free medical care into the North. Prior to this virtually all medical services had been paid for; now GPs were to be paid according to the number of patients on their panel, and, crucially, the patients could choose which doctor they attended. (The so-called 'choice of doctor' scheme for medical card holders—about one-third of the population—was introduced in the South in 1974.) This marked a significant shift in the relationship between doctors and patients and was one which took both sides some time to get used to.

Initially at least this shift of power into the patients' hands was gleefully exploited—as the profession had gloomily forecast it would

" *Next four National Healths, please.*"

The profession feared that free medicine would swamp the surgeries.

be. GPs' waiting rooms were crowded with people with trivial ailments (and many not so trivial that had been held back while the legislation was being passed). Patients did not hesitate to blackmail doctors, threatening to move themselves, their families and their friends to another panel if not satisfied. Stories were told of one extreme case when a dissatisfied seeker of a sick certificate managed to remove 80 of his friends and neighbours from a panel. (Of course, GPs could ask troublesome patients to switch to another doctor. A Moira GP recounted that he 'lost' about a dozen patients in the late 1940s when the annual payment per patient was small. He purchased a dozen hens and claimed that he earned more from the eggs than he lost from the patients!)

As a result of these pressures the patterns of over-prescription that had been common before the war were continued, if not worsened. In a discussion of the NHS in Stormont some months after its introduction, Dr Eileen Hickey of the Mater reported stories of greyhounds being fed NHS cod liver oil and malt, of 'one woman who got a set of false teeth she had not the remotest intention of wearing simply because, as she said, her dentist was a good wee chap and she thought it would be doing him a good turn'. In the same debate Dr William Rodgers reported that so many NHS spectacles had been issued that pawnbrokers had reduced the payment on a pair from 5s to 2s 6d. There was considerable confusion among the public as to what doctors could and could not authorise. This was not surprising, as they now had 48 separate certificates they could issue. Dr Hickey told of 'a doctor friend of mine who was interrupted the other night at twelve o'clock by a patient who said he had heard he could get free sweets and brandy. He thought they would be good for his wife.'[52]

Some of these complaints were echoed (anonymously, as was the practice) by 'A nationalised Irish Doctor living under the NHS' in an irritable article in the *Irish Independent* in April 1950. 'The panel', he wrote, 'has created a nation of hypochondriacs. The service is supposed to be free, so every man, woman and child is taking advantage and cluttering up doctors' surgeries because of the most trivial complaints. There is very little time for real medicine or examination of patients . . . the majority of those attending are seeking certificates for one thing or another.'[53] This article, and another the following January, in which it was claimed that Belfast doctors 'openly acknowledge that their standards are being pulled down by the necessity of dealing with cases on a mass-production basis'[54] must, of course, be viewed in the light of the ongoing debate between Noel Browne and the profession about a state-financed medical service for the South.

Although there were persistent rumours in Northern Ireland that better health care was available privately, the Minister claimed that as many as 96 per cent of the population had registered in less than a year after the beginning of the new service. The effective abolition of private practice put the ordinary GPs into a vulnerable position. They felt, as Dr Hickey reported to Stormont, 'exploited', and 'they resented it bitterly'. In June 1949 Belfast doctors threatened mass withdrawal from the service, and although this did not occur, feelings ran high. One cause of irritation was the overhang of debts from the period before the service started. A number of patients took the opportunity to abandon their previous doctor, and the money owed, and shift to a new practitioner. Even for those who stayed, there was always the possibility that too vigorous a debt-chasing programme might stimulate such moves. One doctor ostentatiously burnt all his old records to reassure his panel that they would not be so harassed.

For the Catholic community it was a source of grievance that unlike similar legislation in England, Wales and Scotland, the Northern Ireland Act did not allow Catholic hospitals to retain partial control. As a result the trustees, no doubt influenced by the same arguments we have seen rehearsed in the South,

(Opposite) 'No one could oppose a scheme with a name like that' thought the inventor of the Mother and Child Scheme, Chief Medical Advisor James Deeny. Note the St Brigid's Cross in the background.

kept the Mater out of the health service, at considerable cost, until 1972. It was curious, as the opposition did not fail to point out, that, despite many admiring references to the British way of life from the Stormont Government benches, in this aspect, at least, Northern Ireland went its own way.

Resisting the process of medicalisation

In the South, partly because of changes in the North and partly in response to a growing feeling that things could and should be improved, several plans and reports in the mid-1940s addressed the question of what might be done with the Irish medical service, and how it might be paid for. Most of these plans were dismissed as impractical. There had long been free health care, of a sort, for the very poor, whether in the voluntary hospitals or by the dispensary system. The dispensary service was not much loved by patients or doctors. Dr John O'Connell, who was brought up in Drumcondra, recalls that

> . . . having a sick child in the house was not peculiar to us. If it happened the options were simple. You nursed him, (in our case this was done by my mother) you prepared the room for the doctor's brief visits, and you waited for the inevitable. Of course not all aspects of the sickness were accepted. My father often talked bitterly of the way we were treated by the doctors. The brusque manner. They came and went without a comment, and there was little you could change about it, because doctors were kings in their own area and talking back or questioning was just not done.[55]

For Terry Eagleton, from an Irish family living in Salford, 'doctors were revered yet also resented, as a kind of a line wedge or middle-class fifth column in our midst, overbearing and something brutish yet armed with the esoteric knowledge people needed to stay in work.'[56]

For those whose incomes and aspirations disqualified them from dispensary tickets and public wards, managing their health was a serious financial problem. In 1943 Sean O'Faolain analysed, in *The Bell*, the expenditures of representative families on varying incomes. On average they seemed to spend at least 6.5 per cent of after-tax income on 'health'. O'Faolain comments that 'in any house where there are children these items run up easily—many prescriptions, M&B, Cough Cures, Cosmetics, MacLeans, Cod Liver Oil, Vitamin tablets, Iron Tonics, TCP and goodness knows what else. If we look at our own medicine chest, or in the lumber press, what hosts of half-used bottles meet our unremembering eyes!'[57] (Over-prescribing and unfinished courses of medicine are not new.) A young solicitor's income of £800 a year bought a reasonable amount of medical care, even if 'in this stratum of society' one might pay 'anything up to £75' for a confinement. For a bank official of ten year's standing on £260 a year, matters were less rosy. A sustained illness could wipe out a life's savings. It is no wonder that the launch of the VHI, in 1957, was an instant success, offering as it did relief from a major life worry for the two-thirds of the population not entitled to free medicine.

The process of expansion of state medical services was resisted by the Catholic Church and, apparently paradoxically, by the profession. In the Church's view the purpose of the physical body was simply to provide a frame for the development of the soul which on death would, ideally, go on to the happiness of unification forever with God. In an address to a conference of Catholic nurses in 1935 already quoted, Pius XI had said 'a nurse must be animated by an intense supernatural life . . . Tend the life of the body, but tend with infinitely more care the life of the soul; it is from the soul that the body derives its value.'[58] In this perspective physical health remained a lesser priority, and was certainly subordinate to the risk that any soul's eternal destiny might be imperilled.

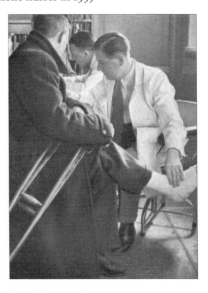

At the same time the Church taught a particular Thomist sociology which maintained that any function relating to the growth and development of the family (specifically health, education, etc.) which could adequately be performed by the family should not be taken over by the state. A fear and detestation of the communist regimes of eastern Europe strongly reinforced this view. In March 1951 (just before the bishops declared their disapproval of the Mother and Child scheme) Bishop Browne of Galway declared: 'Every extension of State control weakens the cause of human liberty and frees weapons for those who would destroy it.'[59] Furthermore, this principle, called subsidiarity, applied to other organisations; as Pius XI wrote: 'It is an injustice, a grave evil and a disturbance of right order for a larger and higher organisation to arrogate to itself functions which can be performed efficiently by smaller and lower bodies.'[60] While it maintained its sway, this elevation of a sociological principle to theological height had the effect of protecting Catholic schools and hospitals from the state.

Mater outpatients (1961); despite the numbers involved doctors managed to maintain the essential intimacy of the doctor-patient relationship.

Doctors also resisted the process of medicalisation, mainly because it led to an increase of control over their professional lives. As the state became more active in health affairs, and a dedicated department of state was finally established (in 1947), the profession had, with difficulty, to adjust to a new and powerful presence in their lives. The problems derived from the fundamentally different objectives and organisational methods of civil servants and professionals.

In their pure forms, the two models (see Table 8.1) represented different views of the world, both quite desirable—'a vigorous population maintained at minimum cost to the state' is an obvious good, but so is the provision of 'the best clinical care' and the development of scientific medicine. In practice all health-care systems have been a compromise in which the profession's desired outcome was mitigated by the state's preferences. The resultant compromise revealed the social power of the profession relative to the state, and in Ireland it is generally believed that the doctors' leaders did well for their members (particularly the consultants). In pushing hard in the direction of the professional model, the world profession often enlisted big corporations such as drug, private health and insurance companies (and in Ireland's case, the Church) in aid.

Table 8.1: Comparison of state-controlled and professional models of health-care*

Function	State-controlled model	Professional model
System objective	To sustain the state by maintaining a vigorous, healthy population at minimum cost	To provide the best clinical care to those who present themselves; to develop scientific medicine to heights
Patient	Any member of society, who also has a duty to keep healthy and fit (exercise, safe sex, not smoking etc.)	An autonomous individual who chooses how to live and when to use the medical system
Power	Centred in the government; maximises value for money	Centred on the profession; maximises practitioner professional development/reward
Organisation	Nationally integrated	Loosely federated private practices and hospitals
Key Institutions	Department of Health	Professional bodies, hospitals
System Finance	Taxpayer	Private individual, insurance
Labour	Fewer specialist doctors, more nurses, midwives; emphasis on care teams	Emphasis on highly skilled individual clinicians; nurses clearly subordinate
Care focus	Prevention, primary care	Specialist clinics
Clinical decision objective	Optimum cost-benefit, as decided by manager/clinician teams	Excellent individual work exclusive of cost considerations
System strength	Standard and chronic illness economically managed	Acute and hi-tech medicine
Pricing	Free, or at cost	Market rate, often variable between customers

* Based on D. W. Little 'Comparing healthcare systems' in P. Conrad and R. Kern *The Sociology of health and illness: critical perspectives* (3rd ed) New York: St Martin's Press 1993

As well as these contrasting goals, there are also the 'work-style' elements contrasted by the organisational behaviour expert Henry Mintzberg.[61] The professional organisational method, adopted by teachers, lawyers, accountants and architects, as well as doctors, envisages each professional deploying a repertoire of more or less standard procedures in varied initial circumstances. Every patient is different, but the palette of solutions to their problems is standardised by common training procedures. The work consists of a repeated cycle of diagnosis and execution; and this is just as true for a solicitor as an obstetrician. Critical to this method of operation are closeness to the student/patient/client and (generally) independence of colleagues. Because the work is done in intimate connection with the patient/client/student it is exposed (as we have seen) to the variability of all human relations.

The so-called 'machine bureaucracy', on the other hand, which is the style of operation appropriate to the national post office, to motor car companies, airlines and the civil service, achieves its standardised, considered output by rigid planning and control. It is designed to iron out the problems caused by human variation, and to ensure consistency and reliability, like a McDonald's burger with French fries or a Japanese motor car. It is the ideal form for simple, stable environments that require an enormous volume of work to be crunched through. The machine bureaucracy emphasises system and regularity, hierarchy, chain of command and clearly defined division of labour.

It is clear that these two working styles are poles apart. Unfortunately, the management of the nascent health service required that they work together, and this inevitably caused stresses. The civil service saw itself imposing controls by way of protecting the public purse. The profession saw such controls and systems as interference with the basic values and freedoms intrinsic to their working methods. Clinical freedom, the right to choose whatever might be the appropriate remedy for any patient was perceived as critical. Frankly, as Leonard Abrahamson (President of the College 1949–51) argued in 1951, 'the medical profession did not want any State control of medical services because it felt that it would destroy the doctor-patient relationship.' If there was any suspicion that these values were being interfered with, tempers flared. Equally, the civil servants saw no more than self-centred resistance to change and better management, and they and others were not slow to ascribe purely mercenary motives to the resisters.

Leonard Abrahamson (1897–1961) cardiologist, President of the College during the Mother and Child row, he played an important part in the IMA's relations with the Department throughout the 1950s.

Curiously, recent European history had provided a potentially powerful argument against state intervention between the profession and its patients. Hitler's Germany had imposed an absolute duty on citizens to keep their bodies clean, healthy and pure ('your body belongs to the nation' was the slogan), it had run an obviously cranky campaign against smoking (particularly for women—'the German woman does not smoke') and finally switched doctors' medical focus from the health of the individual to the vigour of the *Volk*. Specifically the revelations of the Nazi doctors' trials (1946–9) showed how German military doctors, pursuing the health of the people generally, had obeyed orders to perform appalling experiments on concentration camp inmates. These events formed a powerful demonstration of what could happen once the state is allowed to dictate the terms of the doctor-patient relationship. The analogy, however, was not used, probably because (as a consequence of the isolation referred to by Nichevo) neither the profession nor the public had yet internalised the horrors of the Holocaust.[62]

Perhaps the first serious clash between state and the profession came with the question of reporting of cases of infectious diseases at the beginning of the century. The point was not whether notification, as it was called, was a valid public health measure. A strong argument was made that once diagnosis was confirmed, notification should be made the responsibility of the patient. To make doctors report such diseases turned their attention away from the patient's needs to the needs of the state. Despite continued resistance, the doctors' case was lost, and compulsory notification for certain infectious diseases was introduced.

The profound difference of viewpoint between the state-controlled view of how medicine should be governed and the professional (which is by no means limited to Ireland) has proved a fruitful source of conflict since the foundation of the Department of Health in 1947, conflict that has often been expressed in surprisingly offensive terms—on both sides. Part of the problem has been that the characteristic weaknesses of the professional mode of activity are just those that are most unacceptable to bureaucrats. Individualistic and flexible as they have to be to meet the shifting needs of their patients, professionals tend to have problems with co-ordination, with systems innovation and with team responsibility. A prickly independence could result. In Anna Farmar's study of children with terminal cancer, one doctor 'cited a breach of etiquette as a reason for his inactivity in a case; a colleague had asked him to return a telephone call and he found this unacceptable.'[63]

Because of the need for consensus, innovation is often difficult to achieve. Administrators from other traditions found this particularly trying. In the Royal Victoria in Belfast the ex-army Secretary Colonel Field famously compared the difficulty of getting consultants to agree to 'herding cats', and described the great hospital as more like ten cottage hospitals along the same corridor than a single organisation. Senior civil servant Henry Boylan found similar difficulties during his time as Chairman of the Royal Victoria Eye and Ear Hospital in Dublin. Medical professionals, like academics, tend to feel more loyalty to their own practice and to the profession as a whole than to any one institution (though in Ireland this is mitigated by the extraordinary grip the training hospitals have had on their students). Mintzberg's theory of professional structures makes it clear

Sir John Biggart, for many years the dominant figure in medical education in the North, as Dean of the Medical School in Queen's University Belfast.

why the profession has always been unenthusiastic about performance measurement, has scarcely accepted the impact of iatrogenic disease, and has often been slow to accept responsibility for incompetent colleagues.

When James Deeny became Chief Medical Adviser to the Department of Local Government and Health in 1944, he quickly discovered what he called 'the extraordinary animus against the Customs House and the people in it . . .everything we did or tried to do was met with suspicion and resistance'. As well as the fundamental division of organisational objectives discussed above, there was another, unspoken, factor in the relationship between the civil servants and the senior members of the profession—class. Civil servants were generally Christian Brothers boys, clever but without university education, who disliked being patronised by men who, though expensively educated, often owed their positions to family influence. Deeny, who had in fact been to Clongowes and Queen's and was a Member and later a Fellow of the College, naturally resented being told by one of these men that some reform he proposed amounted to 'another Custom House swindle'.[64]

Distressed but not daunted by opposition, Deeny drove the new Department of Health through a radical reform programme. It was needed. Despite Bob Collis' brave attempt to laud the special values of Dublin's 'personal medicine', the Johns Hopkins, research-based model of medical practice was ascendant and successful, and was beginning to make Irish medicine look backward. In 1953 a group of doctors from the American Medical Association examined Irish medical education to assess the suitability of Irish graduates for American medical licences—and to Southern fury only Queen's was found suitable. They found for instance that in UCD, the largest school of medicine in the country, only seven bodies had been supplied for anatomy work to 148 students. The school was, the doctors found, generally understaffed and under equipped; there were no separate departments of pharmacology or bacteriology, the students were not well selected, and clinical work was poorly supervised.[65] A subsequent report by the General Medical Council in the mid 1950s left the clear impression that much should be done to bring the quality of southern Irish medical education up to international standards.

Even Collis himself recognised that 'if the Dublin school is to regain its place in the world it cannot any longer ignore the fact that advancement in medicine must in future come through the interaction of medical science with clinical medicine.'[66] As if to underline the point, about the time Collis was writing this, James Deeny and his colleagues in the Department sent out 40 blood samples in triplicate to the three largest of the 40 Dublin laboratories, UCD, TCD and the RCSI. They were tested for syphilis and, as he recalled 'there was a 20 per cent plus or minus difference in the results. This gave us a strong reason to doubt the quality and accuracy of the work.'[67] When these results were revealed, there was an outcry at the 'dirty trick' of comparing the results of one laboratory with another. When Deeny proposed reforms, the senior men, many of whom had actually founded the laboratories and 'were well satisfied with what they had done', could, as he put it, see no reason to co-operate, especially at the expense of their livelihoods and independence.

Although the medical profession and the Church won a round with the thwarting of Browne's Mother and Child scheme, the ground gained was quietly clawed back by much more effective politicians in subsequent years. From the mid 1950s the state was firmly in the driving seat. By the end of the 1950s, as the historian Ruth Barrington put it,

> . . . Tuberculosis and other infectious diseases had been brought under control. Services for mothers and babies were greatly improved, and maternal and infant mortality reduced significantly. Modern hospital and specialist treatment was made available at nominal or no charge to the majority of the population . . . pathology, radiology and blood transfusion services, vital to the success of physicians and surgeons, were greatly improved. In the space of a dozen years, Ireland had developed a modern

health service which compared favourably with those of more prosperous countries.[68]

This judgement is perhaps partial, but there was no doubt that the health of the ordinary Irish people had benefited enormously from the introduction of antibiotics. In his essay 'How the Irish Died in 1954' James Deeny remarked how the expectation of life at birth had increased by three years for boys and four years for girls since 1946. 'During that period', he comments, 'we can note the virtual disappearance of the infectious diseases as a major cause of death'.[69] In 1935–7 an average of 2,800 people a year died of influenza, diphtheria and other infectious diseases; by 1954 this was down to 398. Since these infectious diseases had been major killers of children, the most significant beneficiaries of this improvement were the young. At the beginning of the century one death in five was of a child of less than ten years; by 1954 it was down to one in twelve. Gradually it was no longer necessary for a family to have to accept that one or perhaps more of their children would die. From this reduction of child mortality stemmed the greatest change in ideas about health since Pasteur and Koch introduced germ theory. From being almost commonplace, the death of a child came to be seen as a scandal, against nature. Sickness itself came to be seen as something that happened primarily to the old, the unfortunate—or, later, to the self-indulgent.

Chapter Nine
The 1970s

'What matters now is not who a man is, but what he can do'

I**T SHOULD HAVE BEEN** the best of times, both for the profession and for the College. After a dazzling series of discoveries and innovations medical intervention was more sure and more successful than it had ever been. The profession was widely respected, and at the best produced levels of professional skill and personal attention unmatchable by other professions. Lawyers and accountants did not, for instance, routinely visit their clients on Christmas morning, as hospital doctors did, or make themselves available on call 24 hours a day, as many doctors still did. Perhaps as a result, doctors and health matters were increasingly in the public consciousness—when Christian Barnard completed the first heart transplant in 1967 he became a world celebrity overnight. Hospitals became a favourite venue for television soap operas, inevitably with doctors as heroes. Across the developed economies the proportion of government expenditure devoted to health continued to rise.

In the early 1950s the profession extended its influence by definitively linking smoking and the dreaded lung cancer. What had previously been a more or less innocent pleasure (even, on occasion, recommended by doctors)was now identified as lethal. Thus was born what health sceptic Petr Skrabanek, a TCD epidemiologist and Fellow of the College, called 'anticipatory medicine', in which treatment was based on a statistical estimate of health risks rather than actual symptoms. A patient might seem and feel perfectly healthy, but a quick test in the GP's surgery might perhaps identify some hypertension ('above average' or even 'pre-hypertensive') and the patient faced a lifetime on drugs, and a self-image of mild invalidity. Occasionally these drugs had side-effects which had to be countered. As a consequence, Risteárd Mulcahy, Professor of Preventive Cardiology at UCD, talking about the 1960s and 1970s, recalled: 'The first thing I nearly always had to do when a patient came into my clinic was to take him off the cocktail of drugs he was taking. Usually he left taking many fewer but more carefully chosen drugs than when he came.'[1]

Over the next decades anticipatory medicine became common discourse, and very often the subtle 'yes, but . . .' of science was drowned by strident health education messages. This was to happen regularly, often based on evidence that when examined turned out to be weakly supported. In the 1970s Denis Burkitt from Northern Ireland noticed that rural Africans suffered less from cancer of the

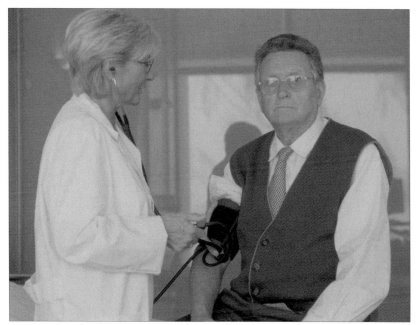

Hypertension was responsible for the high level of deaths from strokes. When drugs became available in the 1960s to control it, the regular monitoring of blood pressure introduced a new form of preventive medicine.

colon than his countrymen and concluded that their high-fibre diet was the reason. The useful recommendation of a high-fibre diet was quickly translated by commercial interests into the useless fibre supplements based on bran. A similar simplistic calculus led to the point where low cholesterol became a fetish and a nagging worry. Anticipatory medicine, wrote Skrabanek, 'promises clients that provided they have their risk factors regularly evaluated and appropriately modified, and adhere to. . . a "healthy life style", most if not all diseases can be prevented, or at least their onset almost indefinitely postponed.'[2] And if this did not happen ran the subtext, someone, probably a doctor, was to blame.

In line with other countries, Ireland's expenditure on healthcare was rising steadily; in 1947/8 health expenditure in the Republic was 1.7 per cent of GNP; by 1957/8 it had risen to 2.9 per cent and by 1970/1 it was 3.7 per cent of a much enlarged economy. Five years later, in 1975, health expenditure had risen to 6.5 per cent of GNP and by 1980 it was 8.2 per cent.[3] In fact this rise echoed a world trend among Western economies, apparently regardless of ideology—in 1960 the USA spent 5.2 per cent of GNP on health and Sweden 3.5 per cent; by the early 1980s both countries spent about 10 per cent, the one still largely relying on private enterprise, the other on socialised medicine.

Since the Second World War the pace of medical development had been unprecedented. New drugs and new treatments followed each other in rapid succession. (The drug companies had not yet learned that 'me-too' was an easier game to play than genuine innovation.) In 1949 steroids, the second of the two bulwarks of the modern pharmacopoeia, after antibiotics, began to be used on arthritic patients. Soon the new wonder-drug was being applied to asthma, eye diseases and numerous other conditions. A new kind of 'black box' medicine became possible. The physician did not need to know exactly what caused many of the numerous diseases that responded to steroids—it was enough that diseases of the blood, skin, eyes, kidneys and numerous others did so respond. But the development of the first steroid, cortisone, was only the first such crucial moment in the development of modern medicine. Others included:

1950: The combination of streptomycin and PAS was successful at last against the white plague, tuberculosis. Within a few years the sanatoria would be virtually empty.

1950: Statisticians definitively link lung cancer and smoking; the use of statistics in this introduces a whole new analytic tool to medicine.

1952: The Copenhagen polio outbreak gives rise to the birth of the intensive care unit.

1955: Open heart surgery.

1961: Hip replacement.

1963: Kidney transplant.

1964: Preventing strokes by careful monitoring of blood pressure.

1971: Sustainable remission from childhood leukaemia.

1973: CAT scanner developed.[4]

In the 1970s the so-called 'biomedical' model of medicine, in which the body was perceived as a series of parts that could (usually) be treated and repaired was dominant. The mind was thought of as another, rather special and mysterious, such part. The patient was under the control and command of the doctor, whose own activities were driven by clinical tests and examinations. The quintessential arena for this activity was the hospital, where the professional ideal, of excellent clinical medicine driven by independent but highly skilled consultants, could be pursued with full vigour.

In the US and the UK the holistic movement of alternative medicine sprang up in contrast to orthodoxy, but this had hardly penetrated into Ireland in the 1970s. The number of alternative practitioners was low, possibly at an all-time low. Certainly there were very few recorded in the *Golden Pages*, though this was to change markedly over the next 30 years. Practitioners such as 'the cancer man' fondly remembered by May Green from Athlone in the 1920s had all but disappeared. 'Johnnie Sweeney', she wrote 'had a cure for external cancer. People came from all over the country looking for the cure . . . Johnnie was famous for his cure. Sadly it died with him. We all knew he used herbs, egg yolk, dandelions and cow dung but that was not the whole secret. He mixed the ingredients in the holy water font from the old church in Geoghegan's yard. He had many, many cures.'[5] She does not say how he came on the ingredient ideas, but herbs (picked perhaps at a certain time), cow dung and the old font resonate with very old magic.

The alternative practitioners who did surface could not offer much intellectual challenge to formal medicine. Acupuncturist John Murphy from Cork told the

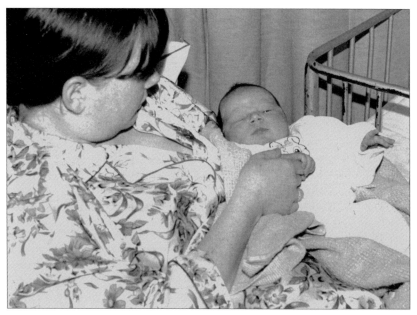

Having a baby is the most common reason for a stay in hospital. In 2001 1 in 6 of all hospital stays were for pregnancy or child-birth.

*Sunday Independe*nt how 'the body's life-force circulates though the organs on a set pattern in 24 hour cycles. Each organ rests for 22 hours and works for 2. The job of the acupuncturist is to switch energy from active to inactive organs.' For diagnosis he reached back to the old tradition that the quality of the pulse could reveal liver, kidney or lung problems. A very highly skilled acupuncturist, he said (modestly admitting he had not quite reached this level) could identify 6 separate pulses on each arm and 28 different 'states' of each pulse.[6] Quack medicines were still advertised, including Radian-B, Flam and the long-running Doan's Backache Pills, but they were dwarfed in prominence by cigarette advertisements, and lacked the bravura of the turn of the century. Where such medicines previously boasted that they successfully cured cases given up by the profession, now 'Pulmo' proudly declared that it had been 'prescribed by doctors for 50 years'.

Religious sources of consolation and aid were still adhered to. The pilgrimage to Lourdes or Knock was well attended, though cracks were appearing—in March 1974 the *Sunday Independent* reported that the annual pilgrimage to Croagh Patrick was switched from Saturday to Sunday to cut down on rowdyism as the 50,000 people 'relaxed' after the climb in Westport's 74 bars. On his travels along the Irish border in 1987 Colm Tóibín saw, near Crossmaglen, a ceremony in honour of St Brigid:

> In front of the altar . . . was a field in which the healing stones stood. Each stone was said to have powers to cure particular parts of the body. There were two indents for knees in the stone marked Knee Stone, with the Irish *Cloch Ghlúine*, printed above it. The people moved from stone to stone, some of them in bare

feet, rubbing their heads against the Head Stone, their waist against the Waist Stone and so on. Streams of materials were tied to the bushes and brambles around the stones, as an offering for luck.[7]

The medical encounter in the 1970s

At the start of the medical encounter the patient has four general questions in mind: two of which address the immediate future—What is happening to me? and, What can be done to stop it? and two which address more long term matters: Why me? and What can be done to prevent this recurring? In the 1970s the answers to these questions (certainly the first two) were sought more predominantly in the surgery of an officially trained doctor than ever before (or since). Although many homes would have had a well-thumbed diagnostic guide, in paragraph after paragraph these guides said 'consult your local doctor', and it was in both parts of the country quite cheap to do so. In the North the NHS service was broadly free, and in the South the average GP's daytime consultation fee was £3.75, the equivalent of €25 in 2004.

In her account of suffering from cancer, the 'Irish Housewife' naturally started in her GP's waiting-room, where she sat with two mothers-to-be chattering about 'pre-natal exercises, relaxation classes, breast-feeding, nappies', and an old lady—obviously very nervous, for there was a slight tremor in her wrinkled, freckled hands. Sharply, the 'Irish Housewife' identifies the sickness script that was being played. She had sat in that waiting room many times before: 'I had come with anaemia, gastric 'flu, ordinary 'flu, and what have you. Each time I had convinced myself that I was knocking on Death's Door. Each time I recovered, of course. Twice I had been given the wonderful news that I was pregnant. That added two more patients to be brought—tonsils, colds, measles, mumps, jaundice.' The doctor was a childhood friend, who had been away to university to study, but had come back to practise on his home patch. His role was to explain what is happening to her body (whether she is pregnant, why there is all that pain), and what if anything can be done about it.

This time he has bad news.

> His voice was not the usual professional doctor-cum-friend. It was a bit shaky . . . 'Ellen,' he began again. 'The news is not so good this time.' 'I know, George,' I said . . . 'I think I have known from the beginning, George,' I said, 'it is definitely hopeless, isn't it?' He looked at me silently.
>
> 'How long George—tell me the truth—how long have I got?'
>
> George gathered his composure and looked at the x-rays again.
>
> 'It is impossible to tell,' he said, 'but the growth is still small. You could have eighteen months to two years at the very outside.'[8]

Curiously, she decides to keep the information about this death sentence to herself, and does not tell either her mother or her husband and children. As a devout Catholic the Irish Housewife does not address the question—'Why me?' to her doctor. This is a matter about which as she says 'nobody knows that answer except the Good Man Himself'. Not that she is too happy, as the last sentence of her book movingly exemplifies: 'Mother of God—I'm not afraid to die, but would you tell your Son—I—I'd like to stay alive!'

Reading this dialogue between doctor and patient, one is struck by the apparent reversal of roles. It is his voice that is 'shaky'; he stays silent as she announces 'it is definitely hopeless'; whereas she 'knows'—and at this point she records the GP muttering '"How," he asked more himself than me, "do people with Cancer always know?"' The fears generated on the patient's side of the medical encounter—of pain, of vulnerability, of indignity, of belittling concentration on the physical body—are mastered in this account by her taking control of the encounter. Some people mentally absent themselves from the encounter (like the young patient in Arthur Miles' painting 'The Doctor'), others assert their individuality against a system that appears to run on regardless of their feelings, by using humour. Thus, businessman Kevin McCourt records his first morning in St Vincent's in September 1993:

Alan P. Grant: President of the College 1977–9, the first Northerner to hold this position.

> . . . 9.55 a girl I have not seen before said 'go to toilet, take your clothes off and put on this robe' (it looks like a girl's pinafore). I was going to say something about indecent exposure, but she didn't look encouraging. 'After it,' says she 'we'll give you your pill—be in bed—it may make you drowsy. . . . ' There cannot possibly be any one else needing something of me. I forgot to mention the bedmakers, the carafe changer and the on-duty nurse who says, peeping in 'Are you alright?' Last peep, I asked her when was I getting my perm.[9]

Medical practice at the GP level had moved on somewhat from the bleak environs of Dr Francis X. Thullabawn, 'the most eligible bachelor in Moymell', in Mervyn Wall's 1950s novel *Leaves for the burning*. 'The dispensary was small and untidy. There was a leather couch for patients and a single chair for his own use. A small paper-littered table stood against the wall; that, the medicine chest and a couple of shelves of empty bottles completed the furnishings. In the passage outside there was a bench on which the patients sat awaiting their turn.'[10]

On locum in Ballyhaunis in the late 1960s, prior to taking up his appointment as head of the Medico-Social Research Board in Dublin, Geoffrey Dean remembered that 'medical practice was very informal: patients would walk into the house at any time of the day, or even late at night.' The wall between the con-

sulting and waiting rooms was not very sound-proof, and one day he overheard two patients gossiping. 'One said: "You know, he is a nice doctor, it's a pity he hasn't his own practice by now." The other replied: "It must be the drink, God bless him."'

The easy-going life implied in this conversation was belied as he learned more about their lives: 'Most of the illnesses were minor, but I was surprised by the large number of people, particularly women, who . . . were taking tranquillisers, usually Librium or Valium, three times a day. Many of them were hooked on these drugs and it was difficult to get them to stop taking them. When the doctor had first prescribed these tranquillisers he had not appreciated how addictive they were.'[11] The over-prescription to the point of addiction of Hoffman-La Roche's benzodiazepines Valium and Librium was an iatrogenic disaster that did not achieve the same publicity as thalidomide, but affected many more lives.

In 1971 James Deeny, having retired from the Department of Health and the World Health Organisation, quixotically took a locum in his family's old stamping ground of Fanad, County Donegal. Dr MacMenamin, the incumbent, was seventy-eight and had been there for more than fifty years. Now his family insisted that he took things easier. 'Universally beloved' MacMenamin had a sharp eye, and 'could spot a sick man or woman from 100 yards and have a diagnosis made before they would come face to face with him.' When Deeny, who had not seriously looked at a patient for thirty years, was faced with his first patients, he examined them as thoroughly as a new qualifier; the word quickly went round—'this man really examines you'. And of course he found things. 'So the word went round that "the new man finds things and tries to cure them".' As he put it 'trade increased, until instead of a couple of hours in the morning, the dispensary session became a day-long affair. Dr MacMenamin watched the whole performance with amusement, since the same thing had happened to him when he began in Fanad fifty years before.'[12]

In January 1972 Deeny and MacMenamin did a study of their case-load, a striking contrast to what Deeny had encountered as a new GP in Lurgan in the 1930s. 'We performed 716 services during the month; 341 were home visits and there were 375 attendances either at his house or at the dispensary. We found that there was a very large number of chronic chest conditions, not tuberculosis, but a surprising number for such an otherwise healthy community. They were probably some unusual form of "Farmer's Lung" possibly from mouldy hay.'[13] In his study of the community he detailed the breakdown: 'respiratory diseases, 182; cardiovascular diseases, 96; digestive disease conditions, 83; diseases of the nervous system, 80; diseases of the organs of movement (rheumatism and arthritis), 78; prophylaxis, 44; skin conditions, 38; genito-urinary conditions, 35; ENT, 25; antenatal examinations, 22; dental, 10; ophthalmic, 6, others, 20.'[14]

The loss of deference

The doctor-patient relationship was in transition in the 1970s, but so was much of the Irish social structure. For the first time in Irish history more people lived in urban than rural environments and farming ceased to be the majority occupation. A country predominantly of self-employed farmers turned, almost overnight it seemed, into a country of employees. Accompanying this change was a shift in sensibility, from a society valuing hierarchy, deference and security to one concerned with individualism, autonomy and enterprise.

New possibilities changed old relationships. In the 1970s young men could find independent jobs in industry at seventeen or younger. As a result, in Ireland, as in other Western countries, the traditional deference given to men of standing (whether nationally or simply in the sphere of the village) began to erode. Duties were replaced in public discourse by rights, enforceable in the law courts; status was replaced by class and interest groups. 'What matters now', wrote Christopher Whelan of the ESRI 'is not who a man is, but what he can do.' This was in fact only partly true. In the Republic restricted access to education (free secondary education was extended to the whole population only in 1967 and barely 5 per cent of the adult population had third level qualifications) curtailed economic opportunities which in turn affected lifestyle choices and health. As Whelan pointed out, in the 1970s social mobility was less in the Republic than in Sweden, France or England.[15] Doctors' sons (and increasingly daughters) left their paid secondary schools and found themselves in the intellectually undemanding medical schools, as they had for generations.

Various other trends towards a new social pattern were just beginning—the marriage rate dropped, and the number of one and two-person households began to rise. Married women were released from 'the ban' and allowed to retain their civil service jobs (and a few years later they were even paid the same as men). Crucially two-thirds of households now had television sets, although the supply of sanitary facilities, especially in the country, was less favourable. The 1971 Census reported that of the 700,000 houses in the state 44 per cent had no fixed bath or shower, and 20 per cent no fixed toilet. In the country, only 42 per cent of houses had flush toilets.

Among the economic changes was a sustained growth in the number of professionals that the new society needed, noticeably architects and accountants, which increased in number nine-fold and eleven-fold respectively between 1926 and 1971. Of five representative professions—lawyers, doctors, architects, engineers and accountants—the traditional pair (law and medicine) represented 70 per cent in 1926; by 1970 there were as many accountants as practising doctors, and more engineers. Where the doctor, the solicitor and the bank manager had been kings of the social walk, now the picture was made complicated by other professional groups. The new professions, for instance the accountants, did their best to adopt the caste marks of 'professional' codes, such as that against advertising, even at the expense of common sense. Thus when Craig Gardner moved offices from Dame Street to Ballsbridge in 1968, the Institute of Chartered Accountants ruled that a general 'change of address' announcement would amount to advertising, and so the firm made no such announcement.[16]

The hugely popular US soap opera Dr Kildare *introduced Irish viewers to the workings of a modern American hospital. A running plot line told of the relationship between the young Dr Kildare (Richard Chamberlain) and his older mentor Dr Gillespie.*

Table 9. 1: The growth of the professions in Ireland 1926-71

	Lawyers	Medical practitioners	Engineers	Architects	Accountants
1926	1,356	2,051	987	199	283
1936	1,759	1,953	1,047	279	673
1946	1,849	2,674	1,765	380	1,414
1951	1,909	2,921	2,126	507	1,446
1961	1,935	2,952	2,744	1,050	2,378
1971	1,963	3,565	3,985	1,935	3,418
Growth 1926–71	45%	74%	303%	872%	1107%

Source: Census

As one of the most highly regarded groups of the traditional elite, doctors inevitably suffered a diminution by these changes. An indication of this process came in early 1974 with the establishment of a Patients' Rights Association—a phenomenon early generations of medics would have greeted with a snort of disbelief. *The Irish Medical Times* commented unsympathetically that 'most doctors will be inclined to view the recent formation . . . with a certain degree of cynicism—as yet another pressure group within the community demanding its own particular rights.' The editorial looked back at the idyllic past when no one talked of 'rights', and the doctor's word was law: 'There is a long tradition in Ireland of a very happy doctor-patient relationship, and the doctor's opinion, advice and indeed decisions have seldom been questioned.' In the unpalatable new situation, the editor noted, 'there is the danger that unnecessary questioning by a patient may influence a doctor's judgement and if there is the possibility now of a threat of litigation or bureaucratic investigation with every medical decision a doctor makes, his work could become very difficult, if not impossible.'[17]

Candles in the dark[18]

In the North the Troubles exposed the profession to a fierce challenge to their professionalism. It provided a vivid demonstration of the truth that medical activity, from the patient's and the doctor's side, is intimately bound with the stresses and prejudices of normal social and political life, and is not a mere technical activity. From the civil rights marches in 1969 onwards violence was endemic, and the victims (and sometimes the perpetrators) inevitably arrived to be treated in hospitals. Two prominent hospitals in Belfast, the Royal and the Mater, were clearly identified as Protestant unionist and Catholic nationalist respectively. The iconography of both had been unmistakable, with the Union Jack decorating the Royal on holidays and Catholic statuary presiding over the wards in the Mater. Ironically, the Royal, the largest acute hospital in Northern Ireland and a pillar of the unionist establishment, is located in 'Republican West Belfast', and conversely the Mater, until 1972 owned and run by the Sisters of Mercy, faces the Shankill Road, and has been treated as the local hospital by generations of the Protestants from that area.

Although senior staff were invariably recruited from the appropriate side by both hospitals, ancillary staff were often locals. So if an injured paramilitary was brought to the Royal, he might bring IRA bodyguards, and be tended by unionist doctors and nurses and otherwise looked after by Catholic staff. In the bed across the ward there might be a policeman, perhaps the victim of an IRA bomb. In these circumstances everyone watched for the slightest hint of preferential treatment, and misapprehensions could easily arise, as when a UDA/UVF member had shot several Catholics and they all arrived in the Royal A&E. The Protestant was treated first, but solely because he had a ruptured spleen.

The location of these hospitals undoubtedly gave rise to fears particularly in patients who were political figures, paramilitaries or members of the security forces, who all had reason to be fearful when in what they considered hostile territory. Perhaps these fears were exaggerated, but it is certain that patients were shot in their beds in three hospitals in Belfast, the City, the Mater and the Royal; the Royal witnessed a gunfight along the famous corridor which linked twenty wards, and staff were shot in the grounds. Hospital routines meant that potential victims could not vary their movements as they usually did.

Nurses in the tower blocks in the Royal Victoria grounds had to be warned not to lean over the balconies of their flats to watch the frequent gunfights between the Army and the IRA.[19] Two small maternity hospitals in Protestant areas had their closures hastened because Catholic mothers and their visitors would not venture there. Derry patients often chose to go across the border to Letterkenny rather than to the local Altnagelvin, where it was feared army or security forces

based in the hospital would arrest them. Prominent unionists, visiting relatives in the Royal, certainly felt uncomfortably that their movements were being noted, and on one shocking occasion a politician visiting his sick child was shot at.

The relations with the state were thrown into relief, as perhaps when the security forces demanded prior access to injured men, or demanded that one of their own be segregated. In 1971 a Statutory Order was passed requiring anyone with knowledge of wounds caused by bombs, guns or other offensive weapon to report the matter to the RUC. The profession instantly united in protest, pointing out not only the breach of patient confidentiality that this would entail, but that any practitioner obeying the law would be at serious personal risk.

The Troubles in the North brought soldiers and the medical profession uncomfortably close.

Their concerns were accepted by the authorities.

Apart from the occasional lapse it was generally agreed that 'with very few exceptions', the behaviour of professionals towards all patients was exemplary. 'No politician,' says James McKenna, in 'Candles in the dark',[20] an oral history on health professionals in the Troubles, 'could quote complaints from patients that they had received inadequate treatment because of their ethnicity. Most denied ever having had such a complaint or even having heard of one.' Some Sinn Féin representatives complained of staff attitudes, but none had a word to say against the actual treatment received. The lapses were few—'one Catholic had noticed Protestant staff asking about patients on the way in "is this one of ours?"'; 'one Protestant observed Catholic nurses being offhand with security forces, while questioning Sinn Féin victims "assiduously"'.

Many of the most critical recognised that the prejudices and personalities of the patients perhaps contributed to problems as well as what was objectively experienced. As one Sinn Féin Assembly member put it: 'I would have to say that it is not the attitude of the doctor or nurse or health professional but it's the perceptions of the patients'. Another politician confirmed that as in all human relationships, a cold, frosty or offhand manner did not necessarily imply prejudice:

'it's "equal opportunity" less sympathetic'.

'Candles in the dark', from which these opinions are drawn, makes it clear that the behaviour of the healthcare professionals transcended the 'great hatred' that consumed so many of their fellow-citizens. 'Every hospital workforce was mixed yet they managed to a remarkable degree to leave their religious and political atavism at the door . . .they sacrificed their own comforts to come unbidden to their workplace when they heard of disasters, making their way through localities torn with active strife. Their colleagues in the community services crossed barriers, both visible and invisible, to attend patients in their own homes.' It was an heroic period of the Irish profession, fit to rank with the fever days of the 1840s.

The medical marketplace

The practical organisation of the profession in the Republic was a matter for fierce political debate as the state steadily increased its expenditure on health. Amid the clamour of debate two key issues can be perceived: firstly, how should doctors be paid for their services? and secondly, what should be the relationship between general practice and the hospital system? At this time the average doctor received £4,327 from the state General Medical Scheme, and perhaps as much again from private practice. This totalled somewhat more than the £7,782 the (married, male) secretary of a government department got. Hospital consultants could expect twice this.

The debate in Ireland, as in other countries, was also something of a civil war inside the profession as medical radicals such as James Deeny confronted the conservative leaders of the profession, who were deeply suspicious that change would undermine both their professional freedoms and their incomes. Because of the great gap between the two points of view, tempers on both sides frayed quickly. The profession did not endear itself by personalised attacks on ministers as for instance the BMA's attacks on Nye Bevan or the Confédération des Syndicats Médicaux on the Gaullist Robert Debré; in Ireland this feature was exemplified by the rudeness in print of William Doolin (editor of both the *Irish Journal of Medical Science* and the IMA's journal) about Minister MacEntee's wife.[21]

Despite attempts to elevate the so-called professional mode of organisation into codes of ethics such as the British 'Family Doctors' Charter', the American 'Ten Principles' and the French 'Medical Charter', it was easy for one side or the other to be characterised as either naïve or cynical. Did the 'fee per service' system preferred by the profession represent the desired clinical freedom, or was it merely a licence to print money, as health administrators believed? International experience was little help, suggesting that whatever system was adopted had advantages and disadvantages as much related to the local culture as to intrinsic merits of the scheme (see Table 9.2). In Sweden for instance 'fee for service' worked well, in the US it was vulnerable to exploitation by doctors threatened by litigation and conscious that insurance companies were picking up the bills.

The Republic's Health Minister Brendan Corish (Labour) wanted to press ahead with a free family doctor service, as recommended by Professor James McCormick of Trinity in a contemporary report, and free hospital care. By reducing private practice to a rump, this would make doctors effectively salaried officials of the state. World-wide there are basically three ways in which doctors are paid—fee per service; capitation (so much for every patient enrolled on a panel) or salary. (There are of course variants or intermediate systems.) Restating the traditional arguments for clinical and financial independence, the hospital consultants in April 1974 threatened to limit their activity to 'vital services' only. Corish was obliged to postpone his scheme indefinitely. Relations between the Department and the profession were at a low ebb.

Table 9. 2: Comparison of GP payment systems

Payment system	Typical abuse	Works well in	Believed abused in
1. Fee per service	Overtesting and over treatment	Sweden	USA
2. Capitation	Excessive referral, demanding patients discouraged	Holland, UK	Austria
3. Salary	Reduced workload, few home visits	Israel, USSR	Middle East, Latin America

Source: B. Abel-Smith *Value for money in health services* London: Heinemann 1975.

Many felt that the often acrimonious debate damaged the profession's standing. Indicative of a change in attitude to the profession was the historian Joe Lee's ascription of purely cynical and mercenary motives to some of the objectors to the Mother and Child scheme of the 1950s. For him, 'many of those who worshipped at the altar of Croesus, while demurely draped in the robes of Hippocrates were shrewd enough to oppose the scheme as "socialised medicine". Some unkind observers suspected that their real opposition was less to "state medicine" than "cheap medicine". Had the much criticised socialised medicine been considered likely to increase professional incomes, its ideological horrors might have been more stoically endured.'[22] This analysis is more ironic than insightful, but it was a sharply critcal note hardly struck in public since G. B. Shaw. An equally unsympathetic later commentator declared that in the debates of the early 1970s 'the medical profession were revealed in their true colours as trade unionists as willing as any other powerful group to defend their incomes by withdrawing their labour'.[23] In January 1974 Dr John Bradshaw noted sarcastically that doctors had 'high incomes, little chance of unemployment, great job satisfaction and they are the most highly respected body of people in the country'. Yet, as he put it, they wanted 'a golden halo and a golden tie-pin to match.'[24] About this time the *Irish Medical Times* commented: 'the public image of the profession has already lost a great deal of its lustre', and remarked at the IMA conference in April 1974 on 'an unsavoury prominence of money.'[25]

In fact, the profession have always been deeply ambiguous about money. Some few have simply exploited their position for financial gain, but the vast majority (while of course unwilling to be paid less than the next person) were primarily anxious to deliver skilled care to their patients. On occasion this delivery called forth extraordinary levels of personal attention to patients—every family has its own affectionate memory of such doctoring. There was, both in the profession's and the public's minds, a gulf between the personal medical service devotedly given and gratefully received, and the cash nexus resulting. (This multi-level image of the doctor is no new thing. In Goltzius' sixteenth-century paintings of the four faces of the physician, the doctor appears first as the healing Christ, next as the ministering angel, then, as the patient recovers, as an ordinary man, and finally, when the bill becomes due, as the Devil incarnate.)

The ambiguity was expressed in different ways. At one conference Dr John Fleetwood, expressing an interest in pensions, was hissed at as a 'moneygrubber'.[26] On locum in Ballyhaunis in the late 1960s Geoffrey Dean recalled visiting panel (free) patients at home—'the man of the house would always insist on pushing two or three pounds into my hand saying "something for your petrol, doctor". After I had trudged through the yard into the kitchen and seen the patient I would be asked what my fee was. At first I was embarrassed about this and would say perhaps "two pounds". On two or three occasions the farmer would then take from his back trouser pocket a wad of £20 notes and say "I am very sorry, doctor, but I have nothing smaller than a £20 note"!'[27]

In *My Uncle Frank* Thomas Bodkin recalls his uncle angrily, even contemptuously, rejecting such proffered payments. The offer and the anger reveal much. In

Lemass' 'rising tide' was very slow to lift some boats. In 1969 the news magazine Nusight *estimated that one-third of children in Ireland were living in conditions of poverty, and had to expect a lifetime of health problems as a result.*

'Our mothers will kill us!' declared one of a feminist group which in May 1971 imported illegal contraceptives from the North as a protest.

a society bound by status, some doctors instinctively felt it was not appropriate for a poor, low-status person to attempt to neutralise the boon of medical care by payment. In the argument about free medicine, those conservatives who insisted that people preferred to pay for their medicine were reporting accurately an ancient reluctance to allow a favour to go unreciprocated. In a society driven by rights and interests a different calculus comes in.

The moral battle

The moral battleground of the early 1970s was contraception, and the profession was reluctantly drawn into the fray, for it impinged intimately on their relationship with most of the women and men in their practices. It had been vexed territory since Pope Paul's *Humanae Vitae* had nailed the Church's colours to the mast in 1968. In practice the moral high ground was shifting fast. The ruling had been quietly ignored by most Irish people, as was evidenced by the continuing trend towards smaller families. The official, formal, public system, however, bolstered by so many absolute statements in the past, took some time to catch up. In 1971 the Archbishop of Dublin, John Charles McQuaid, opening a new UCD department of obstetrics based in Holles Street (of which he was *ex-officio* Chairman) denounced the modern outlook. 'Liberty is often invoked today in the most intimate area of parenthood,' he said. 'But that liberty alone is genuine that knows how to set restraints on itself.' He went on: 'It is the peculiar ignorance of intelligent men, uneducated in philosophy and theology, that they do not see where lies authentic teaching authority . . . with similar nescience they refuse to allow the teaching authority of the Church to intervene in the moral question of applying to human persons the techniques of medicine. That appli-

Himself the son of a doctor, Archbishop John Charles McQuaid, seen here at the opening of the new St Vincent's at Elm Park (November 1970) was a very strong presence in Irish medicine for thirty years. (Photo Stephen O'Connor)

cation is, of its nature, subject to the moral law.' In other words it was for the Church, with its unique understanding of 'objective moral law' to declare how what he called the 'whole complexity of human relationships in marriage' were to be handled.

But this line could not be held. (In a 1974 letter to 'Betty Maguire' of the *Sunday Independent* a nineteen-year-old reported that she had been having sex with her twenty-two-year-old partner but not orgasms—was she frigid?[28] This was *not* a concern her mother would have raised in public, if at all.) A referendum in 1972 had removed the special position of the Catholic Church from the Constitution and in 1973 John Charles himself died. His successor Dermot Ryan did not attend a meeting of the National Maternity Hospital at which the Master, Dr Declan Meagher, declared the importance of freedom of conscience, 'by which he meant particularly the freedom of individual doctors'.[29] However John Charles was far from the only conservative. In the early 1990s the then Archbishop of Dublin, Desmond Connell, forbade Veritas to circulate a pamphlet on how to avoid HIV by safe sex on the grounds that, after celibacy, it recommended the use of condoms.[30]

In March 1974 the Seanad refused a second reading of Mary Robinson's Family Planning Bill. Like much of the rest of the country, the medical profession was generally unenthusiastic. A much touted solution was to make contraceptives available only under prescription (what would later be called 'an Irish solution to an Irish problem')—it was an interesting index of changing attitudes that less than a hundred years after de Styrap had warned the young practitioner against having anything to do with contraception it had become peculiarly the profession's province. The newly introduced 'choice of doctor' scheme for medical card holders—about one-third of patients—meant that doctors were now potentially subject to the kind of pressures we have seen operating in the North in the early days of the NHS. As the *Irish Medical Times* pointed out in February 1974, 'the doctor who cannot in conscience prescribe contraceptives is losing out as patients transfer to the doctor who will.' Perhaps it would be possible to establish dedicated family planning clinics. But this would be the thin end of a wedge, removing the family practitioner from a crucial connection with the family. Dr Doyle of Wexford no doubt spoke for many when he expressed himself as being 'utterly opposed to family planning advice being made available to patients without the knowledge of their family doctor.'[31]

Reforming the hospital system

In 1936 the Hospitals Commission had identified twelve general hospitals in Dublin, with a total of 2,500 beds (not including the 1,000 or so chronic beds in St Kevin's, otherwise the South Dublin Union). The bed total did not include 386 fever beds, most of which (250) were in Cork Street. There were also three special hospitals, notably the three maternities, three children's hospitals, two cancer hospitals and others such as the Westmoreland Lock, specialising in STDs. These hospitals together received the astonishing number of 340,000 out-patient attendances every year from a city population of approximately half a million.

From the time of this first report, published in 1936, it was obvious that 'whatever justification may have existed for such a disproportionate number of relatively small general hospitals in Dublin in those days when the cost of hospital administration and maintenance was exceedingly low compared with modern times, their existence today is beyond all doubt indefensible.'[32] The Commission initially argued that the main obstacle to remedying the situation was financial, but the enormous sums produced by the Sweepstakes soon made it clear that there were other, deeper factors at play. These were discreetly hinted at when a proposal to merge the state-financed Richmond and the Mater, owned by the Sisters of Mercy, to produce a hospital 'which would far exceed anything so far attempted' foundered. There were, as the Commission dryly remarked, 'difficulties inherent in the position' which it was not possible to overcome.[33]

For 40 years, these and similar 'difficulties'—notably a failure of political will to confront the entrenched positions of hospitals boards—meant that little had happened beyond plans and proposals. The effect of the Sweep's riches, in Dublin at least, was to consolidate the status quo; one can only speculate how poverty might have changed the outcome. By the 1970s however it was clear that things would have to change. A series of proposals from the ground-breaking 1968 Fitzgerald Report (the origins among other things of Comhairle na nOspidéal) onwards had proposed that the number of general hospitals in Dublin be reduced to five or six, which would mean a major trimming of the growth of centuries. In practice it was some 30 years before a version of these proposals came to pass. A group of the voluntary hospitals had combined into the Federation of Dublin

Voluntary Hospitals (in 1961), but, as the Hospitals Commission had foreseen, this did not offer a satisfactory solution.

Obviously any consolidation threatened the status quo, and with it established patterns and routines. As we have seen the Irish medical establishment was fiercely loyal to its institutions. Apart from a very human unwillingness to address change, there were also material threats. The key to a consultant's power was access to beds and therefore to the ability to admit patients; at the same time there was, as we have seen, strong pressure to establish consultants on a salaried basis and to minimise lucrative private practice.

Given the importance of the hospital in the biomedical model, it is perhaps not surprising that a remarkable number of Irish people were drawn into the system. As Brendan Hensey, ex-Secretary of the Department of Health commented: 'The number of patients discharged from hospitals was 560,000, about one-sixth of the population—a startling figure even if it does include double-counting of some individuals.'

Inevitably the processing of such numbers led to system difficulties. Weak co-ordination affected, for instance, the professionals' relationship with support staff and with each other in the handling of multi-dimensional cases. The parents of a child with a brain tumour interviewed for Anna Farmar's study of the care of children with terminal cancer told how: '"We had to do all the running; we had to go back to the consultant[s] and try to get them together" . . . another 'spent many hours waiting around on the off-chance of seeing a doctor'. And when the doctor was available 'we were always conscious that his time was limited'. Conversations about seriously ill children too often took place in corridors, and in a style more appropriate to 'a group of medical students, not two people who were in deep shock'.[34] Even when things went positively, a stay in hospital could be bewildering. Kevin McCourt arrived at the Blackrock Clinic in January 1996:

The College in the 1970s—as with many public buildings in Dublin, not much money had been spent maintaining the façade.

> I was here in my room at 3 pm—and then they struck! 3.10: blood sample; 3.20: x-ray downstairs; 3.30: ECG and pacemaker check downstairs; 3.45: upstairs again more blood, weight, pulse, pressure; 3.55: Ursula, matron, wrote down the story of my medical life. Dozens of questions predominantly No; 4.20: menu to book my food—gammon steak.

By far the most common reason for going to hospital, however, was to have a baby. At the beginning of the twentieth century most women gave birth at home; by 1936 the Obstetrical Section of the Royal Academy of Medicine estimated that perhaps half of Dublin births would be in hospital by 1944.[35] Ireland was simply following a world-wide trend in this. As the Obstetrical Section pointed out, in some European and American cities in-hospital deliveries constituted as many as 80 per cent of births. This shift from home to hospital was, thought many, amply justified by the simultaneous drop in Irish maternal mortality. As Brendan Hensey, Secretary of the Department of Health, put it: 'In 1961 20.4 per cent of births occurred at home: by 1971 this had dropped to 0.7 per cent—a change related to a fall in the infant mortality rate from 30.5 per 1,000 to 12.4.'[36]

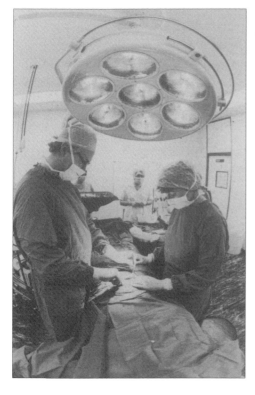

An operation in progress in the Tower unit of Belfast City Hospital, which was begun in 1971 and finally formally opened in 1987. The unit has 18 floors and 1,200 beds.

It was perhaps inevitable, following international trends and the local realities, that childbirth be captured by the hospital system, despite the costs to the state and to mothers. On the other hand the distinguished medical historian Irvine Louden would perhaps see the result as the collective will allowing the obvious to defeat the best. He noted in his magisterial work *Death in Childbirth* that 'wherever a city, a county, a region or a nation had developed a system of maternal care which was firmly based on a body of trained, licensed, regulated and respected midwives (especially when the midwives worked in close and cordial co-operation with doctors and lying-in hospitals) the standard of maternal care was at its highest.'[37] Although the three Dublin maternities did make periodic attempts to develop outside midwifery services, in practice both the hospitals and the Department felt happier to keep things inside.

The few women who did want to have their babies at home found it increasingly difficult. As Mary Maher put in it *You and your baby* (1973) 'having a baby at home is obviously much riskier than having one in hospital and you should be a one hundred per cent safe obstetrical bet before you consider it—or indeed, before any reputable doctor would agree to co-operate'. Part of the difficulty by this time was the lack of midwives accustomed to home births—since virtually all births were now in hospital, all training assumed a hospital environment.

Surveys run by the pressure group the Association for Improvements in the Maternity Services, reported varied hospital experiences. These admittedly unscientific surveys may also represent a snapshot of patients' responses to the general hospital experience, accumulating not just the medical but also the human

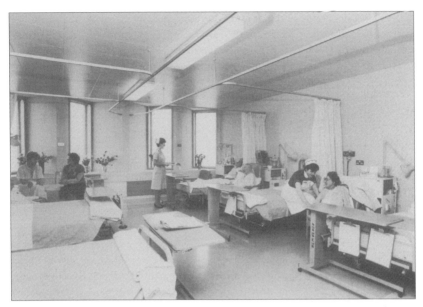

A modern ward in the Tower unit of the Belfast City Hospital—pleasant, airy and light, but certainly not domestic. The first eight floors of the 230 feet high block each contain two 30-bed wards.

experience. Some new mothers were thrilled with the whole event and 'had nothing but praise' for the hospitals, or 'I had first class treatment and thoroughly enjoyed it all'.[38] Others were less enthusiastic especially about 'systems' aspects of being in hospital. 'You were just another cog in a wheel to them' or 'I was satisfied with [the doctor] as a medical technician but not as a human being', 'it is a very emotional time for us on the ward and the hospital system doesn't seem to be able to take this into consideration'. For the fastidious 'other patients' unhygienic habits' could be a trial, not to mention other aspects of communal ward life, such as the food, which ranged from 'awful, stodgy' 'packet soup, greasy fries and rhubarb' to 'excellent and attractively served'.

Some mothers reported that 'these big hospitals can often mean an impersonal atmosphere, hurried staff, long periods of waiting to see doctors and rushed examinations with no time to ask questions or discuss worries.'[39] The events revealed in the case of Dunne *v* the National Maternity Hospital demonstrate how the failures and quirks of an over-stretched system could make childbirth a stressful experience: when Kay Dunne arrived at the hospital in March 1982, already in labour, her file could not be found, so basic details (name, address etc.) had to be taken again; her private doctor was not in the hospital, and then without any examination a ward sister gave her opinion that she was too small to be having twins and that she probably was not in labour.[40]

As usual human relations were variable and (as we have seen in the hospital experience in the Troubles) perhaps the comments reflect as much the temperament of the speaker as the objective situation. Some had good experiences: 'I had a woman doctor and she was actually a source of reassurance and friendship during the whole pregnancy', 'staff could not have been more helpful or pleasant. I really felt that I mattered' and, 'he gave me full attention and discussed all my problems with me'. But others were less happy: 'the medical profession needs courses in human relations', 'I would be absolutely terrified of becoming pregnant again as I have lost confidence completely in the medical maternity services'.

Reinventing the College

Since 1922 the College had sunk to become hardly more than a Dublin medical club. Between 1922 and 1974 there were eighteen Presidents, of whom one was educated at the old Catholic University and one at UCD. Virtually all the rest had attended Trinity. Although perceived in the South as a largely Protestant, Dublin, medical club, in the North it was, ironically, tainted by its Free State connections. The northern medical establishment resolutely faced towards Edinburgh and London, and generally pretended the College did not exist.

The College was run-down, and low in funds. Alan Grant, physician of the Belfast City Hospital and President 1977–9, remembered his election to the Fellowship, in 1954: 'The President, Dr Freeman, and about six senior Fellows sat at a large table. There were no carpets. The walls were a dull mustard colour with brown surrounds. The windows were grimy and the dull light showed flaking paint and cobwebs. It was cold.'[41] For most of his colleagues in the North, the membership examinations of the College in the South were at best a dress rehearsal for the 'real thing' in London or Edinburgh. Some, however, such as Dr Michael Scott, the present Dun's Librarian, found the warm welcome extended by the College staff a welcome alternative to the more impersonal London counterpart.

For a generation or more after 1922 connections between the professions North and South were very slight. This was of course very much in line with the general disdain felt in the North for the Free State. The first crack in the ice came in 1959, with the foundation of the Corrigan Club made up equally of physicians from Dublin and Belfast. Even in this gathering there were entrenched attitudes. When a southern physician gave an after-dinner talk to the Club on 'Irish Medical Schools', the fact that he included Queen's Belfast caused at least one distinguished Northerner to resign, since everyone knew that Queen's was in fact a British medical school.

By the late 1960s it had become clear that the College must radically reform or simply subside. Fences had to be mended with the North and with the Catholic physicians in the South who had been just as reluctant to participate. Because the College was perceived as a largely Protestant, Trinity establishment, it had not been customary for consultants educated at UCD and working particularly at St Vincent's, to become Members or Fellows. In 1968, Bryan Alton, then Vice-President, had been responsible for a bold piece of legislative sleight of hand that enabled this rift to be healed. Since senior consultants could not be expected to

The first eight Fellows elected under new procedures to widen the representativeness of the College. (Front row. left to right.) William F. O'Dwyer (NUI) Jervis Street; Henry E. Counihan (NUI) National Maternity Hospital and St Laurence's; Owen Wade (Camb.) Royal Victoria Hospital, Belfast; Risteárd Mulcahy (NUI) St Vincent's; (second row. left to right.) Denis O'Sullivan (NUI) St Finbarr's Hospital, Cork; Oliver Fitzgerald (NUI) St Vincent's; Timothy Counihan (NUI) Mater and St Anne's Hospital, Dublin; (back) John Vallence-Owen (Camb.) Royal Victoria Hospital, Belfast.

sit a full Membership exam, a by-law was passed to allow the President to conduct a 'special' qualifying examination instead. A consultant cardiologist remembers being solemnly asked 'on which side of the body is the heart?' and on foot of his answer, immediately becoming a Member and very soon a Fellow. Seven others, mostly with a UCD background, were 'made' at the same time. For the next eight years or so some 60 physicians became Fellows under this procedure, greatly widening the College's representativeness. However by 1978 it was felt that the by-law, which was of course quite unfair to those seeking Membership by the examination route, had served its purpose, and a moratorium on admissions in this way was agreed.

In 1969 the then President, Alan Thompson, began to involve Northern Fellows in the activities of the College. His successor as President continued the policy, and opened up the College in numerous ways as well. David Mitchell (1969–72) improved relationships with sister colleges in the UK, and established the College as an equal examining body for medical qualifications with those in the UK. This was to prove crucial and, under Bryan Alton's Presidency (1974–7) candidates began to arrive from the wealthy Gulf States and the Far East. Thus was started a period in which the College steadily regained the influence it had had in previous centuries, as we shall see in the next chapter.

In common with other institutions that had won respect in the era of deference, the profession lost credit in an era of individualism. The heightened expectation stimulated by medicine's success led, conversely, to greater disappointment when things did not go so well, and an increasing enthusiasm for litigation. The tussles in the early part of the 1970s, and the continued sniping between Departmental officials and the profession, certainly adversely affected the public image of the profession.

The 1970s should have been the dawn of a new era of confidence between doctor and patient. Life expectation was steadily rising, more patients were being accurately and effectively treated than ever before, and (more importantly) the physical quality of life offered by medicine was better than ever. But somehow this did not translate into an increased affection for the profession. The era when an author could unselfconsciously refer to doctors as 'the nearest approach to saints on earth' was, for better or worse, over.

Presidents of the College 1922–79

Name	Date	Born	Educated	Hospital	Speciality
Michael Cox	1922–3	1852	Catholic University, London	St Vincent's	Physician
Sir William Thompson	1924–5	1861	TCD, RCSI	Jervis St	Physician
Henry Wilson	1925–6	1865	TCD, RCSI, Leipzig	Rotunda, Richmond & Sir Patrick Dun's	Gynaecologist
William Winter	1927–9	1868	TCD, Edinburgh	Dr Steevens'	Physician
Thomas Moorhead	1929–32	1878	TCD, Vienna	Baggot St & Sir Patrick Dun's	Physician
Francis Purser	1933	1877	TCD, Berlin, London	Mercer's & Richmond	Physician
John Matson	1934–6	1864	TCD, London, Liverpool	Richmond	Physician
William Boxwell	1937–9	1875	TCD	Meath	Physician
Robert Rowlette	1940–2	1873	TCD	Mercer's & Jervis St	Physician
William Harvey	1943–6	1877	TCD, Vienna	Adelaide	Physician/ Dermatologist
Bethel Solomons	1946–9	1885	TCD, Vienna	Rotunda	Obstetrician
Leonard Abrahamson	1949–52	1896	TCD, Paris, London	Richmond & Mercer's	Cardiologist
Edward Freeman	1952–5	1890	UCD, Paris, London	Mater Misericordiae	Cardiologist
Francis O'Donnell	1955–8	1894	RCSI	Mercer's	Dermatologist
Patrick O'Farrell	1958–60	1889	RCSI, Liverpool	St Vincent's	Cardiologist
Robert Steen	1960–3	1902	TCD, London	Baggot St & Meath	Paediatrician
Brian Pringle	1963–6	1905	Cambridge, London	Mercer's & Dr Steevens'	Physician
Alan Thompson	1966–9	1906	TCD, London	St Lawrence's	Physician
David Mitchell	1969–72	1909	TCD, Johns Hopkins	Dr Steevens' & Adelaide	Dermatologist
William Jessop	1972–4	1902	TCD	Meath	Physician
Bryan Alton	1974–7	1919	UCD, Boston, Houston	Mater Misericordiae	Gastroenterologist
Alan Grant	1977–9	1918	QU Belfast	Belfast City	Physician

Note. The importance of TCD to the College in the early years of the new state is obvious. Note also the beginnings in the 1920s of the switch from Europe to the US as the preferred venue for post-graduate education, and the significant reduction in opportunities for general physicians.

Chapter Ten
The medical encounter today

'More medicine than ever before'

S OCIAL AND INTELLECTUAL change generally occurs imperceptibly, in a manner hardly visible to the eye, like the gradual transformation of a summer cloud. Little by little ideas and social customs mutate, each change resting on the last; the process is generally so incremental that only by looking back can we see how far we have come. This book has shown how greatly the medical encounter has changed from generation to generation, in parallel with the society in which the encounter took place. The period between 1975 and 2004 was no different.

At the simplest level, the Irish public at the beginning of the twenty-first century makes much more use of medical facilities than before. More hospital procedures are performed than ever before, more prescriptions written and medicine and medical matters are higher on the national agenda than ever. Over 100,000 people work in the healthcare services (of whom some 5,000 are doctors and 30,000 are nurses). Nearly 10 per cent of the national income is spent on health, a higher proportion than most other European countries (catching up, some said, for the neglect of previous decades). In 2002 the one-third of the population with medical cards (newly including the over-seventies) were provided with just under 30 million prescriptions—twenty years before approximately the same number of patients had to be content with a mere 11 million prescriptions.

Neo-natal intensive care in Holles Street (1996): the tiny patient is dwarfed by the machinery and the staff devoted to keeping him alive.

Health and poverty

Ever since William Wilde had made the facts so explicit in his 1851 Census report, the impact of poverty on patterns of health and sickness in Ireland has been well known. A recent report by the Public Health Alliance of Ireland makes it clear that the impact of poverty on health is still profound. For instance chronic physical illness is 2.5 times more likely for lower socio-economic status people than for the wealthy; death from cancer is four times greater and from stroke three time greater; men in unskilled jobs are twice as likely to die young as professionals; women in the unemployed socio-economic group are twice as likely to give birth to underweight babies than those in the higher professional group.[1] Not only does poverty deprive Irish people of economic goods and benefits, it impedes their life-chances as well. It remains a question how far the structure of the health service, notably its split into private and public delivery, will require to change if there is the political will to improve the health of the poorest citizens.

The broad classification of prescriptions handed out in 2002 to medical card holders gives us a guide to what the poorer part of the population was suffering from. (There is no separate count of the number of prescriptions supplied to the 46 per cent of the population with private medical insurance, or the very unhappily situated group with neither medical cards nor insurance.) Two-thirds of prescriptions related to heart conditions (including anti-cholesterol drugs), nervous system, digestion and chest problems (see Table 10.1).

Table 10. 1: GMS Distribution of medicines by classification (2002)

	Prescribing frequency (000s)	%
Cardiovascular system	6,900	23.28
Nervous system	6,067	20.47
Alimentary tract and metabolism	3,350	11.31
Respiratory system	2,387	8.05
Blood and blood-forming organs	2,218	7.49
Musculo-skeletal system	1,946	6.57
Anti-infectives for systemic use	1,898	6.4
Genito-urinary system	1,314	4.44
Dermatologicals	899	3.03
Systemic hormonal preparations	876	2.96
Sensory organs	790	2.67
Anti-neoplastic and immunomodulating agents	139	0.47
Anti-parasitic products	73	0.25
Various	772	2.61
Total prescriptions written	**29,629**	100

Source: General Medical Services (Payments) Board

The imposing façade of the modern hospital—Tallaght 2004

Although the Irish public made extensive use of the GP and other services, the hospital has consolidated its position as the locus *par excellence* of medicine. It is of course primarily a place of healing, but it is also for all doctors a place of training, for many of life-time employment and for citizens a monument of sociological and political importance. People nowadays go to hospitals (on their own behalf or visiting) more often than they go to church; the recurring thwarting by local political pressure of efforts to establish fewer 'centres of excellence', since the idea was mooted in the 1930s, is eloquent testimony of the community feeling the local hospital generates. Hospitals have definitively migrated from the converted town houses that they started in—their great campuses now dominate their neighbourhoods.

The Hospital Inpatient Enquiry found that 543,000 patients had stayed overnight in hospital in 2001—a total of 3.4m hospital nights at an average stay of just over six days. Four diagnostic categories contributed half of the list of reason for hospitalisation: firstly pregnancy and childbirth (1 in 6 of all hospital stays were for this), then problems related to the digestive system (1 in 8) and the circulatory system (1 in 9); further down the list were (in order) musculoskeletal, respiratory, nervous system, ear nose and throat disorders and so on. A further 205,000 day case procedures were performed in the country's hospitals. In the 1980s the Secretary of the Department of Health had marvelled that over half a million people had been discharged from hospital—the 2002 figure was nearly three-quarters of a million.

Despite a seemingly endless demand both at GP and hospital level for medical attention, market research suggests that fewer people in Ireland categorise their health as 'bad' or 'very bad' than anywhere in Europe, and more (81 per cent) report their health as 'good' or very good'.[2] On average nearly 12 per cent of Europeans (three times the Irish level) perceive their health to be bad or very bad. This may of course be no more than the callow optimism of youth, since Ireland certainly has a younger age-profile than other countries. Only one in 200 of 18–24 years olds in Ireland report their health as 'poor'. Not surprisingly it is this group that bothers their GPs the least; even so 1 in 8 reported visiting their GP within the previous fortnight, compared to 1 in 3 of the over-65s. The powerful impact of life-chances on health can be vividly seen from those groups reporting high levels of visits to GPs: frequent visitors included medical card holders, the widowed and separated, the unemployed and the over-65s.

The alternative challenge

The days when the doctor had sole access to a well of arcane information are over. In the past patients used their own and their family's information sources to assess their conditions. Now the range of advice sources includes (as the *BMJ* put it recently) 'medical and paramedical staff, relatives and friends, practitioners of complementary and alternative medicine, and the latest issue of *Cosmopolitan* magazine'.[3]

For many users, the medical encounter starts with web searches, which make available a flood of information, some of it appropriate, some not. Apart from bias, interest or error, perfectly correct information can be seriously misleading. For instance, because so much of the web is American-based, information about diseases is often posted with the needs of the US population in mind. Sarcoidosis, just to take a case, is particularly dangerous to African-Americans, to the extent of potentially losing limbs; it is much less serious for people from the North European gene pool. To allay fears in his patients, Professor Muiris Fitzgerald of St Vincent's has gone to the trouble of preparing a leaflet pointing out the different prognoses. Pin-point searches for information about a particular drug or diagnosis risk being interpreted completely out of context, and of ignoring the researcher's question: whose interest is being served in putting this information up?

In 1974 *The Irish Medical Times* looked back nostalgically at the era when 'the doctor's opinion, advice and indeed decisions' were rarely questioned. By 2004 that era was long over. Patients increasingly see themselves as consumers, more or less aggressively evaluating treatments, picking and choosing services, informing themselves. In the course of this process there has been mounted a fundamental challenge to the hegemony of orthodox biomedicine.

Following the trend in other Western economies, the market for alternative and complementary medicine has increased exponentially (see Table 10.2). In 2002 the Federation of Irish Complementary Therapy Associations claimed 'approximately 4,000' therapist members—considerably more than the 3,000 or

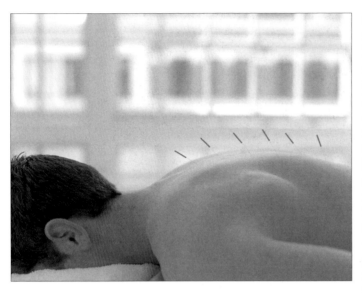

so GPs practising in the country, although the figure perhaps includes double counting of practitioners belonging to more than one Association.[4] Most of these practitioners explicitly or implicitly reject the basis of medicine practised since Koch and Pasteur, with its emphasis on specific invasions and lesions. Their 'holistic' ideal aspires to treat the body and the mind as one, reaching back to the eighteenth century concept exemplified by Laurence Sterne's metaphor of the mind and the body being like a jerkin and its

There are more practitioners of acupuncture in Dublin than any other complementary therapy.

lining—'rumple one and you rumple the other'. The common language of harnessing energy flows inside the body has an equally respectable pedigree.

Table 10.2: The rise of alternative and complementary medicine and counselling in Dublin 1975–2004

Alternative medical services*	1975	1985	1995	2004
Acupuncture		7	60	135
Aromatherapy			37	37
Chiropractic	1	6	27	76
Herbalism	1	1	9	15
Homeopathy		1	30	64
Hypnotism	2	6	28	86
Naturopathy		1	2	2
Osteopathy	4	4	20	27
Reflexology			28	77
Total	**8**	**26**	**241**	**519**
Counselling services*				
Counselling	2	20	172	331
Psychology/psychotherapy	3	7	93	155

* Many practitioners offer more than one service
Source: Golden Pages. The totals should be read as indicative only.

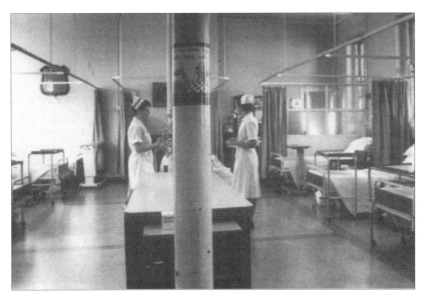

The accident ward in the Meath Hospital a hundred years on (see p. 121).

Despite their rejection of medical orthodoxy (or perhaps because of it), these practitioners clearly meet a strongly felt need. Patients are willing to suspend ordinary scepticism in accepting these treatments—perhaps the most astonishing feat is a revival of the ancient art of cupping (but using mugwort) under the name of moxibustion, backed with the authority of an ancient civilisation—China—that until it accepted some Western medicine had an average life expectancy of no more than 50 years. Many of the therapies evolved from the anti-intellectual alternative cultures of the 1970s. According to Professor Muiris Fitzgerald practitioners in his experience range from 'lovely starry-eyed people' to the 'seriously dotty, daft and dangerous who could mislead or harm vulnerable people.'[5]

The popularity of these new therapies, however, makes it clear that there are aspects of the conventional medical encounter that are failing to deliver expected benefits. Commentators have suggested that this is not so much at the purely medical level, as in human terms. Patients like to feel that they are more than the sum of a series of tests and measurements, and the alternative practitioners provide that attention. Even in purely medical terms sufferers from intractable lower back pain and other awkward ailments might be excused for trying alternatives. Furthermore, it is surely true, for instance, that armed with anti-inflammatory drugs some GPs have abandoned simple traditional alternatives such as massage and dietary advice for rheumatic complaints. The surging popularity of alternative treatments is paralleled by a similar growth in counselling services. Perhaps the two trends are simply a reaction in favour of autonomy, on the part of patients and parishioners alike, and away from the authoritarian style and oppressive rationality of both old-style medicine and old-style religion.

The range of possibilities is wide and increasing; apart from orthodox bio-medicine, the report by the Institute of Public Administration in 2002 identified over 30 separate active disciplines, from aromatherapy to vortex healing, including rebirthing, reiki, endorphin release therapy, aura soma, shiatsu and kiniesology.[6] It is common to move more or less uncritically between medical traditions, with little sense that the therapies might react against each other. Thus 'natural' drugs (which are understood to be simultaneously effective yet harmless) from the herbalist might be taken at the same time as prescribed drugs, typically without the knowledge of the GP. The 4th European Breast Cancer Conference was told in March 2004 that as many as 70 per cent of British breast cancer patients had compromised their chances of survival by using alternative remedies that either did not work or were positively harmful.[7] Studies confirmed that St John's Wort in particular could interact with prescribed drugs and possibly lead to adverse drug reactions.[8]

A wide-ranging eclecticism is reflected in the *Irish Times'* new *Health Supplement* (launched in 2004), which runs from articles about hip replacements and medical cards to fringe diagnoses such as 'Virtual Trauma' and Asperger's Syndrome to out and out fortune-telling (one woman was blandly reported to be using Tarot cards to recommend colonic irrigation and other procedures).

The media

The media ensures that health is constantly in the public eye by regular reporting of scientific medical research, often with sensational headlines—'New cancer breakthrough', or 'Eating our way to an early grave' (red meat linked to cancer of the colon . . .)—and over-emphatic summaries. In one issue of the *Irish Times'* *Health Supplement* for instance (29 June 2004), it was reported that Hungarian scientists had suggested that carrying mobile phones could cut male fertility by one-third; that watching too much TV could distort the hormonal balance of teenagers; that hormone replacement therapy increased the risk of heart attacks; and that drugs taken for Alzheimer Disease had little or no real effect. Some of this 'science' does not survive further scrutiny; it attracts a momentary headline, and some attention for the scientist or laboratory involved and that is all. The Oxford-based think tank Social Issue Research Council has even suggested that many of these stories are mainly to do with competition for funding by the health research and promotion industry.

The media also regularly reports (and it could be argued thus stimulates) an aggressive approach to litigation about alleged medical negligence, and equally aggressive 'doctor-bashing' from pressure groups, at least one of which was not ashamed to assimilate its cause to that of victims of the Holocaust by referring to its members as Survivors of Symphysiotomy. The heat generated against the profession by such groups is remarkable; letter-writers have bluntly referred to this procedure, and by implication the obstetricians themselves as 'barbarous'.[9]

The issues of retained organs and of blood transfusion have stimulated an equally distrusting, ill-informed and venomous rhetoric. For many doctors these are sad, besieged, days.

Despite this grumbling distrust (which has not prevented an enormous rise in demand for quite voluntary cosmetic surgery) in practice the profession is busier than ever. Not only that, but the disillusion of some of the established professionals does not seem to have affected the continuing high demand for places in the country's medical schools. In 2004 over 2,000 Leaving Certificate students applied for medicine, and medical courses (including physiology and pharmacy) were among the few for whom the points requirement continued to rise.

The College's response

The preceding chapters have made it clear that in the 350 years since its foundation by John Stearne, the College has waxed and waned in national importance. It was probably at its peak of national influence in the eighteenth century, when so many men of science and learning were attached to it. In the nineteenth century the College united the great men of the Irish School of Medicine. Stokes, Graves and Corrigan were all Presidents, and in the heroic days of the 1830s and 1840s faced the challenges presented by terrifying cholera outbreaks and famine-induced disease.

However, in the early twentieth 20th century the College, dominated as it still was by the Trinity-educated, largely Protestant, medical élite of the day, found trouble establishing itself in the social and political environment of the new state. It gently became little more than a private medical club, living off its prestige, with hardly enough income to maintain its once splendid premises. In 1963 there were only 160 Fellows, and the total College income (a low year) was a mere £4,924. As Alan Grant (President 1977–9) put it the College had to adapt or perhaps perish— 'the laws of the jungle apply to organisations as well as to persons'.[10] New leadership in the 1960s and 1970s initiated a re-invention, the success of which can be judged by the fact that in 2004 there are over 3,000 Members and 1,400 Fellows.

New Fellows, St Luke's Day 2000, the year John Hume was made an honorary fellow.
(Front row, left to right)
Jonathan Bailey (Secretary),
John Murphy (Treasurer),
Desmond Canavan (President),
T. Joseph McKenna (Registrar),
Ernest Egan (Vice-President).

Presidents of the College 1980–2004

Name	Date	Born	Educated	Hospital	Speciality
Dermot Holland	1980–2	1915	RCSI	Our Lady's Hosp. for Sick Children & Richmond	Pathology
John Kirker	1983–5	1922	TCD, Boston	Sir Patrick Dun's	Neurology
Ivo Drury	1986–8	1920	UCD	Mater Misericordiae	Diabetes/ Endocrinology
Ciaran Barry	1989–91	1928	UCD, London	Mater Misericordiae	Rheumatology
Stephen Doyle	1991–4	1929	UCD, Virginia, USA	Beaumont	Gastroenterology
Stanley Roberts	1994–7	1932	QU Belfast	Royal Victoria, Belfast	Rheumatology
Brian Keogh	1997–2000	1941	UCD	Tallaght	Nephrology
Desmond Canavan	2000–2003	1938	QU Belfast	NI Fever Hospital	Infectious Diseases
T. Joseph McKenna	2003–	1942	UCD	St Vincent's	Endocrinology

Stimulated by the example of the Royal College of Surgeons, the College began to develop its basic Membership examination in Ireland so that it has become the preferred route for post-graduate advancement, and overseas where it is now a valued qualification in over 40 countries. At the same time the College sponsored the establishment of a number of associated specialist associations, with responsibility for developing standards and requirements for its special areas.

The oldest of these was the Institute of Obstetrics and Gynaecology which was initiated in 1966 and was finally incorporated into the College in 1975. The Institute in fact evolved from one of the most active sections of the Royal Academy of Medicine in Ireland which was founded in the late nineteenth century as a purely scientific medical discussion body, and was extremely useful as such. In the modern era of international conferences, however, the Academy has changed its role. The first Faculty was that of Occupational Medicine (founded in 1975). The next Faculty to be founded was that of Public Health Medicine, originally Community Medicine, in 1976. This had long been a concern of an active group in the Academy. The largest of the Faculties, with over 220 members, is that of Pathology which was first mentioned in College minutes in 1977 and finally established in 1982. The Faculty of Paediatrics was set up in the same year. The wide catchment of these Faculties can be judged from the fact that there are, for instance, 165 members of the Institute of Obstetrics and Gynaecology, compared with 76 practising consultant obstetrician/gynaecologists in the Republic; similarly there are 157 members of the Faculty of Paediatrics and 73 practising consultants.

A major activity of the College is the setting and organising of examinations for students from all over the world.

The continuing path of medical education

The original aims of the College, enshrined in the Charter of 1669, were to promote learned medicine against the pretensions of quacks and 'other unskilful and illiterate practisers of physic', to protect the public against 'the frauds and deceits of empirics, apothecaries and druggists' and finally for 'the encouragement of the learned and experienced practitioners in physic . . . for the safety and benefit of [the King's] good subjects'.[11]

The College's modern interpretation of the Charter brief is to concentrate primarily on the establishment of standards, particularly in the development of advanced post-graduate specialist programmes. As the College's mission statement declares, its objective is to promote 'high professional standards in specialist medical practice in order to achieve optimum patient care and to promote the health of the population.' This involves both the training of new doctors and the maintenance of the highest standards among the qualified. The route-map on training is organised by the Irish Committee on Higher Medical Training, a committee which first saw the light of day in the early 1970s, and which represents the College and also the associated Faculties.

Under the auspices of the Medical Council, the College is delegated to design appropriate curricula for the 24 specialities (ranging alphabetically from cardiology to rheumatology) for which senior training is available in Ireland. The focus and symbol of this aspiration to excellence is the examinations set by the College at various levels and disciplines, and sat by more than 3,000 candidates every year.

Modern medical training in the Republic starts with science at school and of course, because of the continuing appeal of medicine, with very high Leaving Certificate points—in 2004 it was estimated that a successful student would require six A1 scores out of eight examinations. The five-year undergraduate course is followed by two six-month internship periods in hospital—six months in medicine and six months in surgery. After this intern year the doctor can apply for full registration with the Medical Council of Ireland.

At this point the young doctor has to choose. The broad division is between general practice, which is the destination for about half of Irish doctors, and hospital work generally in one speciality or another. The young would-be specialist practices at senior house officer level, which generally includes a number of months of exposure to 'acute unselected medical intake'. In general medicine this is extended to eighteen months out of the two years in the admission and follow-up of acute emergencies.

The College Membership examination, generally taken after two years at SHO level, is designed to mark the candidate's suitability for progressing to further specialist training and ultimately for consultant status. In Ireland higher medical training is conducted in the hospital grade of specialist registrar, posts of which are obtained by open competition. Each of the 24 programmes has its own specialist training curriculum lasting between four and seven years. The curriculum is drawn up by the relevant speciality group and is updated regularly. This training is always undertaken with an eye to the requirements of the international community, notably in the US and the UK, where many Irish specialists spend at least some time. On completion of the appropriate specialist training, a physician is then available to be included on the Specialist Registrar of the Medical Council.

A programme of continuous medical education for Fellows and Members of the College, and the associated Institute and Faculties, has been in place since 1995, overseen by the College's Education Committee.

Although the main thrust of the College's contribution has been in the specialist training as described, with the associated monitoring of the facilities provided by training hospitals, the complexity of the modern world of medicine has demanded other activities as well. Not least of these is understanding the requirements of the European Union in providing international standards for the profession, and ensuring that the programmes established for Irish doctors meet those standards. A relatively new development has been the building up of an advocacy role, with the College formulating and expressing its views on major medical issues. The recent release in relation to the Working Time Directive, for instance, was particularly well received, being described by the *Irish Medical Times* as both 'hard-hitting' and 'a badly needed dose of reality'.

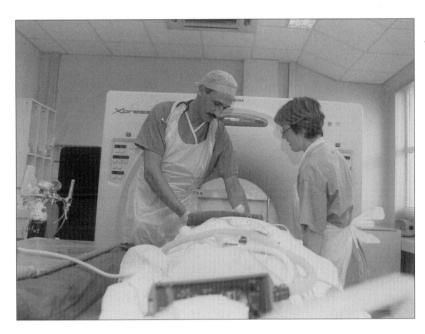

The highly technical face of modern anaesthesia (Tallaght Hospital).

The Irish body in the medical encounter

The medical encounter operates, as we have seen from generation to generation, in the context of well-known social, economic and class contraints. Less well known, however, is the context of deep, inherited attitudes to bodies as such—disabled, healthy, analysed, sexual, sick, reproductive, dead. Contemporary interpretations of bodies by both patient and doctor are signals of character and class and situation and are responded to as such. They are the bedrock of the medical encounter.

Unfortunately the glimpses we have obtained of the somatic experience in Ireland, the physical life of the body in the past, are fleeting. This is partly because our words for the experiences of the body—especially for colour, sensation and smell—are so subjective and so undeveloped. In the clinic patients grope towards a description of pain or discomfort with sadly imprecise vocabularies.

It has certainly not been the practice for doctors to describe in public their physical experience of doctoring. Jonah Barrington recorded that his disgust at human putridity prevented him becoming a surgeon, but normally such matters are concealed by a robust but ambiguous reticence—Lombe Atthill's shudder at the horrors of his youthful experience of surgery without anaesthetic is an exception.

Irish attitudes to the healthy body have long been somewhat shamefaced, a pudeur which was heavily reinforced in the Victorian era but which can be traced back to the eighteenth century. Even washing customs (including hair, teeth, genitals; washing places and water sources) are made obscure by Irish reticence on such subjects—compared say to the forthright French. This was influenced by the religious view that the body was primarily the vehicle for the soul and, as such, of notably lesser importance. It was, taught the Christian Brothers, 'a machine and a lovely clothing of the soul'. Young Catholics (and indeed young Protestants) were told that their body was 'the temple of the Holy Ghost',[12]. Chastity was proclaimed as the great glory of Irish womanhood. At the same time feats of self-harm such as those undertaken by Matt Talbot were lauded.[13]

The sick or unhealthy body is the one doctors have most to do with. In the clinic this is quickly objectivised to the measured body—weight, height, temperature, blood pressure, blood test, x-ray, MRI scan etc. So, when sick, even the squeamish patient takes an unwonted interest in the language of bowel movements, temperatures, test results. For the chronic sick, their illness becomes a part of the way they cope with the world—'my lumbago', 'my back', become almost separate members of the household, as, more sinisterly, does cancer .

The dying body was an object of great reverence, around which numerous rituals and 'scripts' evolved, many with a particular Irish character. The very first hospice for the dying in the English-speaking world was established in Dublin in 1879, and despite its name quickly established a reputation as a place of unexpected peace and consolation. We get some insight to continuing attitudes to the dead body in the fury aroused by body-snatchers in the eighteenth century, in Lady Horne's amputated leg being reunited with the rest of her body on her death in the early twentieth century, and the hurt and dismay aroused by the practice of organ retention.

However, the somatic experience of the past remains difficult to pin down. When Stearne and his contemporaries in the early College spoke of the ague causing 'great pain in the head and the bones', how are we to equate that to our own experience? In the mid eighteenth century the Hospital for Incurables in Donnybrook was established with, among its explicit objectives, that of freeing the public 'from those disagreeable sights [deforming cancerous or tubercular growths etc.] so frequently heretofore met with in our streets'. They had presumably been taken for granted beforehand. Research suggests that the French upper classes first became intolerant of strong smells in the second half of the eighteenth century. It would be interesting to confirm a similar increment of sensitivity (the precursor to miasma theory) in Ireland, where in fact David MacBride, a Fellow of the College, in his explorations of the mechanism of putrefaction had laid some of the ground.[14] We do not know if the nineteenth-century dispensary doctor took human smells in his stride—or was he as nauseated as his twentieth-century counterpart presented with a sick baby misguidedly left unwashed perhaps for days?

Happily the exploration of these elusive aspects of the history of medicine in Ireland is for another book.

Notes and References

Chapter 1

1   *Forum* April 1994.
2   O. W. Holmes 'Currents and counter-currents in medical science' in *Medical Essays* Boston, 1891.
3   R. Porter 'What is disease?' in R. Porter (ed.) *Cambridge Illustrated History of Medicine* Cambridge: Cambridge University Press, pb, 2001, 97.
4   T. Farmar *Holles Street: The National Maternity Hospital—A Centenary History 1894–1994* Dublin: A. & A. Farmar, 1994, 74.
5   H. Hinkson *Golden Lads and Girls* London: Downes, nd [1890s], 171.
6   J. O'Connell *Doctor John—Crusading Doctor and Politician* Dublin: Poolbeg Press, 1989, 6–7.
7   T. Farmar *Ordinary Lives* Dublin: Gill & Macmillan, hb, 1991; pb Dublin: A. & A. Farmar, 1997.
8   L. Sterne *Tristram Shandy* London: J. M. Dent, (Everyman Edition) 1961, Book III, Chap. IV.
9   W. Stokes *Lectures on Fever* London: Longmans, 1874, 152. It should be said that Stokes was quite old at this time, and his opinion was probably a minority one.
10 W. Osler in Countess of Aberdeen (ed.) *Ireland's Crusade against Tuberculosis* Dublin: Maunsel, 1908, Vol. I, 19–20.
11 O. St. J. Gogarty quoted in J. B. Lyons *Oliver St John Gogarty* Dublin: Blackwater Press, 1980, 65.
12 W. R. F. Collis *The State of Medicine in Ireland* Dublin: Parkside Press, 1943, 16.
13 See J. Le Fanu *The Rise and Fall of Modern Medicine* London: Little, Brown, 1999, xviii–xx.

Chapter 2

1   The intellectual framework of this chapter comes from A. Wear *Knowledge and Practice in English Medicine 1550–1680* Cambridge: Cambridge University Press 2000.
2   D. Le Clerk *The History of Physick* translated by Dr Drake and Dr Baden, London: 1699, 207.
3   J. Swift *Gulliver's Travels* (orig. Dublin, 1726) London: Nonsuch Press, 1963, Part IV, Chapter V. Gulliver, it will be remembered, was a surgeon by profession.
4   L. G. Stevenson 'New Diseases in the Seventeenth Century' *Bulletin of the History of Medicine*, Vol. XXXIX (1965) 1–21.
5   A. R. Hall *Henry More and the Scientific Revolution* Cambridge: Cambridge University Press, pb, 1990, 115, 118. More was a great believer in witches and ghosts.

He became in 1666 co-author of *Saducismus Triumphatus* which reiterated the traditional belief in such matters. This book was an important influence on the American divine Cotton Mather, who was deeply involved in the Salem witch trials.

6   J. Pafford *John Clavell 1601–43 Highwayman, Author, Lawyer, Doctor* Oxford: Leopard's Head Press, 1993, 241. This was clearly magical—for instance, if the rag was taken out of the water and dried in the sun or at a fire 'the party [suffers] infinite torments'.

7   D. Macleane *A History of Pembroke College Oxford* Oxford: Oxford Historical Society, 1897, 221; M. Davidson *Medicine in Oxford* Oxford: Blackwell, 1953, 35.

8   Davidson *op. cit.* 36–7.

9   T. W. Belcher *Memoir of John Stearne M & JUD SFTCD* Dublin: Falconer, 1865, 14–15, 32–8.

10   G. Clark *History of the Royal College of Physicians of London* Vol. 1, Oxford: Clarendon Press, 1964, 50.

11   Trinity College Register, quoted in J. D. H. Widdess *A History of the Royal College of Physicians of Ireland 1654–1963* Edinburgh: Livingstone, 1963, 9–10.

12   Widdess *op. cit.* 10, 29. In 1687 Trinity College refused to accept the election of John Crosby as President of the College partly because he was 'not of the Established religion'; however, this by no means necessarily implies, as Widdess assumes, that he was a Catholic.

13   J. Brady and A. Simms *Dublin Through Space and Time* Dublin: Four Courts Press, 2001, 65.

14   Cited in R. Porter (ed.) *Cambridge Illustrated History of Medicine* Cambridge: Cambridge University Press, 1996, 9.

15   W. Petty *Observations on the Dublin Bills of Mortality* London, 1683.

16   J. Graunt *Natural and Political Observations . . . Upon the Bills of Mortality* 1676, quoted in Weare *op. cit.* 107. It is believed that Petty contributed largely to Graunt's book.

17   *The Census of Ireland for the Year 1851* Dublin: HMSO, 1856, Part V, Vol. I, Tables of Deaths, Dublin: HMSO 1856 Vol. I 504.

18   C. V. Wedgewood *Thomas Wentworth First Earl of Strafford 1593–1641* London: Jonathan Cape, pb, 1964, 166, 205, 288.

19   *Analectica Hibernica* No. 4, 21; *Petty Papers* Vol. II, 221; *Orrery Papers* 293; *Journal of the Royal Society of Antiquarians of Ireland* Vol. II, 418. See also E. MacLysaght *Social Life in Seventeenth-Century Ireland* Cork: Cork University Press, 1950.

20   Wear *op. cit.* 213.

21   C. Archer *A Course of Lectures on the Natural History, Composition, Operations, Doses etc. of Various Medicines used in the Practice of Surgery Compiled for the use of Pupils of the Royal College of Surgeons in Ireland* Dublin: 1791, 2–3.

22   Uroscopy, diagnosis by examination of urine, was perfectly respectable at this time, though it became discredited in the eighteenth century.

23   This manuscript, with its obvious Irish connections, found its way to the public library in Tarbes in the South of France and was published in 2000 in Paris by

Editions du Laquet.

24 Wellcome Library MS: Boyle family receipt book. The book is clearly written by two hands (mother and daughter?). This is evidently a general Boyle family recipe book, and receipt 15 makes a reference to Lady Ranelagh as if she were not the author at least of that recipe; receipt 53, *per contra*, in the older hand, says 'To make [?] of roses my brother Robert Boyls way'. The older writer tends to be more magical and more boosterish in commending the recipes.

25 D. Buchan *Folk Tradition and Folk Medicine in Scotland: The Writings of David Rorie* Edinburgh: Canongate Press, 1994, 101.

26 S. Tissot *Advice to the People in General with Regard to their Health* translated by J. Kirkpatrick; Dublin Edition 1766, para 248.

27 R. Burton *The Anatomy of Melancholy* London: 1626, Part 2, Sec. 1, Mem. 4, Subs. 2. Marsh's Library has two editions of Burton's *Anatomy*, dated 1628 and 1660.

28 In 1644, while Stearne was still in Cambridge, the Hebrew scholar Sir John Lightfoot wrote that 'man was created by the Trinity on October 23, 4004 B.C., at nine o'clock in the morning.' In his *Annals of the World* (1658) Archbishop Ussher corrected this by a few days, placing the creation of the world ('and the evening and morning were the first day') to 23 October.

29 Wear *op. cit.* 173.

30 Molyneux to Locke 17 August 1692, quoted in K. Dewhurst *John Locke, Physician and Philosopher* London: Wellcome Historical Medical Library, 1963, 309.

31 Gerald Boate was a Dutch physician brought over from England during the Cromwellian period. His *Ireland's Naturall History* was published in 1652 by Samuel Hartlib, an active promoter of intellectual schemes, and a friend and patron of William Petty. As the title page announces, the book was published 'for the common good and more especially for the benefit of the Adventurers and Planters'.

32 W. Brereton *Travels in Holland, the United Provinces, England, Scotland and Ireland 1634–5* quoted in J. Harrington (ed.) *The English Traveller in Ireland* Dublin: Wolfhound Press, 1991, 113–4.

33 *Census 1851 op. cit.* Tables of Deaths.

34 M. Kelly *A History of the Black Death in Ireland* Stroud: Tempus, 2001, 148.

35 Burton *op. cit.* Part 1, Sec. 1, Mem. 1, Subs 1.

36 *Ibid.* Part 2, Sec. 1, Mem. 3.

37 *Ibid.* Part 2, Sec. 1, Mem. 2.

Chapter 3

1 When they re-emerged at the end of the nineteenth century they were the province of poets and fantasists, not scientists.

2 This *Pharmacopoeia* was originally compiled by the London College of Physicians, and was published in Dublin in 1746.

3 B. FitzGerald (ed.) *Correspondence of Emily Duchess of Leinster 1731–1814* Dublin:

Irish Manuscripts Commission, 3 vols, 1949–57, Vol. I, 61, 17 April 1759.

4   R. McDowell and D. Webb *Trinity College Dublin 1592–1952* Cambridge: Cambridge University Press, 1982.

5   T. W. Belcher *Memoir of Sir Patrick Dun* Dublin: Hodges Smith, 1866, 18–19.

6   *A Directory of Dublin for the Year 1738* Dublin: Dublin Corporation Public Libraries, 2000.

7   P. Fagan *Catholics in a Protestant Country: The Papist Constituency in Eighteenth-Century Dublin* Dublin: Four Courts Press, 1998, 77–100, at 84.

8   E. Underwood *Boerhaave's Men at Leyden and After* Edinburgh: Edinburgh University Press, 1977, 147.

9   H. Dingwall *History of Scottish Medicine* Edinburgh: Edinburgh University Press, 2003, 106.

10   H. Boerhaave *Treatise on the Powers of Medicines* translated by J. Martin, London, 1740, 77–79.

11   E. Foster *Essay on Hospitals* Dublin, 1768, Appendix, 16.

12   FitzGerald *op. cit.* Vol. III, 423, 12 April 1794.

13   S. A. Tissot *Advice to the People in General with regard to their Health* translated by J. Kirkpatrick, Dublin: 1766, Sec. 21.

14   S. Tillyard *Aristocrats* London: Vintage, pb, 1995, 54.

15   FitzGerald *op. cit.,* Vol. I, 10,10 May 1755.

16   *Ibid.* Vol. II, 301, 1 Dec. 1779.

17   Anon [Robert Doussie] *Theory and Practice of Chirurgical Pharmacy* Dublin: George & Alexander Ewing, 1761, 4.

18   Boerhaave *op. cit.*

19   Anon [Doussie] *op. cit.* 9.

20   *Ibid.* 1.

21   A. Day (ed.) *Mary Delany's Letters from Georgian Ireland 1731–68* Belfast: Friar's Bush Press, 1991, 82–3.

22   M-L Legg (ed.) *The Synge Letters* Dublin: Lilliput Press, 1996, 484.

23   Day *op. cit.,* 82–3.

24   FitzGerald *op. cit.* Vol. I, 416, 10 Oct. 1764.

25   M.Wortley Montagu *Letters* London: J. M. Dent (Everyman Edition) [1906], 123–4, 1 April 1717.

26   A-H Maehle 'Conflicting Attitudes towards Inoculation in Enlightenment Germany' in R. Porter (ed.) *Medicine in the Enlightenment* Amsterdam: Rodopi, 1995, 203–4.

27   J. Gregory *Practice of Physic* London, 1788, par. 387.

28   J. Swift *Gulliver's Travels* (orig. Dublin: 1726) London: Nonsuch Press, 1963, Part IV 'Voyage to the Houyhnhnms' Chapter IV, 248.

29   Quoted in D. and R. Porter *Patient's Progress* Cambridge: Polity Press, 1989, ref. 44.

30   B. Robinson *Observations on the Virtues and Operations of Medicines* Dublin, 1752, 146–165.

31   FitzGerald *op. cit.* Vol. I, 898, 17 May, 1759.

32 Legg *op. cit.* 460.

33 Foster *op. cit.* 18.

34 T. Sydenham 'Of Epidemic diseases' *Works* London, 5, 5.

35 FitzGerald *op. cit.* Vol. 1, 555, 10 December 1768.

36 Legg *op. cit.* 283.

37 W. Buchan *Domestic Medicine* Edinburgh: 1769; Dublin: 1781, 98.

38 Foster *op. cit.* 37.

39 L. Sterne *Tristram Shandy* London: J. M. Dent, (Everyman Edition) 1961, Book III, Chap. IV. Sterne, who was distantly related to John Stearne, spent the first ten years of his life in Ireland.

40 Legg *op. cit.* 5–6. Five of the bishop's six children predeceased him, as did his wife.

41 G. Cheyne *The English Malady, or a Treatise of Nervous Diseases of all Kinds etc.* Dublin: reprinted by S. Powell for Risk, Ewing, Smith, 1733, 2.

42 *Dublin Courant* 15 July 1749.

43 Day *op. cit.* 8 Aug. 1758. Arquebuzade is a vulnerary (wound-water) made of rosemary, thyme and other herbs and proof spirit which she would have made up in advance. The black plaster was probably made of seaweed or sphagnum moss.

44 T. Bonner *Becoming a Physician—Medical Education in Britain, France, Germany and the United States 1750–1945* Baltimore: Johns Hopkins University Press, pb, 2000, 48.

45 N. M. Cummins *Some Chapters of Cork Medical History* Cork: Cork University Press, 1957, 11. One of the physicians, Dr Hugh Farmar, was my direct ancestor.

46 Foster *op. cit.* 31.

47 A. Browne *Masters, Midwives and Ladies in Waiting* Dublin: A. & A. Farmar, 1995, 22.

48 Widdess *op.cit.* 28.

49 D. Ó Raghallaigh *Three Centuries of Irish Chemistry* Cork: Cork University Press, 1941, 5–6. I am grateful to Dr Charles Mollan for this reference.

Chapter 4

1 J. Barrington *Personal Sketches of My Own Times* Dublin, 1827, 3rd ed., Vol. I, Chapter VII.

2 The first appearance of the name Hodges on the Dublin bookselling scene was as Gilbert's partner, in a shop in Dame Street. Hodges Figgis later became publishers to the University of Dublin (TCD).

3 L. MacNally *The Justice of the Peace for Ireland* Dublin, 1812, Vol. II, 126–7.

4 *The Lancet* 1829, 1830, quoted in J. D. H. Widdess *History of the Royal College of Physicians of Ireland* Edinburgh: Livingstone, 1963, 37.

5 J. O'Connell *Doctor John* Dublin: Poolbeg Press, 1989, 23.

6 A. Lyons & R. Petrucelli *Medicine: An Illustrated History* New York: Abrahams, 1978, 90, 147, 298.

7 Widdess 1963 *op. cit.* 35.

8 J. Stronge *Andrew Horne: Thirty Years a Master* Dublin: A. & A. Farmar, 1999, 21–2.

9 J. Fleetwood *The Irish Body Snatchers* Dublin: Tomar, 1988, 39. Doctors themselves have often been unenthusiastic about allowing their own bodies to be dissected. In his history of the RCSI (see ref. below) Sir Charles Cameron records how Sir Philip Crampton insisted that his body be encased in cement before interment (357).

10 C. Cameron *History of the Royal College of Surgeons in Ireland* Dublin: Fannin, 1886, 108. In practice the syllabus may not have been as daunting as it appeared. Cameron points out that of the 110 candidates between 1766 and 1796 94 passed, 3 failed for lack of knowledge and 13 because of technical difficulties with indentures.

11 Widdess 1963 *op. cit.* 33.

12 *Instructions from the Army Medical Board of Ireland to Regimental Surgeons serving on that Establishment for regulating the Concerns of the Sick and of the Hospital* Appendix XII. Note the absence of the cautery, traditionally used for the arrest of haemorrhage.

13 E. Foster *Essay on Hospitals* Dublin: W. G. Jones 1768, 61.

14 F. Burney, quoted in D. J. Enright (ed.) *Ill at Ease* London: Faber & Faber, 1989, 133–4.

15 Sir Philip Crampton's 1835 lecture quoted by J. D. H. Widdess in *The Royal College of Surgeons in Ireland and its Medical School* Dublin: RCSI, 3rd ed., 1984, 84.

16 Foster *op. cit.* App. 17.

17 C. Archer *Course of Lectures* Dublin, 1791, 14.

18 *Ibid.* 14 .

19 J. B. Lyons *A Pride of Professors* Dublin: A. & A. Farmar, 1999, 7.

20 Robert Addis Emmett senior was State Physician from 1770 to 1803; as such he was ex-officio physician to Swift's Hospital where he was a major influence in the late eighteenth century. His other son, Thomas Addis, was also a physician, having graduated in Edinburgh, which had taken over from Leiden and Reims in popularity as a medical college. In his history of the Royal College of Surgeons in Ireland Sir Charles Cameron says that 237 Irishmen took medical degrees in Edinburgh between 1775 and 1800 (as compared to 179 Scots and 217 English).

21 C. Ó Gráda *Ireland: A New Economic History 1780–1939* Oxford: Oxford University Press, pb, 1994, 28, 293.

22 Quoted in L. Clarkson & M. Crawford *Feast and Famine* Oxford: Oxford University Press, 2001, 74–5.

23 Figures from the listings in the *Triple Almanack* 1805.

24 Widdess 1963, 59, 88; E. Bishop *The World of Mary O'Connell* Dublin: Lilliput Press, 1999, 7.

25 M. Tuomy *A Treatise on the Principal Diseases of Dublin* Dublin: William Folds, 1810, 10.

26 *Ibid.* 137.

27 W. Buchan *Domestic Medicine.* First published in Edinburgh 1769, Irish edition 1781, last reprinted Boston 1913.

28 Barrington *op. cit.* 30–41.

29 Dineen glosses collough (recte *cailleach)* as 'a veiled woman, a nun, a hag' and *cail-leaca cartaí* as women who tell fortunes by cards.

30 W. Wilde 'A short account of the superstitions and popular practices relating to midwifery and some of the diseases of women and children in Ireland' *Monthly Journal of Medical Science* (Edinburgh) May 1849, 713.

31 Barrington *op. cit.* 78–9.

32 R. Graves *Clinical Lectures on the Practice of Medicine* Dublin: Fannin, 1848, 113.

33 B. FitzGerald (ed.) *Correspondence of Emily Duchess of Leinster 1731–1814* Dublin: Irish Manuscripts Commission 1949, Vol. I, 10 Jan. 1760, 270.

34 *Ibid.* Vol. III, 12 April 1794, 422.

35 Bishop *op. cit.* 142.

36 *Ibid.* 59.

37 *Ibid.* 134.

38 W. Harty *Medical Report of the Institution for the Relief of the Sick Poor* Dublin: Downes, 1808, 15.

39 Widdess 1963 *op. cit.* 88.

40 *Medical and Chirurgical Review* Vol. XIV Jan.–June 1807, xxix, liii. These comments were in response to a questionnaire aimed at regulating the medical profession.

41 'Is there no balm in Gilead; is there no physician there? Why then is not the health of the daughter of my people recovered?' Jeremiah 8:22.

42 E.g. T. Short 'On the Dublin Bills, Air, Weather, Meteors' in *New Observations on the City, Town and Country Bills of Mortality* London: Longman, 1750, 242.

43 'Remarks on the Shortness of Human Life' *Freeman's Journal* 24 April 1804. The category 'other diseases' apparently accounts for 283 people and would include violent deaths such as accidents and suicides. No indication is given as to what the figures are based on—they are perhaps no more than intelligent guesswork.

44 Bishop *op. cit.* 134.

45 M. Lenox-Conyngham (ed.) *Diaries of Ireland* Dublin: Lilliput Press, 1998, 143.

46 Bishop *op. cit.* 139.

47 Trinity College Dublin Manuscripts 4192–4198. Crampton was Surgeon-General, and in 1815 was the subject of a complaint to the College that he had been called in to a case 'without the necessity of a surgical operation', thus putting the physicians on the case in an awkward position. (Widdess *RCPI* 132–3). His main appointment was as surgeon to the Meath, a position he held for nearly 60 years.

48 S. Le Fanu *In a Glass Darkly* London: John Lehmann, 1947, 73.

49 O. Goldsmith *She Stoops to Conquer* Act II Scene 1.

50 Tuomy *op. cit.* 137, 205.

51 T. Mills *Essay on Blood-letting in Fever* Dublin: Gilbert & Hodges, 1813, 222.

52 FitzGerald *op.cit.* Vol. III, 12 April 1794, 422. Gout was believed to attack only the upper classes; in his description in *The Principal Diseases of Dublin*, drawn from experiences in the Dublin General Dispensary, Martin Tuomy does not mention gout at all.

53 D. Corrigan *Lectures on the Nature and Treatment of Fever* Dublin: Fannin, 1853, 2.

54 Tuomy *op. cit.* 117.

55 The Sick Poor Institution was founded in 1794 and was subsumed into the new Poor Law structures in the 1830s.

56 First published in Edinburgh 1769, Irish edition 1781, last reprinted Boston 1913.

57 R. Graves *Clinical Lectures on the Practice of Medicine* Dublin: Fannin 1848. The balance were lectures on gout, nervous diseases, five on venereals, apoplexy, rheumatism, and headaches of young women ('no cases prove more troublesome to the practitioner' he writes hinting at a world of psycho-social distress).

58 *Ibid.* 34.

59 W. Stoker *A Treatise on Fever* London: Longman, 1815.

60 *Ibid.* 17.

61 B. Welsh *Practical Treatise on Bloodletting* Irish edition: Dublin: Hodges & M'Arthur, 1819, 9.

62 *Ibid.* 83, 153.

63 'It is surprising how well the poor of Dublin bear this all-powerful remedy: how much beyond their brethren in the sister kingdom', W. Harty *op. cit.* In a later generation bloodletting became the favourite country remedy for all sorts of ills. The Scottish physician Benjamin Welsh claimed that the English were 'naturally adverse' to bloodletting, and to excuse themselves invented the concept of 'nervous fever'. *Op. cit.* 111.

64 Harty *op. cit.* 10.

65 Tuomy *op. cit.* 264.

66 Mills *op. cit.* table opp. 220, 5.

67 *Ibid.* 5.

68 Widdess *op. cit.* 112–5.

69 W. Moore 'Statistical view of the frequency in which the principal medicines used during the last sixty years have been prescribed' *Dublin Journal of Medical Science* Vol. 10, 1836, 24–29. Moore's son John was President of the College 1898–9.

70 The quotation about Jalap is from Dunglison's *Dictionary of Medical Science* Philadelphia: Lea and Blanchard, 1848, Dr Fleetwood Churchill's copy.

71 W. Stokes *Lectures on Fever* London: Longmans, Green, 1874, 10.

72 R. Carmichael quoted by J. Widdess 1984 *op. cit.* half-title verso.

Chapter 5

1 L. Atthill *Recollections of an Irish Doctor* London: Religious Tract Society, 1911, 119.

2 D. Coakley *The Irish School of Medicine* Dublin: Town House, 1988, 101–2.

3 Elizabeth Smith Diaries, May 1878. Selections from this extensive dairy have been published as *The Highland Lady in Ireland*, and more, describing her life in the 1850s, are forthcoming. The entire diary has been transcribed by Elizabeth McRory, the present owner of Baltiboys House, to whom I am grateful for providing me with

specifically medical references.

4   The child, Prince Leopold (1853–84), suffered from the haemophilia by which Queen Victoria's descendants disrupted the royal families of Europe.

5   *Dublin Medical Press* 22 November 1854, 326.

6   R. Butcher *Essays and Reports on Operative and Conservative Surgery* Dublin: Fannin 1865, 261.

7   O'D. Browne *The Rotunda Hospital 1745–1945* Edinburgh: Livingstone, 1947, 105. The early thermometers were very slow to record temperature. To obviate patient concern a clinical thermometer was available that could only be read from behind.

8   *Dublin Medical Press* Vol. XXXII, 4.

9   This dictionary, edited by R. Dunglison MD and published in Philadelphia, belonged to the Dublin obstetrician and Fellow of the College, Dr Fleetwood Churchill, author of *The Diseases of Children* (1849).

10 R. Graves *Clinical Lectures on the Practice of Medicine* Dublin: Fannin, 1848, 238–41.

11 F. Meenan *Cecilia Street: The Catholic University Medical School 1855–1931* Dublin: Gill & Macmillan, 1987, 5–6.

12 *Ibid.* 38.

13 See D. Murphy *Ireland and the Crimean War* Dublin: Four Courts Press, 2002, Chapter 4.

14 S. Brown 'British Army Surgeons Commissioned 1840–1909 with West Indian/West African Service' in *Medical History* Vol. 37 (1993), 411–31.

15 *Dublin Medical Press* 16 March 1853.

16 A. Knox *Irish Watering Places* Dublin: William Curry, 1845, 217.

17 *Dublin Medical Press* 19 July 1854.

18 H. Dingwall *A History of Scottish Medicine* Edinburgh: Edinburgh University Press, 2003, 127, 197. St Andrew's at this time offered no clinical training whatsoever, and between 1836 and 1862 awarded nearly 2,000 postal degrees.

19 This represents an average of 954 'services' a month, a bit more than the 716 'services' undertaken by Dr James Deeny and his partner in January 1972 in the generally healthy district of Fanad Co. Donegal (see Chapter 8). On the other hand, in 1972 47 per cent of 'services' were home visits, compared to 18 per cent in 1854.

20 Of the 1,490 Irish practitioners listed in the *Medical Directory* of 1852, 290 worked alone. A further 114 towns had two practitioners, very often with the same surname.

21 C. Lever *Barrington* New York: Pratt, 1862, 20.

22 J. Cusack & W. Stokes 'On the mortality of medical practitioners in Ireland' *Dublin Quarterly Journal of Medical Science* Vol. V, Feb. and May 1848, 119.

23 *Census of Ireland 1851* Dublin: HMSO, Part V, Tables of Death, Vol. I, 404.

24 Dr Joseph Pratt quoted in W. Stokes *Lectures on Fever* London: Longmans, 1874, 72.

25 Cusack & Stokes *op. cit.* 113–4. When the income tax was extended to Ireland in 1853 the IMA made a valiant but unavailing attempt to achieve exemption for dispensary doctors on the grounds of the real dangers of general and fever practice. In his acerbic way Arthur Jacob declared that the real reason for the protest was that

doctors did not want to reveal their true income lest people would conclude that a man earning only £100 a year must be a poor doctor. *Dublin Medical Press,* 1853, 298.

26 See for instance *Dublin Medical Press* 9 Feb.1853, 14 Sept. 1853.

27 J. Newman 'Christianity and Medical Science' in *University Subjects discussed in occasional Lectures and Essays* London: 1858.

28 *Dublin Medical Press* June 1853.

29 Smith Diaries 31 Aug. 1853.

30 *Op. cit.* 1 Nov. 1840.

31 *Ibid.* 19 Sept. 1852.

32 An article in the *Annual Register* for 1854 recorded that death did not occur, as had traditionally been believed, at 'the turning o' the tide' (e.g. Falstaff's death in *Henry V* Act II Scene 3) but usually between 5 and 6 am and generally between 2 and 10 am.

33 Smith Diaries *op. cit.* 15 Aug. 1852.

34 D. Corrigan *Lectures on Fever* Dublin: Fannin, 1853, 22–3.

35 Smith Diaries *op. cit.* 27 Nov., 5 Dec. 1851.

36 *Ibid.* 7 March 1842.

37 W. McCormack *Sheridan Le Fanu and Victorian Ireland* Oxford: Clarendon Press, 1980, 128.

38 Smith *op. cit.* 29 April 1852.

39 I. Paisley *The Fifty-nine Revival* Belfast: Free Presbyterian Church of Ulster, 1958, 163.

40 P. Darragh 'Epidemiological observations on episode of communicable psychogenic illness': unpublished D. Phil. thesis submitted to the Queen's University of Belfast 1988, Chap. XV.

41 'Epidemics of the famine years' *Dublin University Magazine* December 1852.

42 Diary of Ellen Palmer of Rush quoted by J. Robins *The Miasma—Epidemic and Panic in Nineteenth-century Ireland* Dublin: Institute of Public Administration, 1995, 144–8.

43 J. Neligan 'Cholera' in *Dublin Quarterly Journal of Medical Science* Vol. XIX, Feb. & May 1855, 153. Neligan had MDs from Edinburgh and Trinity, was a Fellow of the College, editor of the *Quarterly Journal* and also of Robert Graves' *Clinical Lectures.*

44 Smith Diaries *op. cit.* 9 Sept. 1849.

45 As for instance in Neligan 'Cholera' (see above, 153).

46 *Dublin Quarterly Journal of Medical Science* Vol. XIX Feb. & May 1855, 166.

47 W. Stokes *Lectures on Fever* J. Moore (ed.) London: Longmans Green, 1874, 4–5, 17. Stokes died in 1878.

48 J. Babbington 'Bleeding by village practitioners' *Dublin Journal of Medical Science* Vol X (1836) 404–10.

49 W. Stokes *Lecture to the Students of the Meath Hospital* Dublin: Fannin, 1847.

50 R. Lyons *Apology for the Microscope* Dublin: Fannin, 1851.

51 J. D. H. Widdess *The Royal College of Surgeons in Ireland and its Medical School*

1784–1984 Dublin: RCSI [1984], 160.

52 T. G. Wilson *Victorian Doctor* London: Methuen, 1942, 38, 233.

53 A. Corley *Fifty Years of Surgical Progress* Dublin: Falconer, 1888.

54 Browne *op. cit.* 141.

Chapter 6

1 *Dublin Quarterly Journal of Medicine* April 1905, 302–5. Sir John's first contribution to the *Dublin Quarterly Journal of Medical Science* (which he subsequently edited from 1874 to 1920) was 'Mean temperature in its relation to disease and mortality' published in August 1869.

2 W. Osler in Countess of Aberdeen (ed.) *Ireland's Crusade against Tuberculosis* Dublin: Maunsel, 1908, Vol. I, 19–20.

3 E. Culverwell 'Tuberculosis and Consumption' *Dublin Journal of Medical Science* 1903, 91–107.

4 Aberdeen *op. cit.* Vol. I, 35.

5 *Ibid.* Vol. III, 40.

6 R. Tobin 'The bearing of tuberculosis on the condition of Ireland' in Aberdeen *op. cit.* 50. He retorted 'Do you believe all you see through your spectacles?'

7 Aberdeen *More Cracks with 'we twa'* London: Methuen, 1929, 162.

8 Aberdeen *Ireland's Crusade* Vol. I, 80.

9 *Ibid.* Vol. III, 41. The success of the campaign was such that a generation later an etiquette manual declared: 'It is excessively rude and offensive to spit on the floor, or into the fire, or even on the footways in the street. To spit on the floor in church is irreverent as well as rude.' Christian Brothers *Christian Politeness and Counsels for Youth* Dublin: Gill, 1934, 89. The health aspect had by then been converted into a moral or aesthetic commandment.

10 Aberdeen *Ireland's Crusade* Vol. II, 70.

11 Culverwell *op. cit.* 98–9.

12 This was the regime preferred by Dr Walther of Nordach, the leader in the sanatorium movement. As *The Magic Mountain* makes clear, Davos was more liberal. 'These objections', wrote Alfred Parsons, physician to the sanatorium at Newcastle, 'do not carry much weight in sanatoriums for the poor, where all belong to the same class and the majority to the same religion.' *Ireland's Crusade* Vol. II, 50.

13 Aberdeen *Ireland's Crusade* Vol. II, 48–9.

14 H. Burke *The Royal Hospital Donnybrook* Dublin: Royal Hospital, 1993, 181–2.

15 See R. Schofield *et al. The Decline of Mortality in Europe* Oxford: Clarendon Press, 1991.

16 J. Moore 'Clinical Case-taking' in *Dublin Journal of Medical Science* Vol. CXX, (July –Dec. 1895), 392. Moore was quoting, with approval, an article in the British publication *The Practitioner.*

17 See C. Ó Grada *Ireland: A New Economic History 1780–1939* Oxford: Oxford

University Press, pb 1994, 379–382.

18 F. Pim *The Health of Dublin* Dublin: Webb, 1891, 30, 1892, 5.

19 A. Meldon *An Address on Cancer delivered at the opening session 1901–2 in Jervis Street Hospital* Dublin: Sealy Bryers & Walker, 1902.

20 Registrar-General *Special Report on Cancer in Ireland* 1903.

21 Dr L. Symes 'Report of a Country Dispensary' in *Dublin Journal of Medical Science* Vol. CI Jan.–June 1896, 259–267, 350–357.

22 F. Cruise 'Hypnotism' in *Dublin Journal of Medical Science* May 1891, 377–396.

23 According to an article by George Bertrin in the 1910 *Catholic Encyclopaedia.*

24 Quoted in M. McCarthy *Priests and People* Dublin: Hodges Figgis, 1902, 248.

25 M. F. Reaney *The Medical Profession* (Carmichael Prize Essay) Dublin: Browne & Nolan 1905, 103.

26 Burke *op. cit.* 154.

27 W. R. F. Collis *To Be a Pilgrim* London: Secker & Warburg, 1975, 3.

28 A Medical Commissioner quoted in R. Barrington *Health, Medicine and Politics in Ireland 1900–1970* Dublin: Institute of Public Administration, 1987, 10.

29 The Irish Times *The Irish Times Almanac 1898.* This data comes from part of the Almanac taken over wholesale from the Bristol Almanac.

30 J. McCarthy *Five Years in Ireland 1895–1900* Dublin: Hodges Figgis, 1901, 337.

31 R. Kinkead *The Guide for Irish Medical Practitioners* Dublin: Falconer, 1889, 17.

32 L. Atthill *Recollections of an Irish Doctor* London: Religious Tract Society, 1911, 119, 133.

33 *Ibid.* 160.

34 P. Dickinson *The Dublin of Yesterday* London: Methuen, 1929, 26.

35 G. Birmingham *The Search Party* London: Methuen, 1909, 16.

36 *Ibid.* 1.

37 H. A. Hinkson *Golden Lads and Girls* London: Ward & Downey, 1895, 17; G. Moore *Drama in Muslin* London: Vizetelly, 1886, 316.

38 E. OE Somerville & M. Ross *Mount Music* London: Longman, 1919.

39 Reaney *op. cit.* 2.

40 *St Vincent's: A Century of Service* Dublin: St Vincent's Hospital, 1935, 67.

41 J. de Styrap *The Young Practitioner* London: Lewis, 1890, 149. De Styrap was a LKQCPI practising in Shropshire; the book was based on an American original (the problems of the new general practice were universal).

42 *Ibid.* 63.

43 *Dublin Journal of Medical Science* 1903, 384.

44 J. Dowling *An Irish Doctor Remembers* Dublin: Clonmore & Reynolds, 1955, 52–55.

45 T. Bodkin *My Uncle Frank* London: Hale, nd, 57.

46 A Medical Commissioner quoted in R. Barrington *op. cit.* 10.

47 Anon. (J. Johnson Abraham) *The Night Nurse* London: Chapman & Hall, 1913 278.

48 Dowling *op. cit.* 38–9.

49 P. Scanlan *The Irish Nurse* Manorhamilton: Drumlin, 1991, 71–7.

50 *St Vincent's A Century of Service* 165.

51 T. Farmar *Holles Street: The National Maternity Hospital—A Centenary History 1894–1994* Dublin: A. & A. Farmar, 1994, 23.

52 Adelaide Hospital *One Hundred Years of Nursing 1858–1958* Dublin: Capital Press, 1958, 11. In *A Century of Service* the historian and surgeon William Doolin confirms this relatively slow conversion to antisepsis (72). The contrast with the speed with which anaesthesia was taken up is marked (see chapter 4).

53 O'D. Browne *The Rotunda Hospital 1745–1945* Edinburgh: Livingstone, 1947 140.

54 Anon. [Abraham] *op. cit.* 44.

55 *Ibid.* 129–130.

56 O. W. Holmes 'Currents and Counter Currents in Medical Science', an Address delivered before the Massachusetts Medical Society at the Annual Meeting 30 May 1860. Published in O. W. Holmes *Medical Essays* 1842–1882, Boston, 1891.

57 J. Lyons *Oliver St John Gogarty* Dublin: Blackwater Press, 1980, 65.

58 Anon [Abraham] *op. cit.* 225.

59 Reaney *op. cit.* 109.

60 *Ibid.* 108.

61 *Select Committee on Patent Medicines 1914.* This splendidly forthright report was published on 4 August 1914, the very day that Britain declared war on Germany, so its recommendations were not acted upon.

62 Anon [Abraham] *op. cit.* 42, 46.

63 L. Cullen *Eason & Son: A History* Dublin: Easons, 1989, 8.

64 The subsequent quotations are from the four issues of the *Weekly Freeman's Journal* in January 1905.

65 There were only 900 dedicated beds in 1914: G. Jones *'Captain of all these men of death'* Amsterdam: Rodopi, 2001, 162.

Chapter 7

1 The Irish Times *Saorstát Eireann Irish Free State 1922–1932. A Decade of Progress* Dublin: Irish Times 1932.

2 J. Dowling *An Irish Doctor Remembers* Dublin: Clonmore & Reynolds, 1955, 50–51.

3 B. Mitchell *European Historical Statistics* London: Macmillan 1975, Table B7. The infant mortality data for 32-county Ireland is for 1922.

4 Sir W. Thompson 'Mortality from Influenza in Ireland' *Dublin Journal of Medical Science* 4th series 1920, 174. In the 15 months to 31 March 1919 15,867 deaths were ascribed directly to influenza, and 2,009 'excess deaths' from pneumonia may reasonably be attributed to influenza.

5 Sir W. Thompson 'A few outstanding points in connection with the vital statistics of the Irish Free State' *Irish Journal of Medical Science* 5th series, April 1925, 145–62.

6 See for instance the discussion in J. McCarthy *Problems in Theology* Vol. III , 212–18 at 217. McCarthy, Professor of Moral Theology at Maynooth, urged his clerical readers to pass on information about the safe period only individually, 'to those entitled

to use it'. They in turn were exhorted not to pass the information on to others. The actual details of the safe period were best conveyed by a Catholic doctor or, if such was not available, in the last resort by one of the 'acceptable books on the subject'.

7   T. Farmar *Holles Street: The National Maternity Hospital—A Centenary History 1894–1994* Dublin: A. & A. Farmar 1994, 116.

8   *Dáil Debates* 1 Aug. 1934 at col. 2019.

9   Farmar *op. cit.*, 87.

10 Quoted in J. Lyons *Oliver St John Gogarty* Dublin: Blackwater Press, 1980, 157.

11 Hospitals Commission *First General Report 1933–4* Dublin: Stationey Office, 1936, (P. No 1976) 68.

12 W. R. F. Collis *To be a Pilgrim* London: Secker & Warburg, 1975, 72.

13 S. Toksvig *Irish Diaries* Dublin: Lilliput Press, 1998, 67 (16 Nov. 1929).

14 J. Lyons *A Pride of Professors* Dublin: A. & A. Farmar, 1999, 212–3.

15 E. Coey Bigger *Report on the Physical Welfare of Mothers and Children* Dublin 1917. Jellett had clashed with the College in 1910. When he was appointed Master, he was also the Professor of Midwifery in Trinity, and the College, the electoral body to the Professorship, decided that he could not hold both posts, so he had to resign from Trinity.

16 H. Stokes 'Transfusion of blood' *Irish Journal of Medial Science* 1922–3, 21.

17 Farmar *op. cit.* 147.

18 J. D. MacCormack 'Typhoid Fever in Ireland' *Irish Journal of Medical Science* Vol. 302, Feb. 1951, 54–5.

19 C. Saunders 'Address to Foundation Day Meeting, Crumlin Hospital 1973', unpublished typescript.

20 'Medical Education in Ireland' in *Irish Journal of Medical Science* 1925, 454–5; *Statistical Abstract* 1931, 58.

21 G. Jones 'The Rockefeller Foundation and medical education in Ireland in the 1920s' *Irish Historical Studies* Nov. 1997, 564–80.

22 R. Rowlette, review of A. Flexner *Medical Education* in *Irish Journal of Medical Science* 1925, 474.

23 *Ibid.* 476.

24 J. Lee *Ireland 1912–1985* Cambridge: Cambridge University Press, 1989, 616–8. Lee quotes *The Leader* as reporting that 'the medical faculty of one [university] college cast an all but unanimous vote against a candidate upon the grounds (explicitly stated) that he had been guilty of the indiscretion of research work.'

25 Collis *op. cit.* 75.

26 *Ibid.* 72.

27 J. Deeny *To Cure and to Care: Memoirs of a Chief Medical Officer* Dublin: Glendale Press, 1989, 15.

28 *Ibid.* 17.

29 *Ibid.* 16, 17.

30 *Ibid.* 26.

31 Dowling *op. cit.* 59.

32 Deeny *op. cit.* 26.

33 R. Doyle *Rory and Ita* London: Jonathan Cape, 2002, 51.

34 K. Kearns *Dublin Tenement Life* Dublin: Gill & Macmillan, 1994, 35–9.

35 E. MacCarthy 'Public health problems created by louse infestation' in *Irish Journal of Medical Science* 1948, 69. Ethna MacCarthy was a particularly interesting woman who had been friendly with Samuel Beckett at Trinity and lectured in French there before qualifying as a doctor in her forties.

36 R. Barrington *Health, Medicine and Politics in Ireland 1900–1970* Dublin: Institute of Public Administration, 1987, 17.

37 *Irish Journal of Medical Science* 1925: 'gentlemen' 228; 'solemn dignity' 540; McWeeny 336; Blayney 399.

38 E. OE Somerville & Martin Ross *Mount Music* London: Nelson, 1919, 57.

39 Toksvig *op. cit.* 181 (17 May 1932). One of the arguments used against the introduction of the National Health Service in Britain was that it would 'undermine the priestly quality which is inherent in medicine' (*Sunday Express* quoted in H. Hopkins *The New Look* London: Secker & Warburg, 1964, 129*)*.

40 Anon. [J. Johnston Abraham] *The Night Nurse* London: Chapman & Hall, 1913, 17. PUO stands for Pyrexia (i.e. fever) of Unknown Origin.

41 S. O'Casey *Drums Under the Window* London: Pan Books, 1972, 256, 251.

42 Toksvig *op. cit.* 67 (16 Nov. 1929), 149 (23 Dec. 1931).

43 A. J. Cronin *The Citadel* London: Gollancz, 1937, 389.

44 B. Solomons *One Doctor in his Time* London: Christopher Johnson, 1956, 200–1.

45 *Irish Journal of Medical Science* 1928.

46 Dowling *op. cit.* 43.

47 *Medical Press* Students' Number Sept. 1900. More cynically, Tobin continued 'and I have also known a rash use of that virtue cause a doctor's fees to intermit in an even greater degree!'

48 D. Macardle *Fantastic Summer* London: Peter Davies, 1946, 193–4.

49 M. Bodkin SJ *Floodtide* Dublin: Talbot Press, 1927, 185–203.

50 MacCarthy *op. cit.* 67.

51 *Loc. cit.* The O'Farrell quote is from *Forum* April 1994.

52 *Model Housekeeping* 1928, 98.

53 Toksvig *op. cit.* 23 (3 Dec. 1927).

54 *Ibid.* 23 (8 Feb. 1932).

55 *Ibid.* 42, 43 (15, 16 March 1928).

56 P. Logan *Making the Cure* Dublin: Talbot Press, 1972, 133.

57 F. Brett Young *The Young Physician* Severn Edition, London: Heinemann 1934, 346, 356.

58 W. R. F Collis *The State of Medicine in Ireland* Carmichael Prize Essay, Dublin: Parkside Press 1943, 16. Collis studied midwifery under Bethel Solomons (*To be a Pilgrim* 43–4).

59 I. Louden *Death in Childbirth: An International Study of Maternal Care and Maternal Mortality 1800–1950* Oxford: Clarendon Press 1992, 155.

60 L. Atthill *Recollections of an Irish Doctor* London: Religious Tract Society, 1911, 233.

61 Brett Young *op. cit.* 614.

Chapter 8

1   K. Deale *Beyond Any Reasonable Doubt?* Dublin: Gill & Macmillan, 1990, 150. John O'Connell claims that at least one doctor 'continued to do his discreet abortions for years', even on one occasion having the chutzpah to report to the police 'a middle-class businessman [who] brought a girl to him and asked fairly bluntly for an abortion'. J. O'Connell *Doctor John: Crusading Doctor and Politician* Dublin: Poolbeg Press, 1989, 31.

2   Irish Times *Irish Review and Annual 1952* Irish Times: Dublin, 1953, 1.

3   M. Molloy *The Book of Irish Courtesy* Cork: Mercier Press, 1968, 15.

4   W. R. F. Collis *The State of Medicine in Ireland* Dublin: Parkgate Press, 1944, 12.

5   Quoted in *Irish Independent* 5 Dec. 1953.

6   Irish Times *Irish Review and Annual 1950* Irish Times: Dublin, 1951, 5.

7   H. Böll *Irish Journey* London: Secker & Warburg, 1983, 37–8.

8   Irish Times *Irish Review and Annual 1951* Irish Times: Dublin, 1952, 21.

9   M. Colum *Life and the Dream* London: Macmillan, 1947, 399. In 1982 Professor Jack Lyons (to whom I am grateful for this reference) described this as 'a statement some would vigorously reject'.

10 Irish Independent *Guide to Careers* Dublin: Independent Newspapers, 1956, 61. The description of other professions was markedly less lyrical. Of solicitors the *Guide* wrote dourly: 'It is often a question whether the energy and effort expended in reaching qualification has been worthwhile.'

11 Irish Times *Irish Review and Annual 1950* Irish Times: Dublin, 1951, 57.

12 H. Counihan 'The health of student nurses' *Irish Journal of Medical Science* 1951, 305–6.

13 R. Mulcahy *Richard Mulcahy (1886–1971) A Family Memoir* Dublin: Aurelian Press, 1999, 335.

14 O'Connell *op. cit.* 32. 'As a medical student,' O'Connell continues, 'I heard tragic stories every day . . . ' The swapping of such tales reinforced the sense that doctors were privy to a 'reality' about life that was hidden from other middle-class people.

15 *Irish Independent* 1 Dec. 1953.

16 K. Kearns *Dublin Tenement Life* Dublin: Gill & Macmillan, 1994, 104.

17 G. Fielding *Through Streets Broad and Narrow* London: Hutchinson 1960, 186. 'Gabriel Fielding' is the pseudonym of Alan Barnsley, a physician who studied at TCD up to 1940.

18 J. MacCormack 'Typhoid fever in Ireland' *Irish Journal of Medical Science* 1951, 63.

19 D. Coakley *Baggot Street: A Short History of the Royal City of Dublin Hospital* Dublin: Baggot Street Hospital 1995, 79.

20 E. MacCarthy 'Public health problems created by louse infestation' *Irish Journal of*

Medical Science 1948, 67.

21 Mulcahy *op. cit.* 337.

22 J. Fleetwood *History of Medicine in Ireland* Dublin: Browne & Nolan, 1951, 377.

23 A vivid idea of the concerns of Catholic writers on medical ethics can be got from the contents page of J. Kenny SJ *Medical Ethics* Cork: Mercier Press, 1953. The book contains 15 pages on 'Fundamental principles', 17 on 'Professional rights and duties', 33 on 'Morals and marriage', 32 on 'Delivery procedures' (plus 12 on administering baptism) and 30 on 'Man's right to life'. Problems relating to human experimentation or informed consent are not mentioned.

24 Quoted in M. Catherine de Jésus-Christ *At the Bedside of the Sick* London: Burns Oates, 1938, 145–6.

25 W. Heaney *House of Courage* Dublin: Clonmore & Reynolds, 1952, 136.

26 O'Connell *op. cit.* 30.

27 *Ibid.* 36. This story should probably be interpreted as a 'tease' directed at the unease the more solemn medical students would have felt about being paid for professional services.

28 de Jésus-Christ *op. cit.* 60.

29 P. Boylan *Gaps of Brightness* Dublin: A. & A. Farmar, 2003, 94.

30 Counihan *op. cit.* 304. The average nurse had a body-mass index of 24.8, at the very top of the modern 'normal' category.

31 de Jésus-Christ *op. cit.* 44.

32 Hospitals Commission *First General Report 1933–4* Dublin: Stationery Office, 1936, 4.

33 Counihan *op. cit.* 58.

34 The toll of the Industrial Revolution is seen in the fact that in the 1880s army recruiters had to reduce the height requirement to 5 ft (it was 5 ft 6 ins before 1883). Nevertheless they had to reject between 40 and 60 per cent of the volunteers for the Boer War. 'The chief grounds were bad teeth, heart affections, poor sight or hearing and deformities.' J. Drummond & A. Wilbraham *The Englishman's Food* London: Jonathan Cape, 1957, 404. No wonder strapping country lads from Ireland were so important to Queen Victoria's armies. For the Second World War, see R. Titmuss *Problems of Social Policy* London: HMSO, 1950.

35 *Irish Independent* 7 April 1950.

36 T. Mann *The Magic Mountain* London: Penguin, pb, 1960, 195.

37 A. Farmar *Children's Last Days* Dublin: Town House, 1992, 101.

38 Mulcahy *op. cit.*, 334.

39 Fielding *op. cit.*, 187.

40 B. O'Brien 'The treatment of the tuberculous patient' *Irish Journal of Medical Science* 1951, 5. Dr O'Brien describes this account as 'a caricature but not a gross exaggeration'.

41 *The Irish Times* 3 Nov. 2003.

42 T. M. Healy *From Sanatorium to Hospital* Dublin: A. & A. Farmar, 2002, 42. It is no wonder that, as Dr Brendan O'Brien put it, many patients, not feeling particu-

larly sick, 'seek relief from their tedium in the arms of Bacchus or of Venus'. *Irish Journal of Medical Science* Vol. 301, Jan. 1951, 7. John Quinn describes his furtive courtship of a fellow patient (later his wife) by the aid of friendly nurses and porters in *Sea of Love, Sea of Loss* Dublin: Town House, 2003.

43 Quinn *op. cit.* 29.

44 *Ibid.* 33.

45 *Ibid.* 31.

46 O'Connell *op. cit.* 6.

47 C. Cockburn *I, Claud* Harmondsworth: Penguin, rev. ed. 1967, 296.

48 Heaney *op. cit.* 40.

49 Farmar *op. cit.* 135.

50 I am grateful to Dr Paul Darragh for extensive input on the recent history of the health services of Northern Ireland.

51 J. McKenna 'Candles in the dark: health professionals in the Troubles' London: Nuffield Trust, 2004, 18.

52 Northern Ireland House of Commons *Debates* Vol. XXXIII (June 1949). Dr Hickey was of course a Catholic, and interestingly bore the name of the hereditary Gaelic doctors of County Clare—Ó hIcí,—as did the cheerful doctor in *The Irish RM* stories.

53 *Irish Independent* 20 April 1950.

54 *Ibid.* 23 Jan. 1951.

55 O'Connell *op. cit.*, 3.

56 T. Eagleton *The Gatekeeper* London: Allen Lane, 2001, 111.

57 *The Bell* July 1943, 293.

58 Quoted in de Jésus-Christ *op. cit.* 145–6.

59 *Irish Independent* 28 March 1951.

60 Quoted in E. Cahill *The Framework of a Christian State* Dublin: Gill, 1932, 473.

61 H. Mintzberg *The Structuring of Organizations* New Jersey: Prentice-Hall, 1979. I am grateful to my friend the late Dr Geoffrey MacKechnie for bringing Mintzberg to my attention.

62 The Irish Medical Association did cite a somewhat unlikely saying of Lenin's to the effect that 'the first step to absolute power was to gain control of the administrative machinery of medical practice'. The Nazi doctors' activities were discussed in detail in Dom Peter Flood's translation of a Cahier Laënnac title *Medical Experimentation on Man* (Cork: Mercier Press, 1955) but neither of the Royal Colleges purchased a copy.

63 Farmar *op. cit.* 47.

64 J. Deeny *To Cure and to Care* Dublin: Glendale Press, 1989, 93–5.

65 *Irish Independent* 2 December 1953.

66 Collis *op. cit.* 65.

67 Deeny *op. cit.* 100.

68 R. Barrington *Health, Medicine and Politics in Ireland 1900–1970* Dublin: Institute of Public Administration, 1987, 248–9.

69 J. Deeny *The End of an Epidemic* Dublin: A. & A. Farmar, 1995, 137.

Chapter 9

1 Interview with author.

2 P Skrabanek *The Death of Human Medicine and the Rise of Coercive Healthism* London: Social Affairs Unit 1994, 31–2. Skrabanek became somewhat discredited when it emerged that some of his counter-consensus research—such as pointing out that Greece had the highest per capita consumption of cigarettes and the lowest lung cancer rates in Europe—was financed by tobacco companies.

3 B. Hensey 'The health services and their administration' in F. Litton (ed) *Unequal Achievement* Dublin: Institute of Public Administration, 1982, 158.

4 J. Le Fanu *The Rise and Fall of Modern Medicine* London: Little, Brown, 1999, xvii.

5 M. Green 'May's Story' in *Growing up in Arcadia*, privately published, 2004.

6 *Sunday Independent* 3 February 1974.

7 C. Tóibín *Bad Blood: A Walk along the Irish Border* London: Vintage, pb, 1994, 199.

8 'An Irish Housewife' *I'm not afraid to die* Cork: Mercier Press, 1974, 7–8.

9 K. McCourt, unpublished diary in the possession of his son Declan, to whom I am grateful for permission to quote.

10 M. Wall *Leaves for the Burning* 2nd ed. Dublin: Millington, 1973, 53.

11 G. Dean *The Turnstone—A Doctor's Story* Liverpool: Liverpool University Press, 2002, 161–2

12 J. Deeny *To Cure and to Care* Dublin: Glendale Press, 1989, 282.

13 *Ibid.* 282.

14 J. Deeny 'Fanad—a study of a community' in *The End of an Epidemic* Dublin: A. & A. Farmar, 1995, 163. For ease of comparison I have sorted the various ailments in numerical order.

15 C. Whelan 'Class and social mobility' in K. Kennedy (ed) *Ireland in Transition* Cork: Mercier Press, 83.

16 T. Farmar *A History of Craig Gardner & Co: The first 100 years* Dublin: Gill & Macmillan, 1988, 215.

17 *Irish Medical Times* 22 March 1974.

18 This section is based on Dr J. McKenna 'Candles in the dark: Health professionals in the Troubles' (2004) an oral history project exploring how professionals treated members of the 'opposite' community, funded by the Nuffield Trust. I am grateful to Dr McKenna for permission to quote from this document which represents, as he puts it 'a skeleton of a full report of the research'.

19 P. Donaldson *Yes, Matron: A History of Nurses and Nursing at the Royal Victoria Hospital Belfast* Belfast: White Row, nd [c. 1989], 145.

20 McKenna *op. cit.*

21 J. B. Lyons (a doctor) is inclined to palliate Doolin's remarks, but Ruth Barrington (a civil servant) bluntly refers to them as deliberate rudeness. See *A Pride of Professors*

Dublin: A. & A. Farmar, 1999, and *Health, Medicine and Politics in Ireland 1900–1970* Dublin: Institute of Public Administration, 1987 respectively.

22 J. Lee *Ireland 1912–1985 Politics and Society* pb Cambridge: Cambridge University Press, 1985, 315-6.

23 M.-A. Wren *Unhealthy State: Anatomy of a Sick Society* Dublin: New Island, 2003, 51.

24 *Sunday Independent* 21 January 1974.

25 *Irish Medical Times* 26 April 1974.

26 Interview with author.

27 Dean *op. cit.* 160-1.

28 *Sunday Independent* 21 April 1974.

29 *The Irish Times* 25 January 1974.

30 Dean *op. cit.* 194.

31 *Irish Medical Times* 1 February 1974.

32 Hospitals Commission *First General Report 1933-4* Dublin: Stationery Office, 1936, 12.

33 *Ibid.* 14.

34 A. Farmar *Children's Last Days* Dublin: Town House, 1992, 32-2.

35 Hospitals Commission *op. cit.* 21.

36 F. Litton *Unequal Achievement* Dublin: Institute of Public Administration, 162

37 I. Louden *Death in Childbirth* Oxford: Clarendon Press, 1992, 427.

38 D. Neeson *Maternity Services in Ireland* Dublin: Gill & Macmillan, 1986, 133. The subsequent quotes are from this summary of the surveys and also from the 1979 *Report on Women's Experience of Maternity Services* Dublin: AIMS.

39 Neeson *op. cit.* 11.

40 G. Kerrigan *Nothing but the Truth* Dublin: Tomar, 1990, 28, 33. The widely publicised Dunne case was strikingly badly handled by the hospital, and did not increase the public's respect for the profession; it was, however, a landmark case in defining medical negligence.

41 A. Grant 'Impressions of the College' in D. Mitchell *25 Years—An Interim History of the Royal College of Physicians of Ireland 1963–88* Dublin: RCPI, 1992.

Chapter 10

1 *The Irish Times* 17 August 2004.

2 Department of Health *Health Statistics 2002* Section C—data derived from the CSO's quarterly National Household Survey.

3 *British Medical Journal* vol. 329, 3 July 2004, 1.

4 T. O'Sullivan *Report on the Regulation of Practitioners of Complementary and Alternative Medicine in Ireland* Dublin: Institute of Public Administration, 2002

5 *The Irish Times Health Supplement* 29 June 2004.

6 O'Sullivan *op. cit.*

7 *Daily Telegraph* 21 March 2004.

8 E. Mills et. al. 'Interaction of St John's wort with conventional drugs: systematic

review of clinical trials' *British Medical Journal* vol. 329, 3 July 2004, 27.

9 E.g. *The Irish Times* 20 August 2004.

10 D. Mitchell *25 Years—An Interim History of the Royal College of Physicians of Ireland 1963–88* Dublin: RCPI, 85.

11 Quotations from the Charter of 1669 in [T. Belcher] *The Charter of the Kings and Queens College of Physicians in Ireland* Dublin: M. H. Gill, 1856, 1.

12 See for instance *Courtesy for Boys and Girls* Dublin: Gill, 1962, 36. This is a Christian Brothers publication designed for class use. The passage continues '. . . and, please God, will one day enjoy the happiness of Heaven. Consequently, you should make every effort to keep your body clean and properly attired.'

13 When he died Talbot was found with two chains tightly would round his waist; 'both were deeply embedded in the flesh and rusted'. J. Glynn *Life of Matt Talbot* Dublin: Catholic Truth Society of Ireland, 1928 p 77 under the heading 'His fasts and mortifications'.

14 A. Corbin *The Foul and the Fragrant—Odour and the Social Imagination* London: Picador 1994, Chapter 5.

Illustration acknowledgements and credits

A large number of the illustrations in this book are drawn from the collections of the Royal College of Physicians of Ireland. These have been supplemented with images from the archives of the Royal College of Surgeons in Ireland. We are most grateful to the College's Librarian, Robert Mills, and the Archivist of the Royal College of Surgeons in Ireland, Mary O'Doherty, and her colleagues in the Imaging Department, for their generous assistance. We are also grateful to Ms Laoise O'Murchú the Communications Officer at the Adelaide & Meath and National Children's Hospital, Tallaght, for her assistance.

Pictures from commercial collections and galleries are duly credited; other pictures come from the publishers' own archives and private collections. We are grateful to De Vere White Galleries and some others who assisted with pictures which in the end we were unable to use for reasons of space. We are also grateful for the use of images from the following collections: Bridgeman Art Library, David Davison Associates (for the Fr Browne Collection of the Irish Jesuits), ImageFile, Irish Images, the National Gallery of Ireland, the Philadelphia Museum of Fine Art, Science and Society Picture Library, the Tate Gallery, and the Wellcome Trust.

Page

viii: *Allegory of the Medical Profession,* 1578; studio of Hendrik Goltzius (1558–1616), courtesy Philadelphia Museum of Art

1: Woodcut from Panthaleo's *Pillularium* (Pavia 1516) RCPI Library

2: Courtesy Tate Gallery, London

3: From a painting by Philip V. Moon, for Burroughs Wellcome & Co. in the 1960s, *Irish Medicinal Herbs*

5: Thomas Rowlandson (1756–1827), private collection

6: Countess of Aberdeen, *Ireland's Crusade Against Tuberculosis,* Vol. III (Dublin 1909), RCPI Library

7: James Wolveridge, *Speculum Matricis* (1671 ed.), RCPI Library

8: Petrus Morelli, *Methodus Praescribendi* (1650), RCPI Library

9: Artist unknown, RCPI Collection

10: Attributed to Thomas Pooley, RCPI Collection

12: RCPI Library

15: RCPI Library

16: RCPI Library

19: From the title page of the first English edition of *The works of that famous Chirurgion Ambrose Parey* (London, 1634), RCPI Library

21: RCPI Library

22: Engraving by Jonas Arnold for the London edition *Armamentarium Chirurgicum* of Johann Scultus of Ulm (1672) first published in 1655, RCPI Library

24: Jan Steen, *The Sick Woman, c.* 1665, private collection

26: Engraving of the cure of William Maher by William Faithorne Sr for Greatrakes' London pamphlet of 1666, RCPI Library

28: Portrait by Thomas Pooley, statue by unknown artist, RCPI Collection

31: RCPI Collection

32: Attributed to Strickland Lowry, National Gallery of Ireland

34: RCPI Library

37: RCPI Library

38: (Left) Wellcome Library, (right) RCPI Library

39: RCPI Library

41: RCPI Library

42: John William Moore, *Smallpox* (New York 1898)

43: Private collection

44: RCPI Library

45: Science and Society Picture Library, London

46: RCPI Library

48: George [Berkeley], Lord Bishop of Cloyne, *Siris* (Dublin 1744), RCPI Library

51: RCPI Library

52: Royal College of Surgeons in Ireland Library

54: Peter Gatenby, *Dublin's Meath Hospital* (Dublin, 1991)

57: J. D. H Widdess, *An Account of the Schools of Surgery Royal College of Surgeons, Dublin, 1789–1948* (Edinburgh 1948)

58: J. D. H. Widdess, *An Account of the Schools of Surgery Royal College of Surgeons, Dublin, 1789–1948* (Edinburgh 1948)

60: Robert H. Labberton, *An Historical Atlas* (London 1885)

63: Watercolour by Rawdon McNamara, Meath Hospital Collection, photo David Davison Associates

66: Central Catholic Library, Dublin

68: Private collection

70: RCPI Library

72: RCPI Library

74: Private collection

77: RCPI Collection

79: RCPI Collection

80: RCPI Library

81: RCPI Collection

82: Arthur Miles (fl. 1851–80), *The Doctor, c.* 1860. Bridgeman Art Library

85: RCPI Collection

86: Courtesy Peter Costello

89: Central Catholic Library, Dublin

90: RCPI Library

95: RCPI Library

96: RCPI Collection

98: RCPI Library

100: Richard Butcher *Operative and Conservative Surgery* (Dublin 1865) RCPI Library

101: RCPI Collection

102: Countess of Aberdeen, *Ireland's Crusade Against Tuberculosis,* Vol. III (Dublin 1909)

104: John F. O'Sullivan *Belfast City Hospital* (Donaghadee, 2003)

107: Private collection

110: Painting by Philip V. Moon, for Burroughs Wellcome & Co. (The Wellcome Foundation) in the 1960s

111: Central Catholic Library, Dublin

113: National Maternity Hospital

115: Courtesy F. C. Meenan

116: Courtesy Muiris Houston

117: Photo David Davison Associates

121: RCPI Library

122: *One Hundred Years of Nursing 1858–1958, Adelaide Hospital Dublin* (Dublin 1958)

123: RCPI Library

124: Courtesy Bayer

125: *Weekly Freeman's Journal* January 1910

126: *Weekly Freeman's Journal* January 1910

129: Central Catholic Library, Dublin

130: *Dublin Opinion*

133: RCPI Library

134: Publishers' archive

135: Fr Browne Collection, courtesy Irish Jesuits and David Davison Associates

136: St Vincent's *A Century of Service 1834–1934* (Dublin 1934)

139: St Vincent's *A Century of Service 1834–1934* (Dublin 1934)

140: 'Latin Quarter, Ballyscullion' *Dublin Opinion*

143: RCPI Collection

144: St Vincent's *A Century of Service 1834–1934* (Dublin 1934)

146: Fr Browne Collection, David Davison Associates

150: Central Catholic Library, Dublin

152: Irish Image Collection
154: RCPI Collection
155: *Dublin Opinion*
156: Central Catholic Library, Dublin
157: Fr Browne Collection, David Davison
  Associates
159: Private collection
160: RCPI Library
163: *One Hundred Years of Nursing 1858–1958,
  Adelaide Hospital Dublin* (Dublin 1958)
164: *Mater Misericordiae Hospital 1861–1961*
  (Dublin, 1961)
163: Fr Browne Collection, David Davison
  Associates
167: Courtesy Peter Costello
168. Courtesy Peter Costello
171: *Dublin Opinion*
172: Fr Browne Collection, David Davison
  Associates
175: *Mater Misericordiae Hospital 1861–1961*
  (Dublin 1961)
177: RCPI Collection
179: *Pathology at the Royal: The First Hundred
  Years 1890–1990* (Belfast 1990), courtesy Dr
  Michael Scott

183: ImageFile
185: National Maternity Hospital
187: RCPI Collection
189: RCPI Collection
190: Movie Store Collection, London
192: *Nursing Mirror*
195. *Nusight* November 1969
196: *The Irish Times*
197: Stephen O'Connor
199: RCPI Library
200: John F. O'Sullivan *Belfast City Hospital*
  (Donaghadee, 2003)
201: John F. O'Sullivan *Belfast City Hospital*
  (Donaghadee, 2003)
203: RCPI Library
206: National Maternity Hospital
208 Adelaide & Meath Hospital incorporating
  The National Childrens' Hospital
210: ImageFile
211: Adelaide & Meath Hospital incorporating
  The National Childrens' Hospital
213: RCPI Collection
215: RCPI Library
217: Adelaide & Meath Hospital incorporating
  The National Childrens' Hospital

Index